Medical Practice Management

By Horace Cotton

Medical Economics Book Division, Inc.,
Oradell, New Jersey

FIRST PRINTING 1967
SECOND PRINTING 1968
THIRD PRINTING 1970
FOURTH PRINTING 1971

Foreword

For more than 40 years, we at Medical Economics have been doing our best to provide the information and advice about practice management that every private practitioner needs—but doesn't get in medical school. This book exactly fits that aim. We're confident that it can enhance any doctor's efforts to do better for his patients, his family, and himself.

One reason we're confident: The material presented bears directly on a private practitioner's workday. It sticks to its subject; there are no tedious excursions down side roads. Subjects merely related to practice management—such as financial planning, Federal income taxes, medical law—are dealt with (or soon will be) in separate volumes published by Medical Economics Book Division, Inc.

A second reason for our confidence: the book's author, Horace Cotton. He has worked with physicians here and abroad for more than 30 years. His experience includes 10 years of hospital administration, 8 years as a biostatistician, and 14 years as an all-around business adviser to doctors in private practice. His personal client roster passed the 500 mark years ago. He has helped put together over 300 medical partnerships and groups.

His writings in Medical Economics magazine during the last decade have made his name familiar to physicians in all 50 states. In 1963, he wrote "Aid for the Doctor's Aide," and soon afterwards the American Association of Medical Assistants nominated him to its board of examiners. In 1964, he contributed many of the chapters of the books "Medical Partnership Practice" and "Medical Group Practice."

We're proud to put our imprint on this book. It is, we feel, Cotton's best. It's not merely useful; it's good reading.

William Alan Richardson, Editor in Chief
Medical Economics Book Division, Inc.
Oradell, N. J.

October 16, 1967

An acknowledgment by the author

Most of the lessons of this book have been learned during 14 years of grappling with the everyday problems of physicians practicing private medicine in a free enterprise society.

Much of its content has been adapted from material I've contributed to Medical Economics. Some has been plundered from other contributors to the magazine, including physicians, colleagues in the management field, and members of the magazine's superb team of writers and editors. Experts in many fields have been generous in supplying statistics and in reviewing chapters in manuscript. I acknowledge my debt to all of these with gratitude and humility, hoping they'll forgive me for mentioning only one of them by name.

Any acceptance this book may earn among doctors should be credited in substantial part to Gene Balliett, long one of Medical Economics' distinguished senior editors and now, like me, one of its contributing editors and head of his own consulting firm. He, not I, got it finished. His editorial skill, meticulous research, and unwearying patience combined to wage a victorious war against a truly giant sloth—mine. That Gene's name doesn't appear on the cover as co-author is due to his absurd modesty.

Horace Cotton
Albemarle, N.C.

October 16, 1967

To

H. MAX SCHIEBEL, M.D.,

in friendship and gratitude

The author

President, Horace Cotton Associates, Inc.,
a division of Management, Inc., Albemarle, N.C.;
chairman of the board, Management, Inc.
Member, Society of Professional Business Consultants
Contributing Editor, Medical Economics
Contributing Editor, Hospital Physician
Author, "Aid for the Doctor's Aide"
Co-author, "Medical Partnership Practice"
Co-author, "Medical Group Practice"

Contents

Section I
Managing your practice

Section II
Sizing up your practice

Section

I

Managing
your practice

1

Why management matters to you

There are physicians who, even today, regard money as a word that shouldn't be said out loud. Like the Barchester doctors depicted by Anthony Trollope, they hold that "the true physician should hardly be aware that the last friendly grasp of the hand had been made precious by the touch of gold." They like to remind themselves, and each other, and me, that medicine is an art. "Doctors don't mingle art and money," they say.

Sounds fine. Unfortunately, a private practitioner of medicine can't separate them. He practices his art for fees, paid in money.

Most of the doctors I know would keep money out of their practices if they could. None, to my knowledge, has ever found it possible to do so. The wise ones are content to put money in its proper place. I've helped convince many not-so-wise ones that it *has* a place.

It bothers me that tradition, if it's that, inhibits so many young doctors, with their whole careers ahead of them, from even trying to master the economics of medical practice. Some, maybe, are held back by nothing more complicated than a dislike for desk work. Others seem to have an uncomfortable feeling that the silver-haired professors they've most admired wouldn't approve. Still others apparently believe that finding out how their practices stack up against those of other doctors and how they might be improved would destroy their cherished individuality and take all the joy out of practicing.

1

Whatever the reasons for the indifference, one result of it is that few physicians know even the basic economic statistics of the profession they're in. It's rare for one to have a clear idea of how his practice compares financially with other doctors' practices. Thousands think they're doing well when others are so far ahead they're out of fiscal sight. Some think they're lagging behind when they're actually leading the pack.

About one private practitioner in five, or about 35,000 U.S. physicians, nets less than $20,000 a year from his practice. Half that many net $50,000 or more. A competent physician has better than a 50-50 chance of earning $25,000 a year. And he'd better earn that much if he hopes to retire some day, for unlike the corporate executive he'll have to pay for his retirement plan out of his own pocket.

To move up to the $25,000 level takes some management. And in the years immediately ahead, it will take some alert management to do well not just financially but professionally, too. The U.S. today is near the 200,000,000 population mark. The 1970 census will show that there are about 210,000,000 of us. If you intend to look after your share of these potential patients, you'll need to waste less time, work more skillfully, and see to it that your employes and professional associates do the same.

You'll get help, of course, from the seemingly unstoppable march of science. For decades now, you've confidently looked to the boys in the small back rooms to help you cope with ever-increasing patient loads. And they've come through. Two jabs of a needle now can replace two weeks of wearying house calls. You roll no pills, mix no medicines, plod no more behind Dobbin through the winter snows. You see 25 or more office patients a day; the horse-and-buggy doctor worked longer seeing 10 or 12. You funnel 50 patients a year through each hospital bed, against the old-timer's 20. A nurse helps you see more patients, and a secretary does your paper work. All those aids enable you to give your patients top-flight clinical care.

But watch out. There's something following you. Relentlessly.

2

Working ceaselessly against your rising productivity is the phenomenon of ever-rising demand. Just a generation ago, only half the population sought out a doctor in any given year. Today, two-thirds do. There are not merely more of us; we're better educated and maybe more sophisticated. We don't simply want to *get* well; we want to *stay* well. The time isn't too far off when 9 out of 10 Americans will seek a doctor's services at least once each year.

It's becoming clear that computers will soon help you cope with the ever-increasing workload. Already they are beginning to come up with ways of furnishing doctors with precisely the right scraps of information when they're needed. That's great. But computers don't have eyes, ears, fingers, perception, and judgment. Only you have those. Good management is now a prerequisite for the building and maintenance of a successful private practice, and you can't get it on magnetic tapes. Without it, even the most brilliant new physician is apt to find himself in the wrong town, with the wrong office and the wrong help, charging the wrong fees, and wondering why it all happened.

This book's purpose is to help you avoid such blunders—and to assist you in repairing damage that has already occurred. Its larger section, Section I, is addressed directly to the new physician who will soon open a private practice or did so not long ago. Yet the experienced practitioner will, I hope, find much of value in it, too. Fundamentals are always worth reviewing, no matter what the practitioner's level of competency. That's as true of business as it is of medicine—or of football or golf, for that matter.

Section II offers the young practitioner a brisk, down-to-earth review of the bread-and-butter portions of Section I. But Section II is chiefly meant for his older colleague, since the established practitioner has more to gain from an appraisal of his current status. Its frank purpose is to prod him into identifying problems that may be preventing him from realizing the potential he knows he has. If Section II succeeds in that objective, I, for one, will be content. Because over the years I've learned that once a physician identifies a problem he does something about it.

2

Start right:
Go where you're needed

The ad hooked Dr. Patrick Melton. His wife showed it to him a few weeks before his residency ended. It read: "Nandina Beach internist will transfer growing practice, office lease, and all records to purchaser of medical equipment and small equity in new split-level with pool. Payment plan arranged." Nandina Beach, a resort near Daisy Melton's hometown, was the top name on the couple's where-we'd-like-to-live list. They'd honeymooned there. Now they couldn't wait to answer that ad.

Little more than one year later, Dr. Melton sadly mailed much the same ad to the same medical journal. Soon after, he and Daisy shook the sand of Nandina Beach from their shoes forever. The day before they left town, heading for California, Dr. Melton was in the local bank when a hand touched his elbow.

"Going to miss you Wednesday afternoons, Pat," said Dr. Griswold, the dean of Nandina Beach's medical community.

"But not the rest of the week," said Dr. Melton with a trace of bitterness in his voice. "Golf is golf, and business is business, right?"

"Don't be sore, son," said Dr. Griswold. "A town can use just so many doctors. You're the third man to make that discovery here in the last four years."

As the Meltons drove westward, they cheered up. After all, hadn't San Francisco always stood a high second on their list of preferred locations? Pat had served a few weeks of his draft stint

5

there, and he and Daisy had both loved the place. They should have gone there in the beginning, they told each other—without wasting that precious year at Nandina Beach. It stood to reason that a city the size of San Francisco could take one more internist.

If San Francisco had a slot for Dr. Melton, it wasn't visible.

After a depressing year trying to put together some sort of a practice, Pat headed his aging sedan eastward. "This man in Detroit

---

First grade the professional prospects this way

Fill out one column for each area visited. Score 5 for Yes, 3 for Doubtful, 0 for No.

Name of community			
1. I'm personally convinced of the need here for the skills I offer	_____	_____	_____
2. The medical society man was encouraging	_____	_____	_____
3. The local doctors didn't dash my hopes	_____	_____	_____
4. Local lay people think there's room for me	_____	_____	_____
5. I can get hospital privileges	_____	_____	_____
6. Coverage for time off is no problem	_____	_____	_____
7. Consultation facilities are adequate	_____	_____	_____
8. Postgraduate education is accessible	_____	_____	_____
9. I can get office space suitable to my needs	_____	_____	_____
10. Skilled office help can be hired at reasonable rates	_____	_____	_____
Totals	_____	_____	_____

---

says I'll be a 50-50 partner in seven years," he'd told Daisy. "We ought to be out of debt long before then. And, thank goodness, at last I'll be *busy!*"

Meantime, pediatrician Ted Stanton, who'd been a fellow resident of Dr. Melton's, had gone about choosing a location differently. For six months he used up a lot of spare time collecting medical society rosters, Chamber of Commerce brochures, and hospital annual reports, all covering a five-state area. At last, he came up with what he was looking for: a small, growing town with a recently built hospital—*and no pediatrician*. The hospital report told him that Skelthorpe had registered 750 births the previous year. The boosters' booklet announced that 38,000 people lived within 15 miles of the town's center. It also noted that during the last intercensal period Skelthorpe itself had almost doubled its population.

On Dr. Stanton's first free weekend, he and his wife June drove the 200 miles to Skelthorpe. It was no all-American city. But the Saturday and Sunday Ted spent checking up on the local medical picture convinced him of one thing: Skelthorpe needed Stanton.

He talked with all 10 of the town's M.D.s, half of them by phone. None of them actually said, "Thank you for thinking of Skelthorpe as a place to practice, Doctor." But none invited him to beat it, either. A young OBG man said: "I could refer a few newborns to you. But mostly you'd have to depend on people having the sense to take their kids to a specialist." Then he added: "The town isn't much to look at, but it improves on acquaintance. And the fishing's good."

Dr. Stanton took a peek at the hospital, too. The administrator was using Sunday to catch up on some paper work. "Don't quote me," he said, "but *there is work for you here.*"

When the Stantons climbed back in their car, Ted asked June what she thought. "Drive back through the residential section," she said happily. "I noticed a house for rent. It has a pretty front yard."

Two years later, while Pat Melton was glumly taking down his shingle in San Francisco, Ted Stanton was cheerfully taking *his* down in Skelthorpe—to fasten it to the wall of a trim new clinic building, just above a shiny plate bearing the name of his newly arrived partner. Skelthorpe, Dr. Stanton had discovered, needed not one pediatrician but two.

Right there, in the true stories of Drs. Melton and Stanton, you have Management Lesson No. 1: *Go where you're needed.*

If you're looking for a location — either because you're just starting out or because you made a bad pick the last time—do what Ted Stanton did or something like it. It's what any businessman does before deciding where his new product will sell best — some market research. If you're lucky, your research might amount

---

Then grade the economic prospects this way

Fill out one column for each area visited. Score 5 for Yes, 3 for Doubtful, 0 for No.

Name of community			
1. The area's population is increasing			
2. Its industry is diversified			
3. Its employment record is good			
4. New firms have moved in recently			
5. Local bank debits have risen consistently			
6. Consumer credit records are good			
7. Welfare rolls are low			
8. Wages are high			
9. Health care insurance is popular			
10. Going rates for medical care are acceptable			
Totals			

---

to no more than the writing of a few letters and the expenditure of a few postage stamps. There are agencies ready to let you in on their own research into the current need for doctors. For instance, the American Medical Association, most of the state medical societies, and several of the specialty organizations all keep files on openings. For each opening reported to them, they assemble a compact package of information, available to any interested physician. One of those packages could contain the lead you're after.

The A.M.A. Physicians' Placement Service alone helps almost

Now grade the residential prospects this way

Fill out one column for each area visited. Score 5 for Yes, 3 for Doubtful, 0 for No.

Name of community {

1. My wife likes the place ....
2. The residential section is attractive ....
3. Zoning ordinances protect property values ....
4. Price range of houses is within my reach ....
5. Local taxes and assessments appear reasonable ....
6. Public services are adequate ....
7. Shopping facilities are satisfactory ....
8. Good schools are available ....
9. Churches and cultural facilities are adequate ....
10. Recreation facilities are adequate ......

    Totals ....

3,000 doctors each year. It keeps track of the hospital facilities, health activities, economic status, schools, and climate of each of the 3,130 counties in the United States. But don't be misled by the placement service's name. The A.M.A. doesn't actually place anybody anywhere. Its placement service is like a lonely hearts bureau: It introduces doctors to openings and openings to doctors. But there's no fee. If you like, you can hop a plane to Chicago and wade through the entire file by specialty and type of practice. Chances are, it will contain between 1,000 and 1,500 entries for G.P.s alone. But it's easier to lower your sights a little; after all, America's a big country. It's cheaper to use the mails.

Your best bet may be to do as Ted Stanton did—make up your mind about the section of the United States you'd like to be needed by. If you feel you can't be happy outside one particular state, that's that. But it's wiser not to be so firmly pre-sold. Choose a region— Northeast, Southeast, Midwest, or West. Get the atlas out. See if you can narrow things down to, say, a three-state area. Three contiguous states are best, since you may end up visiting all of them, and there's no point in burning up tire rubber unnecessarily.

When you've marked off your region, write to the A.M.A. You'll

---

Finally, compare the towns' total scores

Name of community			
Score for professional prospects			
Score for economic prospects			
Score for residential prospects			
Totals			

10

get back a questionnaire to fill out. When you return it, copies will go to the placement agencies in the states you've named, unless you request otherwise.

Don't just sit back and wait for the mailman, though. If you're a specialist, write to the national office of your specialty group. The people there may be able to help, too. If you know they don't maintain a placement service, write anyway; your letter just might clinch a debate on whether one is needed.

After you've posted that letter, dust off that Journal A.M.A. on your desk, and look through the small ads. If any ad seems worth the price of a postage stamp, answer it. Don't neglect, either, the bigger ads of the privately operated placement services—the so-called "commercial bureaus." Write and tell them what you're after. If they help you get it, of course, there may be a fee to pay—probably 5 per cent of your first year's earnings, tax-deductible. They'll explain the fee when they acknowledge your letter, so you'll have the chance to say No before they settle down to work.

At that stage you'll have done a good job of intercepting the openings that are hunting for you. But that's only half the job, isn't it? You also need to hunt for the hidden openings. Some are in places that need you but don't know it or need you but aren't telling. So you'd better consider writing two more letters.

In the first, ask the medical society of each state you're interested in for its membership roster, plus a list of county populations. When you get the rosters, turn to the geographical listings. For each local medical society, count the number of practitioners in your specialty. Next, using the population list, check any localities that strike you as possibly having room for one more in your line of work. Here are some rough yardsticks you can use:

¶ General practice: one G.P. per 1,500-2,500 population.
¶ Pediatrics: one per 8,000-11,000.
¶ General surgery: one per 9,000-11,000.
¶ OBG: one per 10,000-13,000.
¶ Ophthalmology: one per 19,000-23,000.

Notice I've listed no yardstick above for internists. That's because internists come in different breeds. In one Southern city of 200,000 population, there were, the last time I checked, 80 internists and only 30 general practitioners. Most of the internists there have long functioned as G.P.s. They bar OB and infant care, but not much else. By contrast, a Northeastern city with 50,000 inhabitants had 33 G.P.s and only four internists. The four internists specialize determinedly in cardiac, pulmonary conditions, allergy, and gastro-enterology. They wouldn't treat a drop-in sniffle on a bet. You can see, then, that some internists can get by on a psychiatrist's doctor-patient ratio, while others can barely manage on a G.P.'s ratio.

When you've whittled down your choices to two or three most likely looking possibilities, your homework's over, unless you de-

---

Requirements to meet before opening an office

The regulations on medical licensing vary among the states except in one respect: You must be licensed before you can legally open your door to the first patient. You must be licensed in other ways, too. For guidance, check with the office of your county medical society. It may maintain a checklist of requirements, updated as changes occur in pertinent Federal, state, and local laws. If no such list is available, the society's legal counsel can review this list of requirements with you:

☐ Federal narcotics license *

☐ State basic science examination

☐ State licensure examination

☐ State medical license

☐ State hypnotic drug license

☐ State, county, township, or city professional or occupational license(s)

☐ Zoning permit

* Obtained on application to the nearest office of the Internal Revenue Service. The license must be renewed annually before July 1.

12

cide, as **Dr. Stanton** did, to write the second letter—for some Chamber of Commerce booklets.

Even if you do, though, you'll soon find that legwork is your next order of business. You'll want to visit the towns you've selected and possibly one or more towns suggested by the societies and agencies that have been working for you. Take your wife along. And make sure that one of you has a visitation list something like this:

Local medical society. The state roster should tell you where to find the local headquarters. In small societies, it's apt to be merely the office of the long-suffering physician who's stuck with the unpaid secretarial chores. In more sizable areas, it can be the office of a salaried executive. Whichever it is, the man you'll meet there knows a lot about the local professional climate. Check on whether there are any big groups around. Dig until you're sure no one has your own special field sewn up tight. If he seems cool toward your possible advent, keep questioning till the reason comes out.

Local health department. If this office is within easy reach of the medical society, go there. A public health officer usually knows his area's health strengths and weaknesses forward and backward. He can give you accurate vital statistics. He can brief you on all the local welfare services—and the prevalence of indigents in the area.

Local hospitals. Try to visit at least one. Phone ahead for an appointment with the administrator. If he's available, he'll probably treat you to a quick tour. Find out what provision is made for your kind of work, ask about the procedure for obtaining hospital privileges, pump for information about the local Blue plans and other hospital-medical-surgical coverage in the area.

City hall. You can go there for facts about the local police, fire, water, transportation, sewerage, and garbage collection services. Mainly go there to check on property taxes and assessments.

Chamber of Commerce. Whether it's in a big city or small, it can give you data on the town's trade pattern, its industrial strength and prospects, and its shopping facilities. Don't be shy about asking for information on churches, libraries, clubs, and such pleasures as golf. Discount for civic pride and anxiety to nab a potential new consumer. Just nod politely when you're told that the town needs more doctors. Boosters always say that.

A real-estate office. It's O.K. to pick one from the Yellow Pages. Quiz the broker about neighborhoods, zoning policies, new housing starts, current prices, and rentals. Sure, you'll get a sales pitch with the good information. It won't hurt.

A high school principal. If you have kids destined for college someday, they're either in high school now or they will be in due time. Most high school principals are brutally frank about the worth of the grade schools that feed them, and they're happily proud of their graduates' college-admission successes. And they're accustomed to giving advice to parents.

Some local doctors. It's diplomatic to visit them. But don't limit your calls to those in your own specialty. If you drop anchor later, they'll all be your neighbors and clubmates, and only a few will be competitors. Don't expect them all to be willing to guess at your chances; those who do may cancel each other out anyway. If you can find out the name of a physician who recently settled in the locality, visit him. He's probably charted the professional rocks you'll need to navigate—and has bruises. He just might tell you how he got them.

Should you ever move in on a small town where the incumbents hint broadly that the S.R.O. sign is up? Yes, sometimes. Your best chance of success in such a situation: Offer a kind or quality of medical care the area doesn't have. OBG men and pediatricians have been outstandingly successful in semirural family-doctor areas. Patients come in on their own. Next best bet: Strengthen a weak spot. Not only are there areas where the men in possession aren't numerous enough; there are some where the incumbents aren't *good* enough. Diagnose either situation correctly, and you can move in with confidence.

The big risk is that you—or maybe your wife—will be so sold on a city or town that you'll diagnose a need when one isn't there. Try to avoid making that mistake. If you make it, keep the moving van on a permanent alert. Chances are, you'll be on your way again.

There's no guarantee that, even with all your research, you'll spot a winner. What's certain is that, without research, your chances of finding a loser are high. In any event, picking the wrong place to practice isn't just bad management. It's bad medicine. *Somewhere there are lots of patients who really need you.*

3

Get an office that fits you

A New York City judge once ruled that a doctor's office isn't a store. Later, the judge of an appellate court, upholding him, commented: "A store is a place where people shop. They don't shop for medical care."

They don't?

Well, here's a word for you on the q.t.: Better have yourself a well-situated, well-planned, well-equipped nonstore for people not to shop in. If you don't, they'll do their nonshopping for medical care elsewhere.

Getting the right kind of place may take lots of thought and planning. Here's a rundown of some things a doctor can do to make his office a help to his practice rather than a handicap:

Pick the right spot. It used to be easy for a physician to decide where to hang out his shingle. A general practitioner would mark down a likely residential neighborhood, scout it thoroughly for a suitable house, and hire a contractor to fix him up with a half-residence, half-office. A specialist, on the other hand, would tour the downtown area looking for a vacant suite in a professional building. He'd settle, of course, for what he could get.

Today, except in rural areas, the home-office combination is a disappearing phenomenon in much of the country. I know that's so because I've checked over a list of 617 doctors I know who moved into their present offices during the past 10 years. Out of 112 G.P.s on my list, only two have their offices in their homes. Another 34

17

have fitted up a room at home with a few basics, just in case a patient with a severed artery appears on the doorstep. But those aren't primary offices, and I don't count them.

Of the specialists on my list, surprisingly few have opted for downtown space during the 10-year span. Out of 505 specialists, only 80 occupy business suites in business areas.

All told, 535 doctors out of the 617 total voted against both the home-office combination and the downtown professional building. Here's how they did vote:

¶ 161 moved into small buildings constructed or reconstructed expressly for them, with no special relationship to other professional buildings. Most are near hospitals.

¶ 144 moved into large professional buildings—erected for medical-dental tenants only—almost in sight of a general hospital.

¶ 118 moved into campus-like aggregations of small professional buildings. Practically all of these medical-dental "colonies" are also close to hospitals.

Three books to help you plan your office

Most bookstores and libraries are well stocked with recent volumes on planning an office. These three are of special interest because they deal with doctors' special needs:

¶ "Doctors' Offices and Clinics," Reinhold Publishing Corp., 430 Park Avenue, New York 10022. This book was written by two architects, Paul Kirk and Eugene Sternberg. It's a handsomely illustrated hard-cover guide—the standard in its field. Price: $17.50.

¶ "A Planning Guide for Physicians' Medical Facilities," American Medical Association, 535 North Dearborn Street, Chicago 60610. This booklet is full of valuable information. It's available free from the A.M.A. Division of Socio-Economic Activities.

¶ "Guide for Physicians Office Planning," American Surgical Trade Association, 11 East Adams Street, Chicago 60603. It's an excellent booklet, and it's available free from A.S.T.A. dealers or the association headquarters.

¶ 71 moved into premises more or less remote from hospitals and not restricted to professional occupants. Some are in suburban shopping centers, some over stores, some* in apartment buildings.

¶ 11 (all radiologists) practice in hospital-provided space.

The trend seems clear. Doctors, like hospitals, are outward bound—outward from the department-store and parking-meter areas. To some degree, they're tending to cluster together, to the exclusion of practitioners of other professions. My name for it is "zone practice."

Being a neighborhood G.P., of course, is an excellent reason for not joining the shift to zone practice. And a specialist doesn't have to head for a zone simply because that's where the boys are. But if, in your city, the zone is where the patients go, that's different. You could miss out by swimming against the stream.

Give your patients room. "My waiting room seats eight people," said a doctor who was showing me around his office, "and I never

---

*Not including another 30 in New York City who merely moved from one apartment building to another during the 10 years.

A quick guide to your space needs

The space you need is governed by the work you do. These areas meet the needs of typical practices:

Specialty	Square feet	Specialty	Square feet
Allergy	800	Ophthalmology	900
Anesthesiology [1]	200	Orthopedics [2]	1,000
Dermatology	800	Pathology	800
EENT	700	Pediatrics	900
General practice	1,000	Proctology	700
General surgery	600	Psychiatry	400
Internal medicine	700	Radiology	900
OBG	800	Urology	800

[1] Only business space is required. [2] Add at least 200 square feet if there's to be a physical therapy room.

---

seem to have enough chairs for all the people who turn up. What do you advise?"

It was a familiar question. The doctors who ask it hope, I'm sure, that I'll come through with a surefire way of discouraging patients from arriving early and bringing company with them. Well, there isn't any. So you'd better not figure your reception room space on the basis of your patient load alone. Make room for guests.

Budget space for patients first, of course. But watch it: The average number of patients seen per hour can be misleading. An internist who does two complete work-ups between 10 A.M. and 1 P.M. and then sees 18 other patients between 2 P.M. and 5 P.M. is averaging four patients per hour. He'd be wise to have 12 seats in his reception room. There could easily be that number there if he got back late from lunch—eight patients and four friends.

If you put in enough seats to accommodate the peak load, you'll be able to take care of anything short of a breakdown of your ap-

---

Seven firms that will help plan your office

To boost sales of their products, many manufacturers offer advice and pamphlets on interior designing and office arrangements. The following seven firms offer services that are usually free, even if you buy none of their products.

¶ Aloe Medical Division of Brunswick Corporation, 1831 Olive Street, St. Louis, Mo. 63103. Local sales representatives of this firm will advise physicians, at no charge, on every aspect of office planning. For doctors just starting out in practice or switching to another specialty, the company offers an excellent free booklet called "Equipping Your Office."

¶ American Metal Furniture, Inc., 930 West New York Street, Indianapolis, Ind. 46207. This company will supply, at no charge, suggested interior layouts to physicians who send dimensions of projected suites. The firm also offers, through its surgical supply dealers, a catalog containing several such layouts.

¶ General Electric Company, X-Ray Department, 4855 Electric Avenue, Milwaukee, Wis. 53201. Through its local sales representa-

---

pointment system—and *that* disaster can't be solved by any number of chairs. My thumbnail formula for assessing peak-load needs is simple: 3H. H is the number of revisit patients the doctor figures he can see in an hour. That number varies according to the doctor's specialty and his working speed. Once H has been determined, it should be doubled to allow for the doctor's occasional late arrival and his falling behind schedule because of interruptions or because a patient needs more than the scheduled time. H is tripled to take care of the guests.

If you're a beginning doctor, try to plan ahead by budgeting for the number of revisits per hour you'll schedule when your practice gets busy. And just how many is that? Well, most busy G.P.s I know can go through revisits at a six-per-hour clip. I know some who've raised the figure to 12. I know lots of internists can do eight per hour, though most of them say they don't move that fast. I know plenty of pediatricians who can do 10. So can many general sur-

---

tives, G.E. will execute free interior layouts for X-ray facilities—including X-ray equipment rooms, developing and processing rooms, and diagnostic rooms.

¶ Hamilton Manufacturing Company, Two Rivers, Wis. 54241. Through its surgical supply dealers, this company will prepare free furniture and equipment layouts from architects' floor plans.

¶ Ritter Equipment Company, 400 West Avenue, Rochester, N.Y. 14603. This company executes interior layouts free after the doctor has filled out an office-data questionnaire. A free booklet of such layouts is also available.

¶ Westinghouse Electric Corporation, X-Ray Department, 2519 Wilkins Avenue, Baltimore, Md. 21223. Through its local sales representatives, Westinghouse will execute free interior layouts for X-ray facilities—including X-ray equipment rooms, developing and processing rooms, and diagnostic rooms.

---

geons; I know one who regularly sees 30 follow-up patients per two-hour stretch. (That doesn't mean that a patient is in and out of his office in four minutes. Some stay much longer. But four minutes is the average time a revisit patient is in *his* presence.)

Let's assume that the 3H formula indicates you need 18 reception room seats. To convert them into the square footage required, multiply the 18 by the number of square feet you're willing to allow per person. I can tell you now that 20 square feet per person spells comfort and anything under 12 spells crowd. For 18 people, a reception room measuring 16 feet by 18 feet would be about right; that's 288 square feet.

Give yourself enough rooms. Notice the plural—rooms, not room. You'll understand the reason for this when I tell you about Dr. Callaghan.

His reception room, when I visited him, was packed—with five people. Dr. Callaghan's nurse signaled me to go into the doctor's consultation room. I sat down there. It was tiny, and half of it was

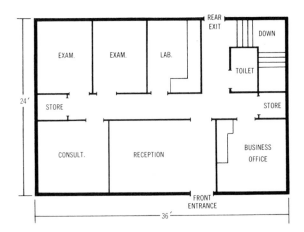

The best layout for a physician's office is rectangular. This layout provides a reception room, front office, consultation room, two examining rooms, laboratory, toilet, and storage space—all within a total area of 864 square feet. The reception room is 160 square feet; the front office, 100; the clinical area, 340; halls, toilet, and storage areas, 264.

curtained off. Behind the curtain, I could hear someone breathing. Suddenly the doctor popped his head into the room from the corridor, said, "Be right with you," and disappeared back into the corridor. I'd merely smiled and nodded to him. *That* was a mistake! If I'd said something out loud, the lady behind the curtain wouldn't have assumed the doctor was talking to her. And she wouldn't have backed into the open, bare. "Doctor," she said, "just take a look at this before I put that damned girdle back on."

The patient, Dr. Callaghan explained later, had been worried about a mole on her gluteus maximus. Thanks to her willingness to believe a face-saving white lie, she left the office that day only worried about the odd impression she must have made on that "visiting specialist" who quickly professed to know nothing about moles.

Thankfully, few doctors I visit are quite as badly off for space as Dr. Callaghan. A surprisingly large number have begun with too little space and too few rooms, though, and have stayed that way. You'd be wise to do your best to avoid the trap of starting practice

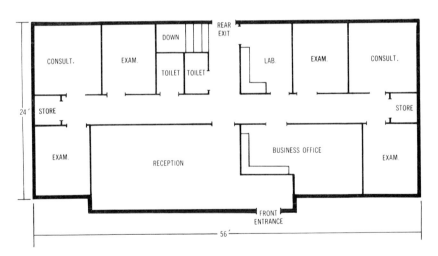

This two-man office layout gives a consultation room and two examining rooms to each physician. The reception room, business office, and laboratory are all larger than a doctor practicing alone would require. Total square feet: 1,400. The reception room is 288; the front office, 168; the clinical area, 600; the halls, toilets, and storage areas, 344.

with a space shortage. To the question "How much space is enough?" the answer is "Always more than you'd think." Enough space isn't, however, a mere matter of area. The square footage of a football field wouldn't help you if the landlord wouldn't let you change the layout. The trick is to get enough rooms.

Some doctors get by with only one examining room. For instance, there's the Pennsylvania doctor I know who runs his office without an aide. After each examination, he tidies up the room, walks into his reception room, and calls the next patient. His practice isn't very busy, and he likes it that way. A doctor with a busy practice, though, does better with several examining rooms. I know a Florida OBG man who compresses all his routine prenatal examinations into three afternoons a week by using five examining rooms. He's been known to see 90 women between lunchtime and quitting time. And he quits at 5:30 P.M. sharp.

For most doctors, an office that has two or three examining rooms, correctly used, should fill the bill. With a good nurse helping, you

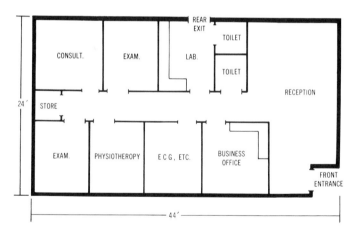

Special rooms in this one-doctor layout permit examining rooms to be used exclusively for examinations. Physical therapy treatments are given only in the physiotherapy room. ECG and BMR have their own room, which is equipped with a wide couch rather than a narrow examining table. The physician handles his patients by circulating through six rooms, interviewing patients, examining them, and supervising their treatment.

may find that seeing 40 patients a day isn't so difficult—*if* you observe these don'ts:

¶ Don't use examining rooms for history-taking, counseling, or chit-chat. The consultation room is the place for those activities.

¶ Don't weigh patients in examining rooms. People weigh the same in the corridor outside.

¶ Don't do minor surgery in examining rooms. If minor surgery is a feature of your office practice, you need a small operating room.

¶ Don't do ECGs or other tests in examining rooms. Set aside a room with a couch, not a table, for such purposes.

¶ Don't give physical therapy treatments in examining rooms. A separate room, cubicled if necessary, is better.

¶ Don't let patients wait in examining rooms for the nurse to come in and give them shots. Until she's ready for them in the lab, they're more comfortable in your reception room.

Some doctors think I overdo my pressure for one room, one job. It isn't actually my own idea. I've picked it up from some efficient doctors I've been watching for years. In the words of one of them: "Half the secret of running a big practice is to walk around opening doors. The other half of the secret is to close the doors behind you. If you do both fast enough, you have no trouble."

Plan for wide corridors. A corridor two feet wide allows one-way traffic only. In a three-foot corridor, two people can pass each other—but not with ease. Try to hold out for four-foot corridors.

Give your secretary enough space. In any well-managed private practice, the front office is the nerve center. It's the reception point, the communications center, the traffic hub, the public relations department, accounting division, credit desk, and teller's cage all in one. So don't settle for a bathroom-sized rectangle grudgingly chopped out of the reception room you originally sketched. Whatever size your consultation room is, the front office should be larger. More man-hours are worked in it. More equipment goes into it. More people are in it at one time.

Once, in Ohio, a doctor's secretary asked me to help her

straighten out some mixed-up figures. We started at 9 A.M. By 10, there were in that room—a six-by-eight foot cubbyhole—the two of us, a patient, the patient's child, and a typewriter mechanic. Then the doctor arrived just as his wife called on the phone. "I'll take it in here," he said, squeezing into the little room. Then: "Did I say something funny?"

What's the smallest area allowable for a one-girl front office? I'd say 100 square feet is absolutely the minimum. For each extra girl, I'd add at least 60 square feet.

Give your nurse some space too. When a doctor employs a nurse as well as a secretary, she'll usually have her headquarters in the lab. If there's no lab, give her a niche somewhere in the treatment area—out of the traffic stream, in a spot where she can weigh patients, sort records, and quietly answer the questions patients forget to ask you. For humanity's sake, see that she has a chair or stool. Office nursing, like waiting on table, gets 'em in the arches.

As that New York judge said, a doctor's office isn't a store. But the smart doctor does take a leaf out of the successful storekeeper's book by providing the best he can afford for the customers, the help, and the goods—as well as for the boss.

4

Look before you lease

et's say you've picked out the office you want. The space is adequate, the layout is just as you specified, the furnishings and equipment are all on order. Now comes your new landlord, waving the lease of your new premises. "Sign here as a matter of form, Doctor," he tells you. "Makes you safe as well as us."

Don't sign.

Not then and there, anyway. Take the document home and bring it back the next day. In the interim, make sure you understand every paragraph, every sentence, and every word. Enlist your lawyer's assistance. Believe me, you'll need him. Once you've signed, you'll have entered a contract into which has gone the skill of a generation of high-priced attorneys—all working for the landlord.

I'll warn you now: Studying a lease is no fun. As literature, it rates nowhere. It has no comic bits. Indeed, it can be distinctly unfunny in parts—especially where it says, as many leases do, that if the landlord considers any act of yours to be "objectionable or improper" he can throw you out, march in himself, and "remove all persons and property from the said premises by force or otherwise."

If one like it is in the lease your landlord offers, can you get it out or water it down? The answer depends on your bargaining strength, and you may possess more than you suspect.

After all, he does want to sell his commodity—space—and he has a healthy respect for the law of supply and demand. If other people are after his space, the chances are that he'll feel he needn't budge. If people aren't battering at his door pleading for a chance to move in, though, you may win a better guarantee of "peaceful enjoyment." The fact that you're a doctor should help you in your negotiations. Many landlords like doctors as tenants. They lend prestige. Also, once a doctor is established, he's less likely to move than, say, a branch business manager whose entire office may be shifted to a new location in three or four years.

In the end, though, your bargaining strength depends on your answer to two questions. How badly do you want the landlord's space? How much are you willing to pay for it? If you have two or three other places in view, at lower prices, or if you can afford to wait, you're in the driver's seat. Trouble is, in the low-priced or moderate-priced rental field, the demand for space almost always exceeds the supply. The consequence usually is that the landlord drops his lease on your desk, announces the rental he's asking, and tells you to take it or leave it. In the higher-priced accommodations, the landlord's position is weaker. The supply of expensive space often exceeds the demand, and vacancies cost a landlord plenty. If he's hurting, he may decide that a reduced rent is better than none at all or that a softer lease is better than empty space.

In a new high-priced building, a landlord may be unusually vulnerable. His project was probably paid for by a small amount of his own cash and a big short-term construction loan from a bank. To repay the bank loan, he needs "takeout money" in the form of a long-term mortgage loan. The "takeout" lender's first question: "How much of the space have you leased?" If the leasing is slow, the landlord is faced with three choices. He can reduce his rentals. He can give what are known as "concessions"—periods of rent-free occupancy to induce tenants to sign. Or he can let up on the strictness of his leases.

To the landlord, the least palatable of these alternatives, is, as you'd expect, a lower rent. He also wants, if he can, to avoid granting any concessions. For him, "softening" the lease has one major advantage: It takes no cash from his wallet.

So when you bring the not-yet-signed lease back, start off with a request for an out-and-out drop in the rent for the full term of the lease. If that fails, ask for a concession: several months' rent-free occupancy. If that fails, make a pitch for the landlord to pay the cost of adapting his space to your requirements. And if *that* fails, try to get him to step-rate the rent over the life of the lease—lower at the start, higher each year thereafter, averaging out to the rate named by the landlord in the first place.

Well, you tried.

Now get down to the lease's fine print. It would, of course, save a lot of time if the landlord would agree to scrap his contract in favor of a contract drawn by your attorney. He won't, though. He wants you to sign *his* lease. Tell him you'll sign it *if* it includes:

A warranty to practice. Ask him to write in a warranty that the local zoning law permits you to practice medicine in the premises, to operate your professional equipment there, and to erect any customary outside signs.

A description of the premises. See that the lease describes in detail what you're renting. Besides listing the rooms you'll ordinarily use, it should mention any other space—in the basement, attic, garage, or grounds—that he's promised you.

A warranty on facilities. Ask for a warranty that the power and plumbing facilities will enable you to operate all your equipment. If any special gas or electric lines have been promised, have them listed. If you don't, you may find yourself with a fat bill for, say, the installation of a high-voltage cable.

Protection of your investment. If you plan to alter the premises, see that the authority to do so is written into the lease. Don't buy any clause requiring you, in such a case, to restore the premises to their original condition; the cost of re-creating a bare rectangle can come high. Guard against valuable equipment passing into the landlord's possession because part of it is fixed to the floor or a wall; have the lease show what you may take with you when you leave.

A guarantee of "services." The lease probably pledges "customary services." This may mean elevator service, hot water, heat, and air-conditioning—and it may not. Ask for each of them to be named in the lease. And check that their availability fits in with your working schedule. In some buildings, "customary services" are deactivated at night or on weekends.

A warning before eviction. Make sure you won't be evicted the first time you inadvertently break a house rule. Ask to be given notice when you're in violation of a rule, and a chance to correct your error. Give a flat No to any clause that says breaking a rule renders you liable not only to be evicted but also to continue paying the rent for the rest of your term.

A definition of "objectionable conduct." Insist that the landlord specify the kind of conduct he can, at his whim, deem "objectionable." Better still, get the clause stricken in its entirety.

Permission to sublet. If the lease is to run over a year, ask for a clause allowing you to move out and turn over the tenancy to someone else. If the landlord insists on the right to veto any proposed subtenant, suggest a compromise like this: "The tenant shall not sublet without the landlord's consent, which consent shall not be unreasonably withheld." If that, too, fails, hold out for an automatic end to the lease within a year (at the most) after you've suffered a disabling illness or accident, and the right to instant release from liability if you're called into military service.

A clause canceling the lease if you die. Of course you don't expect to die during the term of the lease. But you *might.* And your widow could be made to hand over to the landlord a big chunk of what you'd left her, in the form of regular rent payments for the unexpired term of your lease. Protect her against the risk: Dig in your heels until the landlord agrees that your death automatically terminates the lease as of the end of the month in which you die. If his screams unnerve you, it's O.K. to stretch your estate's liability to the end of the month following the month you die in.

A "fire insurance clause." In some leases, destruction of your office by fire doesn't relieve you from paying the rent. Get off this hook if you possibly can.

At this point, you're halfway through your negotiations. You've told the landlord what you want *in* your lease. Now you're ready to tell him what you want *out* of it. Begin by objecting to any clause that says the landlord isn't liable for damage to persons or property caused by falling plaster, broken steam pipes, defective cables, plugged drains, broken water mains, etc. In some states, the law holds a landlord liable for his own negligence even if the lease says he isn't, but don't take the chance. Remember, though, that he's entitled to be told about defects before being made responsible for damage resulting from them. One doctor I know who failed to notify his landlord of a cracked floor in a corridor was himself held liable when a patient tripped on the crack and was hurt.

Object to any clause that gives you a continuing liability after the lease has expired. In some areas, unless stipulated otherwise, a landlord can hold you for a full year's rent if you overstay your lease even by a day. One Midwestern doctor told his landlord that he'd be moving, casually mentioning that he'd need a couple of days to get his equipment out. After he'd gone the landlord wrote: "Since you were in possession of your office after the expiration of your written lease, I'll be billing you for the rent for another year." In court, the landlord won.

Object to tricky renewal clauses. Accept one that says you lose your option to renew if you don't give notice of intention to renew by a stated date. Reject the one that says renewal is automatic unless you give notice of nonrenewal by a stated date. With this second kind, forgetfulness can saddle you with two rents.

Object to an unlimited "viewing clause," giving the landlord the privilege of showing prospective new tenants around your premises at any time. Insist that the viewing period be restricted to 30 days before you leave.

What happens if you deal not with the landlord but with an agent who states flatly that the landlord allows no changes in the printed lease? If your protests fail to budge him, and if you want the space badly, comfort yourself with the reflection that generations of tenants have lived under leases like the one you're offered. You won't be the first doctor to say to himself: "I'm under the gun. But at least it's a gun that's rarely fired."

31

5

The pros and cons of building

S ooner or later almost all physicians ask themselves: "Would I be better off owning my office?" It's a good question, but there's no pat answer. In case the office-owning idea has crossed *your* mind, I'll say one thing in a hurry: Owning isn't necessarily cheaper. Any office you own will probably cost you as much to operate as the one you rent—and quite possibly more.

"But," you may say, "if I build a bigger and better office, and do more and better work in it, I'll earn more. That's good economics, isn't it?"

It sure is. All I want to point out is that the benefits lie in *using* good facilities, not *owning* them. For the improvement of your practice, the space you use needn't be your own.

A few years ago the Midwestern management firm Black & Skaggs Associates made a study of 102 physicians' building projects in five Midwestern states. The earnings of three-fourths of the doctors concerned jumped 15 to 25 per cent in the first year of occupancy of new quarters. Precisely the same results would have been recorded if the new buildings had been owned by Conrad Hilton or Howard Johnson. What mattered was that the doctors moved into good offices, not that their signatures were on the mortgage deeds.

That point established, I've no hesitation in saying that for many doctors there are solid economic advantages in office ownership. They're the advantages inherent in any sound real-estate investment. I've prodded my share of doctors into cashing in on those advantages. But I've occasionally wished that some doctors hadn't been in such an all-fired hurry to become landed proprietors.

Take Dr. Roy Gilbey. He was 30 years old when he finished his stint in the Air Force and set up his general practice in Woodbine, a small community in the South. Inside a year, it was apparent that the tiny office he'd rented for $100 a month wouldn't do. For $150 a month, Dr. Gilbey could have rented a bigger office nearby. With some remodeling, it would have been suitable. Alternatively, the owner of a local store was anxious to build him just the kind of office he wanted on a 10-year lease at $300 a month.

But Dr. Gilbey decided he'd build for himself. One reason, he told me, was that the landlord of the available larger office had said it would be up to Dr. Gilbey to pay for the necessary remodeling. "But I don't care to sink money in another man's property," said the doctor.

If he'd accepted the storeowner's offer to build and lease, he'd have paid $36,000 in rent in 10 years, with nothing to show for it but canceled checks—and the prospect of signing up for a new term. But by building a $36,000 office for himself, and paying for it in 10 years, he'd own a building and have no more rent to pay. "Furthermore, where would I be," Dr. Gilbey asked, "if I got notice to clear out after 10 years? I'd probably be forced to build for myself. Better build now. As owner-occupier, I get the landlord's profit for myself."

The clincher for Dr. Gilbey was that, by building, he'd provide himself—or, at his death, his family—with a capital asset that could either be retained as an income producer or sold outright.

As you see, Dr. Gilbey came up with some excellent reasons for investing in a building of his own. The trouble was that they didn't cancel out these reasons why he shouldn't have committed himself to the purchase of a single brick:

¶ He wasn't sure the location was right for him. It wasn't a cinch that Dr. Gilbey would stay in Woodbine. He was strongly drawn to aviation medicine, and, while in the Air Force, had been tempted to make a career of it. The lure was still there.

¶ He wasn't sure how big to make the building. Dr. Gilbey wasn't at all clear about the scope of the medical care he'd be offering to Woodbine's citizens. That made his building project somewhat iffy. "I've got an X-ray room in the plans," he told me, "but I'm not sure I'll buy a unit."

¶ He wasn't in good enough financial shape to be plunging into the specialty real-estate field. He'd had no time to build up a cash reserve. His life insurance was skimpy. He was in hock for a lot of equipment bought on credit. And he had as yet no substantial equity in the modest home he'd bought.

In due time, Dr. Gilbey returned to the Air Force—with the help of the store owner he'd so curtly turned down. The merchant, still alert to a good opportunity—and able to afford it—bought Dr. Gilbey's office 18 months after it was completed and leased it to Dr. Gilbey's successor. Dr. Gilbey came out of the adventure with no more than a slight financial trauma.

By contrast, consider the case of Dr. Rod Nicholson. At 45, Dr. Nicholson had practiced OBG in Bonniford for nine years. He knew he wouldn't be leaving, ever. For a long time he'd occupied a rented office over a drugstore, and for almost as long a time he'd wanted out. He knew to the last vinyl tile exactly how much new office he wanted.

Checking his fiscal situation, Dr. Nicholson found that he had enough cash in his savings account to buy the lot he'd picked out and leave an emergency reserve.

Owning by now a two-thirds equity in his home, he knew he could refinance the mortgage to raise the down payment on an office building. No need, therefore, to sell or pledge the small portfolio of stocks he'd accumulated in the past few years. His practice was already earning enough to absorb the extra operating costs of a larger office.

Finally, he had enough disability insurance and business overhead insurance to carry him—and his two mortgages—through a long illness, if he should be so unlucky as to have one.

Given ordinary good health, Dr. Nicholson judged, he could pay off the two mortgages—the one on his home and the one on his office—long before old age cut down his working capacity and his income. And, if he were to die prematurely, his life insurance and the stock portfolio would protect his family future.

"I was all set to go," Dr. Nicholson told me. "But I saw one weakness. I had no guarantee that my investment, if I made it, could be quickly sold in an emergency. If I died or was disabled, for instance, a tenant or a buyer might not pop up instantly. Dr. Gordon's office, I remembered, stayed empty for years after his death and finally had to be made over for a beautician. So I made one more decision: I wouldn't build *on my own*."

It took Dr. Nicholson a year to line up four other physicians willing to join him as owner of a new five-doctor office.

"My share worked out at $30,000," said Dr. Nicholson. "For a one-man building, I'd have had to pay more, so right off I had a gain. But the important thing was that all five of us agreed to help find a tenant or buyer for an empty suite. In fact, if one of us dies the other four will immediately buy his interest in the building and later resell it or find a tenant. Now I don't have to worry about whether my investment is safe. I *know* it is."

Most medical men, I'd say, have to wait until they're around Dr. Nicholson's age—40—before they can pass the financial tests he subjected himself to. They're wise if, having decided on building, they get on with it before their 50s arrive, since it's seldom advisable for an older doctor to saddle himself with a long-term mortgage. Ordinarily, the best time to invest in your own office is when you're at the midpoint of your professional life.

Maybe, though, you can swing your share of a building project even if you're just starting out in practice—by getting other doctors to chip in. But is doing so really good economics? One way to reach an answer is to compare your situation with Dr. Nicholson's, since he and his friends plunged the right way.

First off, they bought a lot costing $20,000. The building cost was $120,000, about par for the 6,000 square feet they got. Architects', lawyers', and others' fees peaked out at $10,000, more or less. Total: $150,000. Rod Nicholson's commitment: $30,000. Can *you* take that much financial risk?

The five doctors paid cash for their lot. That called for $4,000 from each man. They paid all fees in cash, requiring $2,000 per

---

Think of who should own your building

It's often advantageous for a doctor to separate his owner-occupied building from his medical practice. Although there's no one best way to do so, one of the following options is generally chosen:

Wife owns building. The physician pays rent to his wife as proprietor. There's no income tax angle. If the couple pays tax on a joint return, the rent is a business deduction on Schedule C, and ordinary income (less depreciation, etc.) on Schedule B. But the doctor gets a clearer picture of his ownership situation if the details aren't buried in his practice accounts. Estate tax savings are possible if the doctor predeceases his wife.

Trust owns building. For doctors who own buildings free and clear, this method offers attractive income tax savings and, with an irrevocable trust, estate tax savings. Complications are plentiful, however, if the building is mortgaged. Trusts can be temporary or permanent. Beneficiaries can be anyone, but, for major tax gains, physicians usually name minor children.

Partnership owns building. This route calls for the formation of a separate partnership, not the one in which the doctors practice together. Since it's a real-estate venture rather than a medical practice, it can ethically include wives and other nonphysicians. No tax gains. Three advantages: A young doctor can be admitted to the medical partnership without having to chip in on building ownership; an older doctor can retire from the medical partnership without surrendering his interest in the building; the building partnership interests can be transferred without disturbing medical partnership interests.

Corporation owns building. This form of ownership is becoming increasingly popular. Stockholders can be anyone, e·g., doctors, wives, outside investors. To the advantages listed under partnership ownership, add these three: limited liability, simplification of transfers of interest, and tax gains.

---

man extra. For the building, they negotiated a 15-year mortgage for $83,500, leaving each doctor to ante up $7,300 toward a down payment of $36,500. So Dr. Nicholson had to dig into his jeans for a total of $13,300. Can *you* raise that much easily?

Dr. Nicholson took the $2,000 for fees out of his savings account. To raise his $4,000 for the land purchase, he borrowed on his life insurance. To get his share of the down payment on the building, he refinanced his home mortgage, leaving the monthly payments unchanged but adding eight years to the term. If you can do something along the same lines, you're in good shape.

When Dr. Nicholson signed for his share of the new office mortgage, he was committed to 180 monthly payments of $144.90 each. Can *you* take on such a long-term liability?

Ignoring operating costs, Dr. Nicholson will have paid out $39,382 in 15 years for his 1,200 square feet of new office. In his town of Bonniford, space of a quality comparable to that in his new building can still be rented for $3 per square foot per year. To rent 1,200 square feet for 15 years, therefore, would cost him $54,000. That's $14,618 more than he'll pay out as an owner. When the 15 years are up, he'll own one-fifth of the building.

Does he have a bargain? To answer that question, we'll have to weigh the investment factor.

The purpose of investment is profit. Dr. Nicholson's office, on the figures I've given you, is going to pay him a profit over renting of $14,618 over 15 years. That's the difference between what he'll pay for his purchased space and what he'd pay for comparable rented space. But he has a $30,000 asset at work. That much money invested in a savings and loan at 4 per cent would earn $24,028 in 15 years—$9,410 more than that $14,608 ownership profit. So add the $9,410 to the $39,382 he'll pay for his $30,000 asset. Now we have a total of $48,792 as the full 15-year cost of Dr. Nicholson's real-estate investment. For that amount of money, he could rent comparable space for 13½ years.

So Dr. Nicholson's investment will be profitable under any of three conditions:

38

1. If he stays in his building 13 years or more.

2. If he sells out at any time for more than his actual outlay to date, plus 4 per cent return on $30,000, less $3 per square foot per year for the duration of his occupancy.

3. If he rents out his space during this period at any figure over $3 per square foot per year.

The point is that owning isn't by any means necessarily better than renting. It depends on your circumstances. Oh, in the end, you're going to kid yourself, I know. You'll closet yourself with your accountant and your tax expert, and you'll fill reams of paper with calculations of tax savings, increased volume of practice, higher fees, and other figures that'll shore up your yen to build—because you *want* to build. Yet what you said you wanted to know was: Is office-owning good economics?

Well, my answer is Yes. *If* you can afford the outlay and can wait for the payoff, it's as sound an idea as owning your home.

Just don't kid yourself that being your own landlord will in itself help your practice. If there's suitable space in someone else's building, your practice will do as well there.

6

Share expenses? Maybe

When young Dr. Kartwright asked me to drop in for a talk, I was puzzled by the address he gave me. It was a small two-doctor building occupied, I thought, by two partners named Huntley and Kuhn.

"I thought you leased a suite in the new Medical Arts Building," I said.

"I almost did," Dr. Kartwright replied, "but Pete Kuhn has gone into a surgical residency, and Fred Huntley decided not to take a new partner. I moved in with him on an expense-sharing deal. That's what I want to talk about."

Dr. Kartwright had done nothing unusual. Thousands of doctors cut their practice costs by sharing them with other doctors. Expense-sharing lets them economize on reception room and business office space, on the costs of repairs and redecorating, and on payroll expenses. Among other items that appeal to them are these:

¶ Each doctor remains in solo practice. There's no sharing of earnings, so one doctor's gross income doesn't depend on another's fee level or patient volume.

¶ They can pool their resources to buy equipment they can't afford as individuals. An X-ray unit is an obvious example. More likely to be overlooked: time saving business equipment, such as a copying machine in a high-price range.

¶ If their fields of work are similar, the emergency coverage problem is easily solved: They sign out to each other. If they're in

41

different specialties, they can refer cases to each other now and then. Either way, they're never far from an informal corridor consultation —a benefit missed by many solo practitioners.

Despite such attractions, Dr. Kartwright was unhappy with his expense-sharing arrangement. "My rent in the Medical Arts Building would have been $300 a month," he reminded me. "Fred and I lease this building for $400 a month. Splitting that down the middle, there was a saving of $100 a month for me right away. Fred's secretary agreed to keep my books. My half of her paycheck is $175 a month. That's a saving of $175 on what I'd have to pay a full-timer."

"You pay your own nurse?"

"Right, so there's no saving there," said Dr. Kartwright. "The saving that swayed me most was in my capital outlay. I'd had my eye on $4,000 worth of furnishings and equipment for the office in the Medical Arts Building. Fred already had everything I needed here, all less than five years old. He offered me Art's half of everything for $1,250, and he agreed to take my note."

"Good deal," I said.

"That's what I thought," replied Dr. Kartwright, "but now I'm sorry I didn't go into the Medical Arts Building. I'm not saving as much as I'd hoped, and Fred and I aren't getting along well. The rent doesn't cover utilities or janitor service. They cost me about $46 a month. I also pay half the wages of a yardman. The Medical Arts Building rent includes *all* services. So, all in all, I'm paying about as much here as I'd have paid there."

"Dr. Huntley told you in advance about the utilities, the janitor, and the yardman, didn't he?"

"He did mention them," Dr. Kartwright confessed. "I just didn't think they'd cost as much as they do. The secretary turned out to be no bargain, either. Fred has a big practice, and he keeps her so busy that my nurse has to help out with my typing and billing. We also have a part-time technician. My share of her monthly pay is $80. All told, what I'm paying for help would get me two full-time girls."

Dr. Kartwright had run up against some other snags:

1. He wasn't consulted enough. Dr. Huntley made all the decisions affecting the property. He'd had Dr. Kartwright's office redecorated in time for the latter's arrival. Dr. Kartwright was pleased about that—until he saw the first month's shared-expense list. He was down for half of the painter's bill. Then: "Makes *my* office look shabby," said Dr. Huntley, so he had his own painted the following month. "At half-price," said Dr. Kartwright.

2. He was low man on the totem pole. Dr. Kartwright wasn't warned that, on Wednesday afternoons, Dr. Huntley, the secretary, the technician, and Dr. Huntley's nurse were all off duty. Dr. Kartwright suggested a revamping of the schedule. Dr. Huntley countered with a suggestion that Dr. Kartwright hire someone for Wednesday afternoon duty. "I'll pay my half," he said.

3. He missed out on new patients. Dr. Kartwright's nurse told him that new patients who asked for him always got to see him—if he happened to be in the office. If not, the secretary explained that Dr. Kartwright was out, but that Dr. Huntley was in. But a patient asking for Dr. Huntley got an appointment for a later date, and Dr. Kartwright's services weren't offered. Patients who merely wanted to see a doctor—any doctor—were automatically steered to Dr. Huntley.

"Just as you'd guess, Fred looks on me as a rival," said Dr. Kartwright. "We sign out to each other alternate nights. Every morning after I've been on call, he phones any patient I've seen for him the night before. And, by the way: Since his is the larger practice, I'm called out for him more than he is for me." What really threw Dr. Kartwright, though, is what happened when he was out sick two months. "Fred brought each month's expense sheet to my home for me to look over," he told me. "There was no allowance for my being out. The second month, I kicked. Fred said he'd have paid *his* half if the situation had been reversed. Maybe he would. I'll never know. I'm leaving at the end of this month."

"Where do I come in?" I asked.

Dr. Kartwright, embarrassed now, laughed out loud. "There's a double suite available in the Medical Arts Building," he said, "and

I'm thinking of sharing it with George Carsden, the surgeon. After all I've told you, is that crazy?"

"Not necessarily," I said. "For a man whose practice is still in the building process, expense sharing *can* be a real help. But if I were you, I'd be more careful this time."

Here are the specific points I suggested Dr. Kartwright watch:

An effective expense-sharing agreement

The following agreement is a composite sample. Since it fits no real-life case exactly, it shouldn't be adapted for actual use without legal advice.

THIS AGREEMENT made this thirty-first day of January, 1968, by and between Harold V. Hawkins, M.D., party of the first part, and Campbell B. Smith, M.D., party of the second part, WITNESSETH:

WHEREAS, the parties hereto are medical doctors and desire to engage in their separate practices in the City of Conway, Indiana, but desire also to share the offices now occupied by the first party at 111 Park Avenue, and to employ office personnel together, and to share the expenses therefor on the basis hereinafter set forth, and also to share the use of their respective items of equipment;

NOW, THEREFORE, the parties hereto, in consideration of the mutual benefits to be derived therefrom, do hereby contract and agree as follows:

(1) That the parties hereto shall share the offices of first party at 111 Park Avenue in the City of Conway, Indiana, and shall share in the joint expenses of operating said offices, including the following items: rent, electricity, salaries for office help, repairs and maintenance, furnishings, drugs, supplies, postage, telephone, and other items of a like nature.

(2) That to provide a fund for the payment of said joint expenses, the parties hereto shall establish a joint bank account, and each shall deposit the initial sum of Two Thousand Dollars ($2,000.00) therein.

(3) That at the end of each month, the said joint expenses paid from said account shall be totaled, and each party hereto shall deposit in said account

Put it in writing. It's a basic error to assume that problems can be satisfactorily settled as they crop up. They often can't, as Dr. Kartwright discovered when he found himself paying for space and help he couldn't use during the two months he was out sick. You'll do better to anticipate problems in advance, agree on how they'll be handled, and have your decisions written into a contract.

---

a sum computed by prorating the gross business done by each party in said month against the said joint expenses.

(4) That each party shall continue to own the equipment which he now owns and shall continue to own his separate accounts receivable.

(5) That each party shall separately collect monies due him and may deposit said funds in his own bank account, but that each shall keep careful account of all professional charges and cash receipts and shall make such figures available to the other party as needed for the computation of the said joint expense-sharing.

(6) That each party shall have equal authority as to personnel, but neither shall obligate the association for any sum in excess of One Hundred Dollars ($100.00) without the consent of the other party.

This agreement shall become effective on the second day of March, 1968, and shall continue until terminated. Either party may discontinue this agreement by giving the other a notice in writing of such intention on or before the ninetieth (90th) day prior thereto.

IN WITNESS WHEREOF, the parties hereto have hereunto set their hands and seals to this instrument, executed in duplicate the day and year first above mentioned.

Witnesses:

_____

First party

_____   _____

Second party

_____

Be specific about which expenses you'll share. Include office rent, compensation of shared employes, repairs, maintenance, utilities, phones, and supplies used by both doctors. Exclude the salary of any employe who works for only one doctor, automobile expenses, personal or specialized instruments and supplies, and other items of interest to one man only.

Choose a fair way of sharing expenses. Split them on a dollar production basis or an office use basis. A measure of dollar production is the number of dollars a doctor charges or collects. Use of an office can be measured by the number of patients seen there.

Huntley and Kartwright cut their expenses down the middle. But Kartwright, who saw fewer patients, grossed only $1,500 a month to Huntley's $4,000. And Kartwright didn't even see the inside of his office during the two months he was sick. So to him the 50-50 split was less than equitable.

On a dollar production basis, his share in a normal working month might have been $3 to every $8 from Dr. Huntley—reflecting their 3-8 gross income ratio. And he wouldn't have minded paying a *fair* share of the expenses while sick—say, half, his regular monthly contribution.

Sharing expenses according to dollar production isn't always the right answer, though. When doctors in different fields of work share an office, the appointment books are often a truer guide to a fair division of the tab than the bankbooks. Sharing with Dr. Carsden, a surgeon, Dr. Kartwright, a G.P., will be in the office more, see more patients there, receive and make more phone calls, mail out more bills. But the surgeon might have the larger earnings.

Watch the depreciation allowance. If you intend to share capital costs—medical, surgical, or business equipment—remember that expenditures on them aren't operating expenses. The annual depreciation on them is. Make sure you're credited with your share.

Suppose that as low man in a 60-40 arrangement, you nevertheless agree to chip in $3,000 on a $6,000 X-ray unit. Instruct your accountant to split the annual depreciation allowance on it 50-50, not 60-40, or you'll lose out on the tax angle.

Spell out how the expenses are to be paid. Pay shared expenses through a joint bank account, depositing enough to cover the first two months. Each month, restore the account to its starting level by making contributions in the agreed proportions. That's better than having one doctor pay all bills one month and the other pay them the following month, as is sometimes done. It's also better than having one man pay everything, recovering the other's share when funds run low. The joint bank account keeps both men up to date and fully informed.

Decide who can spend what. Dr. Huntley, you remember, had Dr. Kartwright's office painted, then his own—and Dr. Kartwright was miffed. Guard against such resentment by stipulating that any spending higher than, say, $25 shall first be agreed to by both parties.

Prohibit walkouts. If your co-tenant suddenly leaves in a huff, you can be stuck for the entire expense for quite a while, if a replacement is slow in showing up. Cover the risk with a 90-day notice clause.

If you do have to call all bets off in a hurry (as did a surgeon who discovered that his co-tenant was an abortionist), add words something like these: "Professional misconduct shall be sufficient ground for the innocent party to terminate this agreement without notice."

Who stays on when sharing ends? If you move into an office owned by another doctor, there's no problem about who stays on when the contract terminates. But sometimes, when expense-sharers separate, there's a hassle over whose name stays on the office door. The time to hassle—or to spin a coin—is *before* you sign the joint lease.

There's a lot to be said for expense-sharing, especially for the beginning doctor. Just watch the points I've listed. Dr. Kartwright did when he joined Dr. Carsden in the Medical Arts Building, and he's happy now.

7

You can't do good work without proper tools

When a management consultant visits a doctor for the first time, he sometimes gets an immediate tip-off on his client's main problem from the contents of the doctor's office. If the consultant sees an attractive reception room, a front office containing modern business machines, and a treatment area amply fitted out with up-to-date diagnostic and therapeutic equipment, he figures he's about to meet a busy physician. If, on the other hand, the reception room is gloomy, the girl in the front office is thumping a battered old typewriter, and the back rooms are cluttered with chipped Army-surplus tables and cabinets, he can get ready for the plaintive query: "What's good for an ailing practice?"

The consultant knows that any physician today who's under-equipped or badly equipped is under a handicap as great as that of a golfer setting out to win the U.S. Open with a set of hickory-shafted clubs. He knows, too, that a beginning doctor almost invariably asks himself: "What's the least amount of equipment I can get by with until my practice gets going? How much will it cost?"

He'd do better to wonder: "What can I use in my new practice? And what are the prices of the best goods?"

Over the years, I've collected some dos and don'ts that have helped many physicians to make satisfying choices:

¶ Do buy equipment now if you can use it now. Seeing how long you can put off the purchase of a needed item is false economy.

¶ Don't buy anything with the intention of replacing it with a better model later. Later, you'll find, will turn out to be *much* later.

¶ Do indulge any preference you have for a particular make or model. Familiarity breeds contentment.

¶ Don't fail to get competitive bids on all major items and on groups of smaller items, except where you're specifying a preferred make or model.

¶ Don't invite bids from suppliers who cannot offer prompt and reliable service on their sales and temporary replacement of equipment taken away for servicing.

There's a hallowed tradition, it seems, that a doctor's reception room should contain at least one settee. Sometime, when you're visiting in the office of a colleague, note his patients' choice of seats. Even if the room is pretty full, it's a safe bet that the middle place in each three-seat settee is still open. In *your* reception room, aim at individual seating throughout. Buy comfortable armchairs with upholstered seats, with a straightback chair here and there. If you want to know what it's like for a woman in the third trimester to struggle out of a deep armchair, sit in one with a typewriter in your lap. Now, still holding the typewriter, get to your feet.

Checklist for your reception room

A patient gets his first impression of a doctor's office from the reception room. Here's what he should see:

- Armchairs, straight chairs, all with upholstered seats
- Center, corner, end, and coffee tables
- Magazine rack

- Coat, hat, umbrella stands
- Both floor and table lamps
- Pictures
- Mirror
- Ashtrays, smokers

The following earn extra points:

- Plants, flowers
- Carpet
- Aquarium

- Children's corner
- Water cooler
- Recorded music

If you call in a decorator to fit out your reception room, watch that he doesn't load you up with chi-chi table lamps that throw two-foot circles of dim light onto the tables the lamps stand on—and nowhere else. Most waiting patients like to read. For reading, light should come from above. Include overhead lighting.

Don't overlook the importance of "patient-pleasers" in your reception room. Music is one of the best. Be sure, though, that the sound is kept low; loud music hinders conversation and distracts people from reading. Limit the output to instrumental music.

If you're a pediatrician, you'll almost certainly think to install a tank of tropical fish, a few soft toys, and some games that make no noise. But also think to rail off an area for the tiniest tots—where they'll be secure and maybe even out of Mommy's hair.

Other patient-pleasers: carpet on the floor, pictures on the wall, plants in boxes, flowers in vases, a water cooler, a wall mirror, and a bulletin board carrying health hints and funnies about doctors.

Checklist for your business office

The essential items are:

- Counter for reception and registration of patients
- Desk or built-in work station for secretary
- Table or other extra work surface additional to desk
- Chairs (posture for personnel, straight for visitors)
- File cabinets (or shelves)
- Supply cupboard
- Typewriter
- Adding machine
- Copier
- Safe (if receipts are kept in the office overnight)

The following may also be needed, according to the size of your office and the business systems in use:

- Dictation equipment
- Intercom or paging system
- Check protector
- Postage meter, scale, and electric letter opener
- Bookkeeping machine, mimeograph machine, and other specialized equipment

---

The champion of patient-pleasers is the magazine rack. Keep only current issues there. One copy each of 10 magazines gives readers a choice; 10 back numbers of the same magazine isn't by any means an equivalent. Don't be tempted to save on magazine subscriptions by bringing issues from home after the family's through with them. If you must save that way, do it the other way around; take the office magazines home when the new issues arrive. And don't let your own enthusiasm for, say, boating show itself in a rash of magazines devoted to that sport. Even though you may not read mass-circulation magazines, they're the ones you need in your reception room. Almost any newsstand operator can tell you the names of the 10 biggest sellers.

The front office is an area that's easy to fit up on the cheap. Don't let yourself be tempted, though, because it's also an area where the best equipment pays big dividends by helping to get a greater volume of paper work done. So:

¶ Don't handicap your secretary with a small desk on which she's expected to keep an open appointment book, typewriter, telephone, in-tray, out-tray, and other desk-top furnishings. In her job, plenty of working surface is vital. Get her a 60-inch secretarial desk with separate typewriter table set at right angles to it. And don't forget a posture chair.

¶ Drive-it-yourself typewriters have had their day. Start your secretary off right with an electric typewriter.

Checklist for your consultation room

These are the essentials:

- Desk and chair
- Armchairs for visitors
- Table or credenza for journals
- Bookcase or bookshelves
- Carpet
- Overhead, floor, and desk lamps
- Pictures
- Ashtrays
- Coat closet

¶ Don't even look at a hand-cranked adding machine. Tell your supplier you want an electric with direct subtraction, credit balance, dial, *and tape.*

¶ The greatest economizer of secretarial time to appear since World War II is the office copier. Include one in your starting equipment. The dry-copy kind is the kind you need.

What goes into your consultation room? My main concern is that what goes there be good. Your desk keynotes the room, so get a good one. Choose wood over metal. Position the desk so that you face the door, not a wall. Add a matching table or credenza for your waiting-to-be-read medical journals. Without it, you can resign yourself to the loss of your desk top as a working surface. Along the same line, if you use a dictating machine, buy a stand for it. And I'm all for carpeting, draperies, and a picture or two.

For each of your examining rooms, your supplier will probably suggest a small desk or table with matching chair. Turn him down. If you feel you must make on-the-spot notes, equip each examining

---

Checklist for your workrooms

Examining room equipment is available in matching sets, wood or metal, in a variety of colors. Standard equipment:

- Examining table—regulation, special, or all-purpose
- Instrument cabinet
- Treatment stand
- Gooseneck lamp
- Stool
- Waste receptacle
- Foot-controlled sink
- Wall desk—which can be installed just outside the room, on the corridor wall
- Shelf for female patients' clothing
- Hooks for male patients' clothing

Special-purpose rooms may contain such diagnostic aids as:

- Electrocardiograph
- Exercise tolerance steps
- Ultrasonic equipment (may be combined with diathermy)
- Diathermy equipment
- Other therapeutic equipment according to specialty

---

room with a small, chest-high wall desk—and write standing up. Better still, locate your wall desks *outside* the examining rooms, and make your jottings while the patient is dressing inside.

Of the private physicians I know, about one in four regards a laboratory as an indispensable part of his office equipment. To him, the facility is good medicine and good economics. "Making money from my lab isn't its prime purpose," says a Virginia G.P., "but I've got to admit it's profitable."

A lab doesn't have to be fancy. It can be tucked into a small jog in a corridor. A factory-made bench, with all the fixings, can run into money, but you don't need one. Nor do you need a great deal of expensive equipment. Thousands of doctors get by with no more than a microscope, a colorimeter, a water bath, and an autoclave. A doctor in solo practice can usually train his office nurse to do the simple tests he requires: urinalyses, blood counts, prothrombin times, cholesterols, and blood sugars. When these are done on the premises, patients are saved many trips to hospitals or commercial laboratories. And there *is* that point about profitability.

Should your office contain X-ray equipment? Many doctors who once said No changed their minds later on. "What made us get our own X-ray unit," says an Indiana G.P. who practices with a partner, "was that we sent a patient to a radiologist who canceled the appointment to go on a luncheon date. The patient never was X-rayed by him. She then went on her own to an internist who,

---

Checklist for your X-ray room

It should have:

- Radiographic-fluoroscopic unit
- Viewing boxes
- Dressing space
- Darkroom
- Cabinets (or shelves) for records
- Closets (or cupboards) for supplies

54

with his own X-rays, found a pulmonary lesion. For a while, we thought we'd be sued. We installed X-rays for our own protection."

Some doctors pass up X-ray equipment because they can't read films well enough. Others learn how to read them. "You have to take time out for a good course," one told me, "and keep up to date with review courses."

If you don't want to read films you can have them made in your office and farm them out to a radiologist. His reading fees will cut into your X-ray receipts, of course, but there'll still be a surplus over costs.

Some physicians balk at X-rays because the equipment's so expensive. Two New Jersey G.P.s have an answer: "Our unit cost us $6,000. We bought it on time. In four years, we've grossed $35,000 with it. Materials have cost $3,500, and we've paid our technician $20,000. So we're ahead financially. The gain in convenience, to us and to our patients, has been incalculable."

A doctor who orders ECGs frequently should weigh the pros and cons of buying his own electrocardiograph. Can't read tracings? You can learn as others have. Or you can run the tests in your office and pay a consultant to interpret them. "The first 100 ECGs recouped the cost of my equipment," says a Georgia G.P. "Even if I'd paid an internist for interpretations, 200 tracings would have recovered my initial outlay. More important, though, I've stopped the seeping away of patients that occurred when I referred them outside for the tests."

Don't close out your equipment list without deciding for or against the purchase of physical therapy appliances. Many doctors have found that sending patients outside for treatment isn't entirely satisfactory. "Where I practice," says a country G.P., "the hospital is 20 miles away. My patients won't go that far. They *say* they will, but they duck it. So some conditions that could have been cleared up by physical therapy have dragged on and on. I finally invested in a diathermy machine and an ultrasonic machine. Now I order treatments knowing they'll be given. My investment? I recovered it in three months."

8

How to decide which office appliances to buy

I once walked into the office of a general practitioner in Pennsylvania and heard the crisp ping of a bell. No, it wasn't a bell on the door alerting the doctor's aide to my arrival. The ping came from an honest-to-goodness cash register—complete with no-sale key and shoot-out drawer.

"*That,*" I told the doctor, "is a piece of business equipment you'd do better without. A safe, yes. A cashbox in your aide's desk drawer, yes. But *not* a cash register!"

Not long afterward, in Virginia, I asked a doctor's secretary if I might use her adding machine. "If *you* tell him we need it, maybe we'll get one," she said hopefully. "I do my addition and subtraction the hard way—and get them wrong most of the time." She did, too. I found out by running a test tape on a few pages of her daybook, using a small adding machine I carry in my car.

Somehow, where office appliances are concerned, it's either feast or famine in a doctor's office. Some physicians have enough business equipment to run General Motors. For example, there's the Southern country doctor who boasts a bookkeeping machine, twin sets of dictating equipment, a shiny monster that folds, stuffs, seals, and puts postage stamps on his monthly statements, a copying machine—and no less than six electric typewriters. The marvel is that he employs only one aide. "She can type at her desk, my desk, and in either of my two examining rooms—since there's a typewriter at each location," he explains. "And in case I want her to type something at my home, I have a machine in the living room and another in the den. I also have two electronic calculating machines, one here and one at home."

By contrast, some medical offices seem to make out with nothing more complicated than a ballpoint pen, a card index drawer, and a box of paper clips.

As you'd guess, there is a middle road between being gadget-rich and equipment-poor. Let's try to identify it in this chapter. We needn't discuss desk-top impedimenta; your office supply salesman, I'm sure, sees to it that you and your aide are well equipped with desk calendars, tape dispensers, staplers, and all the rest of the useful clutter to be found wherever paper work is done. Let's concern ourselves here with the more costly aids to office efficiency.

An electronic typewriter does it by the numbers

If yours is a practice with a heavy load of repetitive reporting to other doctors—radiology and pathology are outstanding examples—it might be worth your while to install an electronic typewriter. It types reports and letters from a magnetic tape on which you've previously recorded standardized paragraphs and sentences. You say into your microphone: "Write to Dr. Jones. Use paragraphs 4, 9, 23, and 46." Your secretary then addresses a letter to Dr. Jones and pushes buttons to select the paragraphs you've named. The electronic typewriter forthwith rips off the right bits of text at 186 words a minute, error-free, while your secretary busies herself with some other job. The machine is flexible enough to let you modify any taped paragraph, sentence, or word at will.

The typewriter can also be used to transcribe "original" dictation. Your secretary transcribes the material at normal speed, and it is simultaneously taped. If you then make editorial changes in her transcript, she corrects the tape in the appropriate places, then punches a button for a top-speed rerun. She doesn't have to type the whole thing over.

Interested? Then first make sure you can get your money's worth out of the gadget. It costs around $7,000, leases for about $200 a month.

The office appliance I'm most often asked about is usually, though inaccurately, called a bookkeeping machine. If you're a stickler for correct names, call it a ledger-posting machine. Its primary purpose: to debit the ledger (account) cards of individual patients with the charges they incur, to credit them with the payments they make, and to show the balances due. Its secondary function is to duplicate each posting on the patient's current monthly statement, thus keeping it ready for instant mailing. Third, the machine churns out a running log of all the postings it makes, totaling each day's debits, credits, and balances. It discharges all three functions in the same posting operation.

An efficient machine? Yes, indeed. Should you buy one? Not necessarily. To decide pro or con, ask yourself the six questions I've listed on page 61. If you come up with fewer than four affirmative answers, you don't really need a ledger-posting machine in your office. (I know the salesman will tell you differently. If I were a salesman, I would, too.)

Another high-cost item of business equipment I'm frequently asked about is the dictating machine. It comes in great variety, using tape, belt, disc, wire, and even magnetic-coated paper. You can get one that lets you and your aide out of handling any of these accessories, if you'd rather not be bothered with 'em. All the name-brand machines I've tried work well. If you have dictation equipment, it doesn't matter if your secretary never learned shorthand or speedwriting. It doesn't even matter if she isn't in the office when you get around to catching up on your mail. Nor does it matter if *you're* away from the office when you get the urge to dictate. You can dictate to a machine at the hospital, at home, in your car, in an airplane. And there's always the luring thought that dictation equipment could mean the end of the hen-scratchings that masquerade as your medical records. Rare is the physician who hasn't, at some time or other, dreamed of emancipating himself from the tyranny of writing up his office charts by hand.

With so many good reasons for installing them, why then do I see so many dictating machines gathering dust in doctors' offices?

Look at the six questions on page 62. If you can't answer Yes to four of them, you won't get value out of dictating equipment. If you can score four affirmatives and don't already have the equipment in your office, you're missing a smart bet. And if your objection is to the impedimenta that comes with most mechanical devices, take a look at the box below, where you'll find a description of a dictation system that doesn't require you to change discs, belts, or tapes.

I'd guess that the most popular new item of business equipment for the small office is the copying machine. More and more doctors are using a copier to prepare patients' monthly statements, to reproduce medical records asked for by other physicians and attorneys, and to speed up many other jobs around the office. There are

---

A dictating system without accessories

Maybe you'd take more kindly to machine dictation if it were as simple as dictating to a stenographer. Many physicians don't want the bother of changing discs, belts, tapes, wires, index slips, and suchlike accessories. They prefer just to talk. If you're one of these doctors, there's a system available that'll suit you to a crossed *t*—or a dotted *i*.

All *you* do is talk into a miniature phone-type handset. You can play back, erase, and correct at will. All your secretary does is listen to a peewee transcriber. She can start, stop, and repeat at will. Neither of you ever touches the recording medium, which is a sealed endless belt of magnetic tape stuffed away in a storage closet or even in the office basement or attic.

You can hook up any number of handsets to the remote tape and thus be able to dictate from anywhere in the office. If you have more than one aide who types, extra transcribers enable them to work at their own desks without having to shuttle machines around the office. Bonus feature: Giving you a bare 10 seconds' start, an aide can start transcribing while you're still dictating.

For a one recorder-one transcriber installation, figure on a capital outlay of around $1,200 or a monthly lease-purchase payment of $50 for two years. But once the master tape is in, the cost of extra recorders and transcribers is trifling.

---

dry-heat copiers, diazo copiers, photo transfer copiers, and electrostatic copiers. None would earn its keep for you, unless you say Yes to four out of six in the quick quiz on page 63. If you do, forget about diazo and photo transfer copiers. Spend your time looking at the latest dry-heat and electrostatic machines. Solo practitioners like the lower cost of the dry-heat jobs. Doctors in partnership and group

---

Would a ledger-posting machine help you?

Four affirmative responses will justify your investigating the use of a machine-posting system:

	Yes	No
1. A posting is a record of a charge, a payment, or both of these at one time. Does your office have 2,000 postings a month—i.e., an average of 100 postings per working day?	___	___
2. Is your aide currently posting transactions more than three working days in arrears?	___	___
3. Check this Yes if your aide does all three of these jobs separately by hand: post to a daybook, post to ledger cards, post to itemized monthly statements.	___	___
4. Check this Yes if you want a system that will give you a running daily total of accounts receivable, prove your listed collections against deposited cash, classify your daily work and earnings by the types of service you render, and, if you're in partnership, yield ready data on the billings of the respective partners.	___	___
5. No machine can work unaided, and if your operator falls sick you'd be in trouble if there's no one available to take her place. So do you have at least two aides who can learn to operate the machine?	___	___
6. Can the time your aide saves by switching to a machine system be put to good use?	___	___

61

practice like the work turned out by a good electrostatic machine, and they can afford its higher cost.

The phone-answering device is still somewhat of a newcomer to medical offices. It invites callers to record messages for you to hear later, and at least one model will play back the message to your home phone (or any other) when you sound a special signal from a

---

Would dictating equipment help you?

Four affirmative responses will justify your inviting bids from your local dictating machine salesmen:

          Yes   *No*

1. Do you sometimes fail to originate or answer letters because your aide can't take shorthand dictation, write fast notes in longhand, or compose an acceptable letter on brief instructions from you? ____ ____

2. Would you often like to reply to a letter immediately on reading it, answer mail at odd moments during the day, or do some of the answering in your den at home? ____ ____

3. When you're at the hospital, does your aide have time on her hands at the office that she could use to type up dictation? ____ ____

4. When you handwrite patients' histories and examination findings, do you tend to write less than you really should because it takes so long? ____ ____

5. Since a machine won't say "What was that again, Doctor?" are you willing to think out what to say before you start, to speak clearly, and to spell out unusual words? ____ ____

6. Realizing it's cheaper to do your drafting on a scratch pad than on engraved stationery with six useless carbon copies, are you willing to leave material alone after it's typed? ____ ____

---

device you can carry in your bag. No doubt of it: The gadget is almost as good as having a human being take your messages. I'd recommend it *if* there's no answering service in your community— or if the quality of your answering service is awfully low.

Would it be a good idea to install an office intercom system? It would if you haven't got a Girl Friday literally at your elbow all day long. If intercom units would save you steps or stop you hollering down the corridors for an aide, by all means get them installed.

A postage meter? The ads in the business journals are certainly persuasive, and you do (or probably will) use 400 first-class

---

Would a copying machine help you?

Four affirmative responses will justify your looking seriously at photocopying machines:

	Yes	*No*
1. Would it help if your aide could prepare several hundred monthly statements in one hour?	____	____
2. When referring a patient, would an instant copy of all or part of your office record help the consultant?	____	____
3. As a member of, say, a medical society subcommittee, are there times when you'd like to circulate several copies of a document?	____	____
4. Does it often happen that you send off an insurance report and later receive a request for a duplicate?	____	____
5. Do you often get letters you could easily answer by scrawling "Yes," "No," or "Sorry, can't make it" across the top and mailing them back—keeping copies of the letters and answers in your files?	____	____
6. Is the convenience of doing these things so easily worth, say, 10 cents per sheet copied?	____	____

---

postage stamps each month. A meter would be bound to save time, wouldn't it? Well now, would it? Not necessarily. Suppose a breakdown of your stamp usage shows that on 25 working days in each month your aide mails an average of just six letters. Then toward the end of the month she has one big mailing day—when she gets out the monthly statements. Metering *that* day's mail would save time. But at what cost? The monthly machine rent might actually exceed the whole month's postage bill. In larger medical offices, I'll

---

Would a postage meter help you?

Four affirmative responses will justify your looking seriously at postage meters. But if yours is a big office with a heavy daily mail, skip this quiz; without further ado, I'll say you *do* need a meter.

	Yes	No
1. If your outgoing mail is typical—about 500 five-cent pieces a month—are you willing to pay about $4 for each $3 worth of postage stamps?	___	___
2. Could your aide save about $50 worth of time in the next 12 months if she printed stamps on envelopes instead of sticking them on?	___	___
3. Would a machine that wets the envelope flaps while printing the postage save enough time to reduce your annual mailing costs by another $25?	___	___
4. Does your aide run out of stamps so often that she spends several hours a year at the post office replenishing the postage drawer?	___	___
5. Have you any reason to believe that someone is walking off with large quantities of stamps from your office?	___	___
6. Four out of five postage-meter users spend more than $600 a year on postage. Do you spend that much?	___	___

---

admit, the case for a postage meter is often strong. But in the smaller offices, if the affixing of adhesive stamps to envelopes is really too abhorrent to consider, there's always the cheapest, fastest solution of all: prestamped envelopes. Get them from the post office. (If you ask, you can have your return address imprinted on them.) To see whether your outgoing mail is voluminous enough to warrant a meter, answer the questions on page 64.

Will it save enough time?

If you're told that a new piece of business equipment will "pay for itself in time saved," the table below will help you decide whether the claim's soundly based.

Figure the annual total cost by adding the yearly depreciation cost (purchase price divided by useful life, usually 10 years) to your estimate of the annual extra cost of new supplies and the maintenance contract, if any. Look for the nearest round number to that total in the left-hand column below. Then look horizontally across until you come to the column headed by the salary you pay the girl who'll use the equipment. Finally, circle the figure at the intersection—the number of minutes per day the equipment will have to save your girl in order to justify its expense.

New equipment's annual total cost	*Minutes per day it must save your aide if her salary is:*					
	$3,000	$3,500	$4,000	$4,500	$5,000	$6,000
$ 25	4	3	3	3	2	2
50	8	7	6	5	5	4
75	12	10	9	8	7	6
100	16	14	12	11	10	8
125	20	17	15	13	12	10
150	24	21	18	16	14	12
175	28	24	21	18	17	14
200	32	28	24	21	19	16
225	36	31	27	24	21	18
250	40	34	30	26	24	20
275	44	38	33	29	26	22
300	48	41	36	32	29	24

Earlier I mentioned a doctor who owns two electronic calculators. Should you buy one? Only if you do lots of multiplying and dividing in your office. I haven't been in many medical offices that do.

Electric adding machines are quite another matter. I haven't seen a single medical office that couldn't get its money's worth out of at least one. If your unfortunate aide is still hauling away at the crank of a manually operated adder, take it from me that the electric job is much faster and worth the extra cost.

I'll say the same for electric typewriters. They really are faster than manual typewriters. And your aide may gain as much comfort as speed from one. To anyone who has become used to an electric typewriter, the old drive-it-yourself kind steers like a truck. Give the electric two more gold stars for evenness of impression and clarity of carbon copies. The power jobs are good buys even in offices that don't have much typing. And if by any chance yours is an office that churns out lots of letters and reports of basically common content, think about an electronic typewriter such as the one described on page 58.

In the final analysis, your decision on any one piece of business equipment should turn on the issue of time saved—*if* the time saved can be put to good use. So you'll find the table on page 65 handy when the salesmen come to call. It's a ready reckoner you can use to figure the dollars-and-cents value of the minutes gained.

If you're starting up in practice, say Yes to an electric adding machine and an electric typewriter. Dictating machine, copier, and intercom? Probably. Postage meter? Maybe. As for the phone-answering device, bookkeeping machine, and electronic calculator, they can wait. They'll be available when you need them.

9

You'll need help, and finding it isn't easy

N ow it's time to look for the help you're going to need when the patients start to arrive. You need an aide, and you need a good one.

They're not easy to come by.

There's a pediatrician in Florida who got one of the best aides I know by sheer good fortune. Deciding she wanted to work in his city, she started one morning at the end of "Doctors' Row" and walked from one office to the next. She found him in the third office she entered—watching the decorators at work in his new quarters. Ten years later, her employer was still thanking his stars she did.

Don't count on finding a good aide so easily. "Most of the girls I interview are little more than literate," a surgeon once told me. "If I find one who can type, chances are that she'll fizzle out in patient relations or some other part of the job. There ought to be at least one source in every town where a doctor could apply for— and get—a girl who's capable of doing medical office work."

In an effort to discover the best ways of locating topflight help, I've sifted at one time or another through reams of advice from physicians, personnel experts, employment agencies, schools for medical aides, and management consultants. And I've had years of personal experience in helping doctors find aides. All I know for certain is that there's no single best way to find a paragon. You have to be prepared to work through all likely methods—seven of them, by my count.

Let's examine all seven, but don't assume that I'm listing them in order of preference. The right way for you might be any one of them—or a combination of them.

Advertise. An ad in the classified section of a newspaper is a favorite way to recruit office help, and one that's almost guaranteed to get some response fast.

Many doctors feel that the main drawback to the help wanted column is the risk of being swamped by unsuitable applicants. "When I advertised in our local paper, I got 40 replies," says a Stamford, Conn., doctor. "I interviewed every last one of them—and found none satisfactory."

That's chiefly why the heads of two New York agencies that specialize in finding doctors' aides say they think doctors are foolish to advertise. Even allowing for a natural bias in the agent's approach, they do have a point. "Why plow through a hundred letters or take a hundred phone calls," asks one of these agents, "when an agency can whittle down the prospects to two or three?"

A North Carolina doctor knows there's another side of the coin, though. "I got my best aide through a classified ad," he reports. "She was listed with two employment agencies, both of which failed to route her to me, though they'd had my vacancy on file for several weeks. Besides, a good thing about classified ads is that they are seen by aides who already have jobs but are open for a change."

Sometimes such a girl may be especially eager to move to another town. So don't stick slavishly to the local paper when you advertise. There may be an aide in a city 50 miles away who's longing to live in your snug community. A small-town Alabama doctor got a jewel of a secretary through an ad in a Birmingham paper. His town happened to be her birthplace, and she wanted to come back home.

How should you word your ad? The specimens given on page 71 will give you some ideas.

Note that they all include mention of the salary. Some of the experts advise against stating it, but I'm all for saying what you're willing to pay. If you show the bait, you'll automatically weed out those who want more than you can afford to pay. And if your bait is attractive, showing it can't hurt. If Dr. Titewad's treasure, Miss Jones, has abandoned all hope of a raise in her $70 per week stipend, your $90 may be the clincher.

In other respects, too, be specific in your ad. If you want an experienced girl, say so. State the skills you're looking for. If you're willing to take a trainee, announce the fact.

Another tip: Always use a "blind ad." In other words, give no address or phone number. Instead, ask for written replies addressed to a newspaper box number. You'll screen out many third-raters that way since a letter of application is an aptitude test in itself. And the blind ad keeps the merely curious off your telephone.

List your vacancy with an employment agency. I've already indicated the big plus factor for agencies. It's that they do your screening for you. They are experts at it.

As one agency head says forcefully: "Only people who make a business of it know how to interview. Employment interviewing takes long experience. Many a prospective employer will see a pretty face and some good clothes, and if the girl is two steps ahead of being an idiot, he'll hire her. We don't work that way."

Another point in favor of the agency is that its assistance needn't cost you a cent. The job-seeker pays the freight. Of course, there's nothing to stop you from offering to pay the successful applicant's placement fee. Myself, I think that's a good idea. It starts the aide off with a reservoir of goodwill in your favor.

Good agencies take great pains to classify their registrants accurately and in detail. They take voluminous histories, apply psychological and aptitude tests, and supplement them with intensive interviewing. Many physicians I know have found first-class aides through agencies.

It's true that an agency's range of choice is limited by the size and variety of its own list of registrants. It's true also that agency lists carry the names of many near-unemployables, and that the same deadheads register with many agencies. Going for you, on the other hand, is the fact that no agency lasts long if it doesn't deliver the goods. A well-established agency is worth trying.

Shop around the schools. I mean all kinds of schools. Every community has a high school. Many have vocational and technical schools, business schools, junior colleges, colleges. There are schools for nurses, schools for X-ray and laboratory technicians, schools for medical-record librarians. In a few areas there are special schools for medical aides.

I've found excellent girls for clients simply by phoning high school principals. One principal said I was a godsend; he had the very girl, and he'd been wondering how in the world to locate a doctor who might need her.

A New York State physician once asked his chief aide how she managed to come up with such splendid trainees. Her answer: Whenever a new girl was needed, she called a friend who ran a business college and asked him to send over the pick of the crop.

Unless she's a graduate of a nursing school or of a technician-training school, however, the girl you get from an educational source must learn how to apply her background skills to the unique requirements of a medical office. Don't expect a ready-made aide from a college, high school, or even a commercial business school.

The specialized schools for medical office assistants are different. Their training hardly ever lasts less than a year, and it may last up to four years. A typical curriculum will include courses in basic secretarial skills, medical terminology, and paramedical skills. The students may also get on-the-job training in doctors' offices and in hospitals.

Naturally, such schools have little difficulty placing their graduates. Says the placement officer of one long-established New York City school: "We get calls for more medical assistants than we can supply. And because there aren't enough to go around they can get pretty snooty. Some will turn their noses up at any job away from Park Avenue. Or a girl who lives in Brooklyn, say, won't work outside Brooklyn. And—rightly—they expect good salaries."

All schools for aides and all agencies say amen to that word "rightly." A common complaint among them is that doctors don't want to pay enough. Comments a respected school head: "The

70

doctor says, 'No beginners for me; I want an experienced girl.' Then I ask the doctor what salary he has in mind. Ten to one, he'll offer less than I was planning to ask for a beginner."

What's the word, then, on applying to the placement bureau of a school for aides when you're hunting a Girl Friday? Just this: If there's such an institution in your vicinity (try the Yellow Pages), pick up the phone and make the necessary inquiries. If you really want a good aide, be ready to pay a good salary.

Use the grapevine. Pass the word around everywhere you can think of. Ask other doctors' aides to talk it up in the drugstore, the church, and the neighborhood. Let all your friends know you're on the lookout. Tell the detail men who call on you.

The grapevine probably finishes in a dead heat with the classified ad as the most popular way to find a new aide. *And it works.* Through this inexpensive method, a Tennessee internist ended up

---

Three aide-wanted ads that work

Here are three model classified ads that can help you locate an aide. The italicized words are the key ones:

For a one-girl office
Experienced aide for physician, *start* $400 per month. *All duties,* including nursing, reception, telephone, appointments, bookkeeping, typing from machine dictation; *no other aides employed;* R.N. *preferred* but not essential. Interviews to *selected applicants only.* Write *fully* to Box 000.

For a secretary in a two-girl office
Experienced secretary for physician, *start* $350 per month. *No nursing duties;* reception, telephone, appointments, bookkeeping, typing from machine dictation, *knowledge of medical terminology.* Interviews to *selected applicants only.* Write *fully* to Box 000.

For a trainee
Physician will employ *inexperienced* girl, *start* $300 per month. High school graduate; *must type well,* be good at figures. *Other aides employed. Will train* as medical secretary. Interviews to *selected applicants only.* Write *fully* to Box 000.

---

with two sisters working for him. The elder offered to train the younger if the doctor would take her. He did, and she did.

Similarly, a bookkeeper came all the way from Washington, D.C., to South Carolina when her sister-in-law dropped her a note mentioning a clinic job. And I know a secretary who's the daughter of a detail man; her dad handpicked the doctor-employer.

Many doctors have aides who were formerly patients. But there's a danger in recruiting from this source. If the girl doesn't turn out well, you can easily have quite a kickback. You can lose an aide, a patient, and, likely as not, some of the misfit's friends.

There's one special advantage in the grapevine method: When friends and associates become involved in your search, they tend to screen their nominees fairly well. Knowing you, they have a fair idea of the kinds of personality you like and dislike. And—unless you're mighty unpopular—they're likely to "sell" you as a boss.

Speaking of friends and associates, don't forget to drop the word at your local medical society meeting. And call the executive secretary of your state medical association; he may have a file of hopefuls. If the American Association of Medical Assistants has a chapter in your locality, be sure the chapter secretary knows you're looking. Moral: If you're in search of an aide, don't keep it secret.

Raid a hospital. Excuse me. I stated that too strongly. What I meant to say was this: Just let it be widely known in your hospital that you're looking for an office aide. Chances are that, in a day or two, one or more staff girls will phone you to ask about the job.

A Michigan ENT man hired two aides away from a hospital where he's on the staff. "Sure it was a raid," he said. "But what's a man to do? I knew the girls were good, and they wanted to work for me."

Of course, hospital administrators don't usually see it that way. I remember one who beefed to me that in three months he had lost four employes to doctors who happened to be my clients. What the girls didn't tell the administrator when they left was that they'd all intended to give up their hospital jobs anyway.

I can't condone raiding the hospital for personnel, so don't ask me to defend it—though I fully appreciate why it's done. My advice boils down to this: If a hospital employe applies to you for a job, you needn't have pangs of conscience about hiring her. But it isn't cricket to lure one away with a dollar-baited hook.

Get help from a management consultant. Medical management consultants aren't in the employment agency business, as such. But they do know lots of doctors' employes, ex-employes, and some would-be employes. They can often put a client in touch with a suitable aide. I've done it on numerous occasions.

Bring the little woman into the office. Much has been said about the wisdom of doctors' using their wives as aides. Is it wise? That's a moot question. I happen to belong to the "no wives in the office" camp. I'm convinced that most patients prefer the office girl, for social and psychological reasons, to be someone other than the doctor's wife. Though there are brilliant exceptions, I remain unrepentant on the point.

But there's no reason why you shouldn't disagree with me.

Of those seven ways of finding an aide, four seem to me the wisest, since they are the beaten paths. They have signposts that say: Advertise, Try the Agencies, Tap the Schools, Use the Grapevine.

10

*It takes time
to pick the right aide*

If you're thinking of advertising for an aide, as in the preceding chapter I suggested you should, the prospect of interviewing a slew of applicants may give you pause, as it did a Pennsylvania doctor of my acquaintance. "I don't much relish the idea of going over the same ground with 20 or more females in succession," he said. "Doctor," I replied, "you needn't. See only the two or three most promising applicants. Weed out the others in advance."

He told me later that the procedure I then outlined for him saved much needless repetition and hours of his time. So I'll repeat my suggestions here; you may find them equally helpful. Naturally, some of the steps I'm going to suggest can be taken for you by an employment agency or school placement bureau—if you're within range of one that places medical aides. But I'm assuming that for one reason or another you've decided to tap the market at large by running a classified ad.

Also, I'll assume your ad specifies that applications be sent to a box number, care of the newspaper. That way, you'll be sure the respondents are serious about applying, and you'll have in hand clear evidence of their minimum skills.

That brings us to this first step in screening out deadwood:
Don't consider a sloppy application. If it's written in pencil, rule it out. The girl ought to be go-getter enough to look for a pen or borrow a typewriter. She's not likely to overcome her laziness in your employ if she can't overcome it when applying for a job.

If her penmanship or typing is poor, rule out her application. Many records in a doctor's office must be filled in—legibly—by hand. And a poor typist will get her work out late.

Also watch out for spelling mistakes. A client of mine spent a lot of time correcting errors in his letters after hiring a new secretary. He could have spared himself the chore if he'd attached more importance to the girl's "aplication," which she'd signed "respectfuly yours."

Don't consider an applicant who's too young or too old. It's true that laws in some states bar job discrimination on account of age, but that's not to say you have to ignore an applicant's age.

If you are going to employ more than one aide, it's a big mistake to bring in one who's a generation older than the others—unless you plan to make her boss. But in such specialties as urology and gynecology, maturity may be an important asset in an aide who'll deal directly with patients.

Don't consider an applicant who fails to meet your education standard. You probably will insist on a high school education, but some doctors I know demand more. For example, there's a surgeon in Chicago who won't look at an application from a girl who lacks a college degree. He reasons that in a practice like his—consisting of 100 per cent referrals—he needs an office staff with a high polish.

You may require an R.N. or L.P.N. if paramedical work is a major part of the job. If not, you'll almost certainly feel that business school or other formal secretarial training is a must.

Whatever your educational standards, my advice is: Stick to 'em. Later on it's unlikely that you'll be able to repair big holes in your aide's schooling, even if you're willing to try. And a semi-educated girl is likely to be semi-satisfactory in her work.

Don't interview a girl unless she seems to have the skills you need. If a girl has the skills you advertised for, she's unlikely to fail to say so; you can safely rule out applications that don't. If you need both stenography and bookkeeping, don't bother with the girl who says she has one and is willing to learn the other. It doesn't pay to provide on-the-job training in a skill that's needed right now.

Don't see an applicant till you've checked two of her references. Yes, I know that's the opposite of custom, but it pays to do it my way. At least 10 per cent of job applicants, it seems, tell lies. One New York personnel agency has said, "Of 25,000 applicants in two years, around 3,000 were found to have falsified their applications." Even assuming that the statements made by aspiring medical aides are more dependable than that, I can't lose sight of the many cases I know of where physicians have unwittingly employed thieves, drunks, psychotics, and even prostitutes.

This form will help you judge aides sight unseen

A simple checklist like this can help you eliminate unqualified job applicants from consideration—*before* bringing them in for interviews. In this example, Mary Smith is eliminated in favor of Jane Wilson and Ann McNeil, who *do* have the medical-office experience that the doctor advertised for.

Name	Looks of application	Legibility, spelling	Age	Education	Skills	Experience	Reference check with last employer	Second last employer	Special notes
Smith, Mary	O.K.	O.K.	O.K.	O.K.	O.K.	?	O.K.	None	Worked for insurance company. I really need medical office experience.
Wilson, Jane	O.K.	O.K.	?	O.K.	O.K.	O.K.	O.K.	O.K.	Age 45. Still young enough to learn my office routines?
McNeil, Ann	O.K.	O.K.	O.K.	O.K.	O.K.	O.K.	?	O.K.	She resigned last job because she didn't get along with senior girl. Will it happen again?

77

Do you remember the case of the aide with 22 aliases who embezzled $100,000 from a Georgia clinic before she fled with her two cars and her 50 cocker spaniels? Or the Midwestern psychiatrist who had to defend himself against a false rape charge brought by a newly hired aide? Also, consider the plight of a surgeon I know in North Carolina. His new office girl practiced the world's oldest profession with some success among his male patients, until the surgeon belatedly discovered her scarlet past and present.

Beyond such wild excesses, I know of numerous instances when doctors hired girls unsuited to the jobs by reason of temperament or attitude. Let two examples suffice. If a South Carolina G.P. I know had checked references first, he wouldn't have paid $1,800 in salary before getting around to firing a bone-lazy secretary. Nor would a certain Brooklyn internist have taken so long to find out that the aide he'd hired liked to play doctor; the physician she'd last worked for could have warned him, but he hadn't checked.

Trouble is, lemons often look good, talk well, and appear to have had the requisite experience. And once you've interviewed a girl and told her you'll hire her, it's hard to reverse yourself later on the basis of reference checks, even supposing you make them. So the advantage of checking beforehand is obvious.

Naturally, you won't start checking the references of any candidate until you've weeded out all who failed the other tests I've mentioned. With those that remain, you'll proceed as follows:

¶ Where previous employers are named, phone the last two. Ask direct questions about the girl's efficiency, punctuality, sickness record, honesty. And don't forget to ask why she left.

¶ If an applicant has failed to list her past employers, but seems promising otherwise, call her or write her for the names. (If you phone her, you get a chance to check her voice and diction.)

The girls who pass the screening tests are the only ones you'll need to interview. If they number more than you want to see, go through the list again, applying the criteria more strictly.

Before sending for the applicants on your final list, make a small checklist like the one on page 77.

11

How to limit the risk in selecting a helper

How can you be sure that, of the three or four girls you've decided to interview for the key job in your new office, you'll pick out the best? Well, I don't know that it's possible to be 100 per cent sure, but of course it *is* possible to improve your chances. In this chapter I'm proposing that you use some interviewing gambits to do so. And they're not usually found in personnel department manuals.

The first of them was given to me by a Connecticut pediatrician. "When I'm interviewing a prospective aide, one of the first things I ask is how she got to my office," he advises. "If she says she drove in her own car, I ask her how many miles it gets to the gallon. If she came by bus, I ask her to tell me the route number and how often the bus runs. I don't really care what the girl knows about such minor matters, but I want to see how she reacts to unexpected questions. A girl working in a medical office must be able to field surprise or offbeat questions."

A different device is used by an Iowa G.P. when interviewing a job candidate. He hides his pen and pencil before the girl enters his office. Then he finds an excuse to ask if he may borrow hers. "I watch like a hawk when she opens her handbag," he says. "If I see a jumbled mess inside, it's a tip-off to me. Girls who jumble their pocketbooks are likely to jumble my office, too."

Then there's the New Jersey internist whose interview with a would-be aide invariably includes the following query: "Do you know any of my patients?" As the doctor explains it: "That inno-cent-sounding question can bring a very telling answer. It nails a gasbag every time. One girl had the nerve to tell me a scandalous story about one of my own relatives!"

Most physicians, I've found, are less skillful at employe inter-viewing than the three I've mentioned. The majority, in fact, seem to be more like a Georgia client of mine who employed five suc-cessive aides in a single two-year period. Advertising a sixth time, he stated in the ad that the working hours were 8:30 to 5:30. He interviewed several of the respondents and hired one, but he ne-glected to ask whether she'd mind working late once in a while. So she goes home every day exactly at 5:30, regardless of the work that's piled up. He doesn't have the heart to fire her and start all over. "Sometimes I suspect I pick the wrong girls," he confessed to me. "Tell me, how do other doctors handle this interviewing procedure?"

Applicant *Grace Kern* Date *1/5*			
	+ +	+	-
General appearance		✓	
Height and weight		✓	
Grooming	✓		
Dress	✓		
Teeth, hair, nails		✓	
Voice, diction			✓ (*nasal*)
Fluency		✓	
Alertness	✓		
Mannerisms			✓ (*Seems nervous & edgy*)
Poise			✓

Personal attributes to watch. As soon as a job applicant has left your office, it's a good idea to fill out a plus-and-minus chart like this. Later, you can use it to help choose the best girl.

Applicant _Grace Kern_   Date _1/5_

	+ +	+	-
1. Why do you (would you) like to work with a doctor?	✓		
2. Where did you learn the skills mentioned in my ad?	✓		
3. In what jobs have you used those skills?	✓		
4. Why did you leave your last job?	✓		
5. What were the other employers like?		✓	
6. What family responsibilities do you have?			✓
7. How long do you plan to continue working? (recently married)			✓
8. We get a bit pushed here sometimes. Will that bother you?		✓	
9. Like most doctors, I work late sometimes. Will it upset your home life if you don't always get out on time?			✓
10. How do you feel about pressing people to pay a doctor?		✓	
11. Do you think it's best to stay home with a cold?	✓		
12. Are you willing to be bonded?	✓		
13. Have you handled money for anyone before?	✓		
14. Would you like to ask me any questions?	✓		

Leading questions to ask. It's best to go over this checklist before interviewing a prospective aide and again after she's left your office—when you can record your evaluation of her answers. Too obvious use of such a list while you're talking with the girl may inhibit her replies.

I gave him six pointers that have helped many doctors over the hurdles of employment interviewing:

Allow enough time for the interview. How much time is enough? About half an hour, I'd say.

Of course, if you discover in the first five minutes that the applicant won't do, you can cut things off then and there. But the more promising the girl seems, the more time you should spend in talking with her—or, rather, in getting *her* to talk.

It's best not to schedule the interview immediately ahead of a "must-keep" appointment. A job interview should always be conducted at a leisurely pace.

Have a mental picture of the kind of girl you're looking for. Then judge the candidate by how closely she fits it. You think an aide's physical characteristics don't matter? But you surely have likes and dislikes in the people you associate with. Such predilections can play an important part in the daily relationship of a physician and his assistant.

To take an extreme example, I know a surgeon who left Florida for Ohio rather than accept a group manager's adamant choice of a nurse for him. The woman was a six-footer; the surgeon is five feet, four—with his shoes on.

If a doctor is dedicated to helping patients fight obesity, he probably hasn't much use for a big, fat secretary.

In Virginia, there's an allergist who won't hire a girl who smokes. Once he found out later that the girl he'd hired had fibbed about not smoking. He fired her.

Perhaps you have no such special prejudices. But at least you expect certain standards of dress and personal grooming. The time to decide how a candidate meets those standards is during the interview. To that end, you can use the checklist on page 80. Fill it out the moment the girl has left. Later on, when you're making your final decision, it will help recall the impression she made.

One word of caution: Don't set your personnel standards so high no one can meet them. A certain big-city practitioner I know once did that. Though he hired the 40th girl he interviewed and she turned out to be a fine worker, he was never satisfied with her. She never could precisely fit the perfectionist's image he'd created beforehand. No one could.

Prod her into revealing something of her normal self. Few people behave with complete naturalness under cross-examination. They tend to clam up.

"In interviewing, the most profitable technique is the nondirective approach," says a top personnel man who has hired hundreds of girls. "The trick is to get the prospective employe to *volunteer* information. If you ask specific questions all the time, she'll give you the answers she thinks you want. So your best plan is to pitch her a fast one, sit back, listen, and hope she'll touch all the bases."

When you do ask questions, make sure you ask such basic ones as those I've roughed out in the 14-point checklist on page 81. But don't ask them too directly. An interview is usually most revealing if it's carried on so informally that much of what's said seems like small talk. Suppose you say to a girl, "Why do you want to work with me?" She's likely to become tense and tongue-tied. She'll relax and open up in response to such a remark as this (by you): "I can't help wondering why anybody wants to work with a doctor—when there are so many easier jobs around!"

If you want to know about a nurse's operating room experience, casually ask her what surgeons she has worked for. She'll take it from there with hardly an assist.

If you want to be sure that a prospective secretary is as well versed in the vocabulary of your specialty as she claims, wonder out loud about getting her a copy of the latest textbook in your field instead of expecting her to rely on your 10-year old medical dictionary. Her reaction will tell you a lot.

Of course, you'll ask outright questions about such specific things as time spent in various jobs and names of schools. And there's one direct query you should never omit: "What do you want to ask *me* about?"

A surgeon in Tennessee recalls his sad experience with a secretary who, at the end of her first day in his office, said, "Doctor,

83

may I have three months' pay in advance?" If he'd solicited important questions at the interview, he'd probably have heard that one. He'd then have asked why she needed money so badly— and he'd have learned that she'd just been handed a stiff fine for drunken driving.

Here's another example of why it's important for a doctor and an aide to understand each other during the hiring interview. An agency head reports: "We sent a girl after a job in a doctor's office, and she got it. The doctor had mentioned a five-day week, meaning that she'd get Wednesday and Saturday afternoons off. But she thought that a five-day week meant no Saturday work at all. She quit after one week."

One more suggestion concerning my evocative score sheet: Mark the score as soon as a candidate leaves, before the next girl comes in. If you mark three or four sheets at once, a few hours later, it's easy to get mixed up. (Naturally, you won't openly check your list in the applicant's presence.)

If you're going to test prospects, give the same test to each. Only uniform testing can give much of a comparison. So your test must be thought out and readied in advance.

You'll find that it isn't easy to dream up a fair test of a girl's ability to do the job you want her for. That's why some doctors —especially those in big cities—depend on outside firms that make a business of testing basic skills. For a small fee, such companies will check a girl out on her training, office skills, general level of education and knowledge, "attitude," etc.

One unusual—and simple—test is suggested by the senior partner of a seven-man West Coast group that employs 19 girls. Says he: "We have an applicant lunch with some of our own girls. And we listen seriously to their opinions of her before committing ourselves." If you're new in practice, perhaps you could ask another physician to let *his* girls chat with your candidates.

Bend over backward to represent yourself and your job accurately. Suppose your typewriter came out of the Ark, and your adding machine really belongs to the dentist next door—and can be borrowed only twice a week. In such an event, it's doubtful that anybody you hire—no matter how good she is—will manage to do her work on time in the way you want it done.

Or if you're chronically late for morning appointments, can you really expect the new girl to placate your restive patients? If you're slack about keeping medical records, isn't there bound to be trouble ahead when your aide tries to wrestle with insurance forms? Are you casual about jotting down charges for house calls and hospital work? Then, even with the best of aides, your collections will very likely be poor.

So give your prospective aide a realistic preview of what the job will be like. If she'll work with other aides, tell her where she'll stand in relation to them. She may like teamwork. On the other hand, she may react badly to such a situation if she's a loner.

In this same spirit of realism, it's up to you to state your policies on vacations, holidays, sick leave, etc. Many jobseekers are too nervous or timid to ask about those things. In time, though, if they don't like your time-off policies, they may get up the courage to leave quietly for employment elsewhere. Better to get matters straight at the beginning, isn't it?

Don't deprive yourself of a good aide by overemphasizing permanence. It's natural to hope that a new employe will be a star who'll stay with you until you retire. But that's wishful thinking.

The turnover in medical offices is high, and you'll be wise to make up your mind to live with it. So don't feel that you must stake everything on a girl's answer to Question 7 on my job-aptitude score sheet. If a top prospect indicates that she plans to take up motherhood as a career in two or three years, why cross her off your list? Two or three years' good service is worth having.

One final point: When your interviewing has reached a successful conclusion, remember that a trial trip is always advisable. After, say, 30 days, if either of you is not satisfied, you may still work things out by talking over what's wrong. If that's impossible, it's easier to call all bets off—if that's what was agreed on in the first place.

12

*It pays
to be a good boss*

I once dropped in at a Bosses' Night staged by a chapter of the American Association of Medical Assistants. It was fun. Compliments were as plentiful as rice at a wedding, and an astonished surgeon was crowned Boss of the Year—with plastic laurels. The occasion set me thinking about an ad I'd seen in a California newspaper the preceding year. It read: "UNSKILLED LABOR: Assistant, part-time, for doctor's office, $1.50 per hour." It will be a cold day in August when *that* M.D. is named Boss of the Year.

But how about you?

You could qualify, perhaps, by following the lead of an Oklahoma G.P. who treats his half-dozen aides—and their spouses —to a biennial overseas vacation or by paying your secretary $10,000 a year, as does a neurosurgeon of my acquaintance.

But you really needn't bid *that* high for the garland.

After 14 years of aide-watching, I'm satisfied you can challenge all comers if you'll follow these not-too-difficult rules:

Pay the going rate. A Virginia internist once put a plaintive question to me. "How is it that the secretaries in commercial offices are so superior to mine? Those offices have crackerjack girls who stay in one job for years. I'm continually replacing one mediocre girl with another."

"For one thing," I replied, "commercial employers hereabouts pay their secretaries $95 or more a week. You pay $70. In this area, that's the going rate for a junior typist or a file clerk."

I showed the complaining internist the current U.S. Department of Labor bulletin giving the going rates for women office workers in his locality. In it, he read this definition of a secretary: "Performs secretarial and clerical duties for a superior. . . . Duties include making appointments for superior, receiving people coming into office, answering and making phone calls, handling personal and important or confidential mail, writing routine correspondence on own initiative, taking [shorthand] dictation . . . and transcribing [recorded] dictation."

"If you want a girl with all those skills, plus the ability to keep your books and collect your accounts," I said, "you'd better meet your competitors' salary offers."

Secretaries aren't the only medical assistants whose pay seems low in comparison with what's offered elsewhere. Nurses and technicians in doctors' offices generally get less than those doing comparable jobs in hospitals and industrial medical departments. And the results are as predictable as the coming of spring: undistinguished performance, high turnover, employer dissatisfaction.

Years ago, when I said those things before a meeting of doctors in the Midwest, a fretful G.P. rose to demand, "Are you aiming to be the Walter Reuther of the doctor's office?" I'm not, of course. I'm simply convinced that even a doctor can't get the cream of the crop for skim-milk pay.

Give raises voluntarily. A Florida aide said to me last year: "Ask for a raise? Not me. My boss knows how much I'm worth. He should offer me a raise." I've heard the same gripe often enough to be concerned about it.

Resentful aides have been known to steal rather than ask for raises they felt they'd earned. "The doctor said nothing about a raise this year—for the third year in a row," sobbed an aide who'd come up short in her cash. "So when that bill collector turned up here in the office, I thought to myself: 'Damn the boss! Just $5 a week more and I wouldn't be in this mess.' Then I gave the bill collector the doctor's money."

Your aide's value to you should increase as time goes by. If it does, pay her a little more. If it doesn't, you probably should replace her. Whether you review salaries once a year or twice a year doesn't greatly matter. The important thing is that you do review your staff salaries regularly and voluntarily.

Spell out fringe benefits. Some forms of compensation don't show up in an aide's pay check. The commonest fringe benefit is the assurance of free medical care from the employer within his particular field. The offer may cover the assistant's children and sometimes her husband. To a G.P.'s aide, it can be a valuable benefit—and an expensive one for the doctor. To a plastic surgeon's aide, it doesn't amount to much.

Two men I know have recognized these problems and taken steps to solve them. One, a Texas G.P., prefers not to be the family physician to his three aides. "They go to doctors they've had for years," he says. "I've talked with all three doctors, and they've agreed to give my aides a discount. They get better care that way. You know the proverb about the shoemaker's children."

The other doctor, a Maryland surgeon, says: "I pay the health insurance premiums for my two girls and their families. That, I feel, makes up for my not being available to them for free run-of-the-mill surgery. And if they or their families ever do need my services, they won't feel they're imposing."

Some other fringe benefits I'm in favor of:

¶ A Christmas bonus, handed out in plenty of time for Christmas shopping. An extra week's pay for a full year's service isn't too much. Prorate it, of course, for girls who haven't been with you the whole year. Two weeks' extra pay isn't too much for a girl who's been with you five full years.

¶ Sick pay. Ten days of sick pay a year won't break you. The lack of it, however, can easily wreck an assistant's budget.

¶ Paid vacations. Most aides get two weeks off with pay each year. I'll go along with that—until your girl has put in five full years with you. At that point she's earned three extra days. And after 10 full years, a three-week vacation isn't excessive.

89

¶ Emergency leave. I suggest you allow your aide three extra days off during the year. This emergency leave protects her vacation time against inroads made by relatives' funerals, weddings, and illnesses.

¶ Seven paid holidays are now commonplace in many parts of the country. Some employers give more. The basic seven are New Year's Day, Memorial Day, Independence Day, Labor Day, Thanksgiving Day, a half-day for Christmas Eve, Christmas Day, and a half-day for New Year's Eve.

Close the office on time. No aide pretends that pay isn't important to her. But money doesn't buy off the resentment that boils up inside her when you consistently ignore quitting time. She'll willingly stay beyond the closing hour—whatever it may be—to help you with an emergency. But the aide isn't born who doesn't get mad at being kept late unnecessarily. And—let's face it—your aide knows the difference between those two situations.

"The office is supposed to close at 6," a New Jersey aide told me, in explaining why she planned to resign. "But 6 o'clock comes, and patients still stream in. The doctor sees them all. He says that's what he's there for. If my husband isn't home, I call a baby sitter. In six months I've paid the sitter for 100 hours. No, a raise won't help. I want to go home at 6."

She knew and the doctor knew that most of the patients he saw after 6 were people with minor ailments, dropping in on their way home from work or after an early supper.

"But it's not my fault!" her employer would protest when the office had finally emptied out sometime after 7 o'clock. "I'm working late, too. Why should *she* do all the grousing?"

"Because she isn't getting paid for seeing patients," I told him, *"and you are."*

If you're going to work late every night, hire a part-time girl for duty after an agreed hour. And if the real reason for all the overtime is that you have more patients than you can handle in a normal day, you may well need another full-time girl—and a partner.

Pay your aide overtime. In the past I've counseled doctors not to pay overtime. Now I'm convinced that overtime in doctors' offices should be paid for.

No, I don't think you should install a time clock. Just pay for overtime in 15-minute periods, ignoring the first 15 minutes but paying for any 15-minute periods—or parts thereof—after the first.

The rate can be straight time, time and a half, or double time —whatever you feel is fair. But, having set the rate, make one unbreakable rule: You pay for no overtime you don't first authorize. That takes care of the rare aide who prefers an extra buck to going home.

Why have I changed my mind about the payment of overtime in medical offices? It finally dawned on me that less overtime is worked in offices where it's paid for than in offices where it isn't.

Help a new aide learn her job. If you employ more than one assistant, ask your senior aide to show a newcomer the ropes. But what if your only aide is a girl-of-all-work? Here are five suggestions:

¶ Hire the new aide before the old one leaves. Otherwise the new girl will lose a lot of time figuring out simple routines and finding out where things are kept.

¶ Have your old aide write a guide before she leaves. This description of what she does and how she does it will serve as a reminder for the new aide. And a job description will prove especially helpful if the departing aide has to leave before the new one starts.

¶ If there's a local chapter of the American Association of Medical Assistants, encourage your aide to join it. At their meetings, these chapters discuss job details and hear talks by doctors, lawyers, drug and equipment men, insurance agents, and many others.

¶ Get your accountant to come in and check your new aide out on her handling of the office financial records.

¶ Give your new aide some helpful books. You can choose some from the list suggested by the American Association of Medical Assistants.

You'll still need to do some of the training yourself. For instance, brief your new aide on what she can do without first checking with you—and on what she must never do without your authorization. Tell her how much time to allow for a visit by a new patient and how much for an old one. Tell her your preferences in O.R. hours. Fill her in on the idiosyncrasies of your referring physicians.

And don't forget to tell her *why* you want things done a certain way. "I've told my new girl time and again to attach the patient's chart to phone messages from inquiring parents," a Pennsylvania pediatrician grumbled to me not long ago. "But she never learns." She's learned now. He explained to her how impossible it was to answer a mother's questions about her child without first refreshing his memory. When a girl understands *why* it's best to do a job a certain way, she learns fast.

Give her good tools. How would you feel if you had to listen to a patient's chest sounds through an old wooden stethoscope? Handicapped, I'll bet. So does an aide when she cranks out the day's charges and collections on a manual adding machine. She needs an electric.

And if she's learned to type during the last few years, she probably feels handicapped punching the keys of a drive-it-yourself typewriter. Same cure: Go electric.

See that she has a copying machine, the most-needed office invention. Sure, it isn't in use all day and every day. But when copies are needed in a hurry, her other work won't be dislocated.

Thinking of buying a dictating machine or changing from your present make? When you sit down with a salesman, bring your aide into the discussion. She would be the one to suffer if you bought a lemon.

Be considerate. You've hired the paragon you've been seeking. You're paying her well. She's happy with her fringe benefits. With rare exceptions, her busy day ends on time. She has enough space to do her work and all the equipment she's asked for. You're a front runner for the Boss-of-the-Year title. To cinch it, do one more thing: Be considerate. Like this:

¶ When you arrive in the morning, say "Hi." When you leave at night, say "Thanks."

¶ When she puts notes on your desk, read them.

¶ When she's filing an armful of charts, give her a chance to dump them and grab her notebook before you begin reeling off instructions.

¶ Don't tell patients to "Come right over" or "Drop in this afternoon." Put them through to your aide, or push the hold button while she checks on the state of your appointment book.

¶ Don't let patients out through the back door unless you're sure your aide doesn't want to see them before they leave.

¶ Let your aide know where you can be reached at all times. She feels stupid telling another doctor, "I don't know where he is."

¶ If yours is a one-girl office, subscribe to an answering service, or your aide won't be able to leave the phone unattended for even a minute. And she *does* have to go to the washroom now and then.

And by the way, be sure your aide knows your size in crowns. It would be too bad if those plastic laurels slid down and hid your blushing face.

13

If these outsiders can help, ask them in

There are doctors whose appointment books are kept by girls they've never seen. Others have their phones answered all day long by girls who never come within miles of their offices. Still others have their phoned dictation transcribed by typists they'll never meet. In a few towns, doctors' fees are plunked straight into bank accounts even though neither the physicians nor their employes touch the patients' checks. In a growing number of towns, patients are getting doctors' bills and health insurance claim forms that were prepared by a service firm's computer, not by the doctor's aide. And in most towns, a doctor who can't prod slowpokes into paying need only whistle to summon an army of bill collectors to his aid.

I'm not necessarily trying to sell you on such outside services; I'm just telling you that they're available. I do recommend, however, that you *consider* turning to an outside service firm whenever there's a chance that it can do a job for you better or cheaper than an extra aide-in-residence can. In a fast-growing practice, hiring outside services may be smarter than moving into a bigger office and hiring a bigger staff.

Here's a rundown on half-a-dozen services that are widely available, with some tips on how to decide whether you might benefit by hiring them:

Accounting service. Understandably, the physician who can personally handle the accounting chores of a busy practice is a rarity.

95

And though some doctors have aides who know a debit from a credit and a journal from a ledger, many don't. So by and large I'd say you should ask a professional to score your fiscal hits, runs, and errors.

Be on guard, though: An accountant is anyone who chooses to call himself an accountant. He can be a man boasting a college degree, a couple of years of graduate study, and a five-year apprenticeship. He can also be a tallyman at the local pickle factory who moonlights by keeping books of uncertain accuracy for a handful of private clients.

Top banana in the accounting world is the certified public accountant; those letters C.P.A. after his name testify that he got the nod from a bunch of tough examiners. Though fewer than half the states demand that all C.P.A. candidates be college men, the test is so difficult that the odds against a high-schooler's passing it are high. In more than 30 states, a second accounting title is recognized: public accountant. It's good, too.

While no one can use the letters C.P.A. or P.A. unless he's licensed by the state to do so, anyone, licensed or not, can keep your accounts, prepare your tax returns, and audit your financial records. The C.P.A. and P.A. designations are, of course, cast-iron assurance of an accountant's qualifications. But don't reject *every* non-C.P.A. out of hand. Many thoroughly capable men have never sought the appellation. Be on your guard against expecting too much from the accountant you finally choose. If what you want from the man you hire for the job is management know-how as well as accounting skill, don't bank on getting it from a man whose training has equipped him only to turn out balance sheets and tax returns. You may of course strike it lucky—and then again you may not. The safe play: Ask among your colleagues for the good word on their accountants. If several have nothing but praise for the same man, he's the one to send for.

Answering service. If you're liable to be needed on short notice by patients, other doctors, or the hospital, there's no help for it: Someone must answer your phone around the clock. In office

96

SERVICE REPORT

MC 163 (REV 10-66)

| | COMPLETE FOR GOVERNMENT PROGRAM | COMPLETE FOR CPS MEMBERS |

PATIENT'S NAME AND ADDRESS

PERRY PATIENT
123 MAIN STREET
HOMETOWN, CALIF.

CALIFORNIA MEDICAL ASSISTANCE PROGRAM (MEDI-CAL)
PATIENT'S IDENTIFICATION NO.

| CO. | AID | CASE NO. | FBU (FBS) NO. |

FEDERAL MEDICARE (SEE ITEM 28 ON REVERSE SIDE.)
H.I. CLAIM NO.

CPS GROUP NO. **952-690**

CPS MEMBERSHIP NO. **532-76-8920**

PATIENT'S RELATIONSHIP TO SUBSCRIBER

[X] SELF [ ] SPOUSE [ ] CHILD

SUBSCRIBER'S NAME (IF PATIENT IS A DEPENDENT)

PATIENT'S BIRTHDATE **11/22/29**

PATIENT'S SEX [X] MALE [ ] FEMALE

IF TREATED IN HOSPITAL OR NURSING HOME—
I.P. OR O.P. INDICATE NAME AND LOCATION

MEMORIAL HOSPITAL
ANYTOWN, CALIF.

ADMISSION DATE **07/02/68**
DISCHARGE DATE **07/14/68**

NAME AND ADDRESS OF PHYSICIAN OR OTHER SUPPLIER OF SERVICE OR APPLIANCES

J. C. CONWAY, M.D.
218 POWELL STREET
ANYTOWN, CALIF.

CERTIFICATE NO. **C-12345**

OTHER HOSPITAL, MEDICAL COVERAGE INCLUDING MEDICARE, IF "YES", NAME OF COMPANY OR PLAN.   [ ] NO [ ] YES

CONDITION CAUSED BY [ ] INJURY [ ] ILLNESS [ ] PREGNANCY
IF INJURY, INDICATE DATE, HOW AND WHERE SUSTAINED

[ ] HOME [ ] AUTO ACCIDENT [ ] OTHER

IF PREGNANCY, DATE OF COMMENCEMENT—
IS THIS A NEW ILLNESS? [ ] NO [ ] YES
IS CONDITION DUE TO INJURY OR SICKNESS ARISING OUT OF PATIENT'S EMPLOYMENT? [ ] NO [ ] YES

IF PATIENT WAS - REFERRED INDICATE FROM DOCTOR OR TO DOCTOR

"I certify that I offer and provide medical care services without discrimination based on race, color, religion, or national origin."

SIGNATURE OF PHYSICIAN OR OTHER SUPPLIER OF SERVICES OR APPLIANCES (REQUIRED FOR GOVERNMENT PROGRAM)

DIAGNOSIS AND CONCURRENT CONDITIONS

2620 FIBULA FRACTURE
CLOSED REDUCTION OF FRACTURE
CAST APPLIED 07/04/68

REMARKS

DATE OF SERVICE	64 RVS (OR SMA) PROC. NO.	DESCRIBE EACH SERVICE OR APPLIANCE SEPARATELY	IN OUT HOSP HOSP / HOME / OFFICE				YOUR FEE	FOR CPS USE ONLY
07/04	0921	FRACTURE, CLOSED REDUCTION	X				50.00	
07/17	9005	OFFICE VISIT				X	10.00	
07/17	7306	XRAY FIBULA				X	15.00	
07/29	9005	OFFICE VISIT				X	10.00	
07/29	7306	XRAY FIBULA				X	15.00	
07/31	9005	OFFICE VISIT				X	10.00	
08/23	9005	OFFICE VISIT				X	10.00	
08/23	7306	XRAY FIBULA				X	15.00	

DATE PROCESSED		DIAGNOSIS	DISP.	PAY CODE	CPC	MEDICAL ADVISOR	LINE OF COV.	RVS MULT. VISITS	
MDE	FEE	PROF.	HOSP.	MISC.	QUAL.	REL.	PERS.	ORIG. EFF. DATE	EXPL.

DATE OF CHG. OR CL.   SEE REVERSE SIDE.   NUMBER _____

Computer-prepared forms for health insurance claims are one outgrowth of electronic billing. The various scraps of information needed for the claim in a complicated case can be collected bit by bit over a period of months, stored in the computer till needed, then printed out on signal—whenever the doctor specifies. This computerized claim form was developed by Peninsula Professional Services, an electronic billing company that was launched by five physicians in San Mateo, Calif., in 1964.

hours, your aide will answer it, but after she's gone for the day you'll need outside help. Answering service is available in all except the smallest towns. (If your town is one of the exceptions, turn to Chapter 8 for mention of a gadget that will take your messages when nobody's home.)

Many an answering service will take your calls throughout the 24 hours, if that's what you want. Some, though, will cover your phone only till midnight or so. Some will make your appointments for you, if you'll give them clear instructions on how you want your day set up. "I look on my answering service as a full-time secretary working night and day for me," says one New Orleans surgeon.

		SERVICE ANALYSIS REPORT 06-30-67						
257	JOHN D. JONES M.D.							
SERVICE CODE	SERVICE DESCRIPTION	CURRENT MONTH AMOUNT	%	QUARTER TO DATE AMOUNT	%	YEAR TO DATE AMOUNT	%	
100	PATIENT PAYMENT	3,653.00CR	100.0	9,513.62CR	99.8	19,528.62CR	99.7	
101	INSURANCE CO. PAYMENT	.00	.0	22.50CR	.2	63.47CR	.3	
	TOTAL PAYMENTS	3,653.00CR	100.0	9,536.12CR	100.0	19,592.09CR	100.0	
110	ROUTINE OFFICE VISIT	1,292.00	37.6	3,623.00	33.5	8,457.00	36.1	
111	OFFICE VISIT & PEN	12.00	.3	42.00	.4	64.00	.2	
112	FIRST OFFICE VISIT	84.00	2.4	546.00	5.0	1,118.00	4.8	
113	OFFICE VISIT & DPT	405.00	11.8	1,050.00	9.7	2,075.00	8.9	
114	OFFICE VISIT & POLIO	354.00	10.3	831.00	7.7	1,742.00	7.5	
115	OFFICE VISIT & VACC	9.00	.3	313.00	2.9	642.00	2.7	
116	OFF VISIT & TBC TEST	147.00	4.3	258.00	2.4	498.00	2.2	
117	OFFICE VISIT & D-T	18.00	.5	27.00	.2	63.00	.2	
118	DPT	79.00	2.3	204.00	1.9	516.00	2.2	
119	POLIO	137.00	4.0	281.00	2.6	743.00	3.2	
120	VACCINATION	6.00	.2	98.00	.9	213.00	.9	
121	TETANUS TOXOID	.00	.0	3.00	.0	10.00	.1	
122	MEASLES VACCINE	190.00	5.5	685.00	6.3	1,285.00	5.4	
123	GAMMA GLOBULIN	5.00	.1	30.00	.3	72.00	.4	
124	DIPHTH - TETANUS	6.00	.2	12.00	.1	12.00	.1	
125	INJECTION	3.00	.1	18.00	.2	42.00	.1	
126	MINOR SURGERY	60.00	1.7	219.00	2.0	558.00	2.4	
127	CONSULTATION HOSP	.00	.0	75.00	.7	115.00	.4	
128	CONSULTATION OFFICE	.00	.0	15.00	.1	23.00	.1	
129	HOUSE CALL DAY	63.00	1.8	274.00	2.5	432.00	1.9	
130	HOUSE CALL DAY & INJ	.00	.0	55.00	.5	157.00	.6	
131	HOSPITAL CARE	381.00	11.1	976.00	9.0	2,088.00	8.8	
132	NEWBORN CARE	180.00	5.2	770.00	7.1	1,746.00	7.4	
133	NEWBORN & CES SECTN	.00	.0	250.00	2.3	457.00	1.9	
134	PREMATURE CARE	.00	.0	112.00	1.0	227.00	.9	
135	HOSP EMERGENCY ROOM	.00	.0	42.00	.4	94.00	.5	
136	TBC TEST	4.00	.1	8.00	.1	20.00	.1	
	TOTAL FOR SERVICES	3,435.00	100.0	10,817.00	100.0	23,469.00	100.0	

Unique collating ability enables a computer to compile and rapidly print out information that can help the doctor, his accountant, and his management consultant keep tabs on key elements of his practice—all as a by-product of his charge slips. The service analysis shown here, for instance, provides the doctor with a recapitulation of both payments and services, broken down by current month, quarter, and year to date. The report includes entries for initial office visits and for office, hospital, and house consultations.

"It costs $35 a month, and I couldn't get a girl to do the job as well for 10 times that amount."

It's unwise, though, to expect the service's operators to function beyond their ability. If you ask them to take down phoned lab or X-ray reports, you're in for some gorgeous garblings. My favorite: A radiologist's alleged finding of "caulifloweritis" in a patient with gallstones.

When you're going out of town, give your answering service the

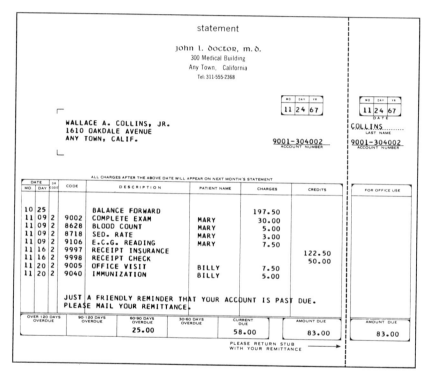

Personal messages of the doctor's choosing can be imprinted by computer on the patient's monthly statement. This example, produced by Standata, San Francisco, carries a computer-printed reminder to the patient that his account is in arrears, and a request for payment. A computerized statement can also remind the patient he's due for a checkup. Many doctors who have tried computer billing say patients like the professional look of their statements and appreciate the way services and charges are itemized.

names of at least two covering doctors. "When we have the name of only one," says a service supervisor, "we often can't get him because he's off somewhere on a case of his own."

Bonus tip: Ask how many subscribers the service has for each operator it employs. If the ratio is higher than 80-1, shop around a bit more—or you may run into trouble with patients who can't even get the answering service to answer.

Comprehensive banking service. Banks will do lots more than mind your money for you or lend you some of the money they're minding for other people.

Some banks will send out doctor's bills, for instance—and some will even collect them. The doctors enclose return envelopes with their patients' bills; they're addressed to a post office box number. The number is the local bank's, and a bank employe picks up the envelopes. Each day, the bank credits incoming checks to the doctor and sends him an itemized deposit slip.

Similarly, some banks collect rents for their doctor-customers; the doctor's tenant pays his rent to the bank—or, if he doesn't, the bank jogs his memory. And some banks will collect your stock dividends, if you authorize them to.

Some banks also make paying bills just as easy. There are banks that will make out a doctor's payroll checks and mail them to his aides, not forgetting to send Uncle Sam his share of each girl's pay at the appointed times. And in some cities, banks will relieve you of the chore of paying many of your regular bills. Once you've given 'em the O.K. to take the funds out of your account, they'll pay your insurance premiums, for example—life, office, home, automobile. Or they'll shift cash from your checking account to your savings account (so it can earn interest) any time the checking balance goes over a figure you've specified. Also, some banks offer credit-card plans that let you charge many of your purchases around town— or borrow "instant cash" of $350 or more.

So any time you have a money-handling problem, it never hurts to ask your banker for a solution. He may go a long way to accommodate you.

Billing service. If you haven't yet been invited to let your monthly statements be churned out by a machine—likely as not a computer—you will be. You'll be assured that they'll be itemized, dated, enveloped, stamped, and mailed out on time. You'll be told that they'll cost less than your present statements do. You may also be told that your collections will zoom.

By all means listen to the man's pitch. Cut him short, though, when he goes into his rhapsody on the speed with which a computer operates. That's important to him, but to you it's irrelevant. You're concerned with results, and it's all one whether your statements are produced by a computer or by a one-armed man chiseling figures into stone tablets.

When you've heard the pitch, ask the salesman to put it all in writing and guarantee it.

All outside billing services have two features in common. They bill your patients regularly—monthly, weekly, or even daily. And they furnish you periodic reports showing the age of each unpaid account as of the reporting date.

In other respects, the billing services can differ a good deal. Some limit themselves to billing and age analysis, as it's called. Others supply a broad spectrum of data—e.g., how much you earned in the office, how much at the hospital, how much from lab tests, how much from X-rays, and so on *ad infinitum.* Some services will, on request, include in a patient's bill a reminder that the time is approaching for his annual physical examination.

The billing services vary also in their methods of collecting the data they need from you. Some want you to phone it in. Most want a daily written record of patients' charges and payments.

Chiefly, though, the services vary in performance. Some have done so poorly that they've gone broke. Others are doing jobs that rate all the way from fair to excellent.

In a Medical Economics survey of 200 doctors who'd tried computerized billing, 75 per cent said they'd recommend it to their colleagues. The doctors who said they wouldn't recommend it sounded some warnings well worth listening to. The clearest:

Don't buy outside billing service unless your aide is sold on it. If she can't make it work, it won't. As one West Coast G.P. explained, "There's a painful learning process for the aide to go through." Another Western physician added, "Some aides resent having control taken out of their hands." The "painful learning process" seems to be the larger part of the problem; some girls can't *or won't* learn to do things differently.

The second-ranking problem, mentioned by 7 out of 10 of the doctors who'd dropped outside billing, was that the firms they had dealt with hadn't made good on their promises. A New England internist reported, "The computer was supposed to free my girl for other office duties, but it hasn't." A California pediatrician grumbled: "The billing man said my aide would reduce her bookkeeping and billing chores 15 minutes a day. Well, that just hasn't happened." From a Southern general practitioner came the plaint: "The man told us that health insurance cases would be no problem. But we ended up having to take care of all our insurance billing by hand."

Third-ranking problem: too many programing errors. According to a West Coast dermatologist, his accounts receivable had balanced to the penny every month for seven years. With outside billing, they were off as much as $500 during the three months he tried it. Three East Coast specialists said they lost a lot of money through programing errors: "The books and the monthly statements were a mess, and cleaning it up cost us about $2,000 in extra salaries."

What do *I* think? I'm sure there's a big future for outside billing. Someone—and before too long—is going to get the bugs out of it. But until that happens I'm from Missouri. Inside billing—by your aide in your office—is still a pretty good method. It doesn't cost much, and patients like it. Meantime, if you're thinking of farming out yours, I'd suggest you check and recheck these three points:

¶ Make sure you can use all the frills the salesman offers. If you're not greatly interested in knowing how long it takes patients to pay you, how many people pay by check, or how much of your income comes from surgery and how much from urine tests, why pay for such statistics?

¶ Satisfy yourself that the firm you're considering has a thorough grasp of doctors' billing problems, and that it's already giving satisfaction to other doctors in your locality. Billing for haberdashery is one thing; billing for medical care is another.

¶ Watch out you don't pay for your billing twice over. You may find you're sending a good-sized check to the billing service every month and paying your aide to put in the same hours on billing as she did previously.

Collection service. People who can pay you don't belong on your charity list. And they certainly shouldn't get on it by the simple maneuver of ignoring your bills.

It bothers me when a doctor refuses point-blank—as some do —to send delinquent accounts out for collection. Oh, the cash the collector recovers doesn't matter. What does matter is this: Any doctor who lets himself be bilked encourages the bilker to repeat— *on other doctors.* So by all means send an outside collector after a patient who can pay but won't.

Don't send just *any* collector, though. Shun the trim stranger who says: "This local collection firm is taking you to the cleaners. They're grabbing off 50 per cent. We operate nationwide for 30 per cent. Sign here." You may find, when you finally read his document, that you've agreed to pay him 30 per cent of *every bill you turn over to him.* So if you hand him $1,000 in old accounts and he collects $100 on them, he won't send you $70. He'll keep the $100 —and send you a bill for $200. By comparison, the local collector who was supposed to be so high-priced would have charged you nothing at all for the uncollected accounts. Instead of billing you for $200, he would have mailed you a check for $50.

Any reputable collector will tell you that his operating costs eat up at least 35 per cent of the money he collects. So when an agency offers to collect for less than 40 per cent, look for the catch. It's there somewhere.

Watch out, too, for the pitchman who stresses his nationally known firm's readiness to return all of your accounts any time you ask for them. Sure, they'll return 'em. They rushed $3,500 worth of accounts to a Midwestern doctor—with a demand for $1,400. His contract said that if he pulled back any accounts "in process of collection" he'd pay the firm as if they'd collected every dime.

Don't let my warnings scare you off. There probably *is* an ethical collection agency near you. Take the time to locate it. Check that it's really local, and not just a maildrop for a so-called national organization. Ask for a list of some other doctors it serves, and call them for opinions on its work. Look over the collection letters the agency uses in its pursuit of debtors. Insist on a monthly squaring-up of accounts between you and the agency. Reserve to yourself all final decisions on abandoning accounts and suing debtors. Check that you can get your accounts back on demand without penalty. Don't pay anything down. Don't sign a contract.

And don't gripe if the agency asks for half of each dollar it recovers. You'll still be ahead four bits.

Management service. This kind of service for doctors isn't the newest thing around; some was available back in the 1920s. Today, there's even a national consultants' organization: The Society of Professional Business Consultants, headquartered in Chicago. Yet the field is still largely untilled; I doubt that more than 5 per cent of U.S. physicians use an outside management consultant on a regular basis.

Though the services performed vary from one management firm to the next, some generalizations are possible. If a management consultant makes routine monthly visits, his services will generally include a check of the practice's financial records and a continuing review of collections and unpaid accounts. He'll also report to the doctor on his personnel's efficiency, advise him on business methods, keep him up to date on new and useful equipment, and confer with him on a medley of matters. Topics may range from office salaries to the doctor's need for a partner or to his tax liability. In effect, the consultant who makes frequent visits functions as the doctor's visiting systems expert, tax adviser, and all-around business counsel.

Not all consultants offer monthly services, though. Some visit quarterly. A few specialize in annual diagnostic surveys of practices. A very few specialize in advising doctors how to build *big* practices. Others specialize in guiding partnerships and groups. Some concentrate on collection techniques. Some pay lots more attention to personal financial problems than to practice management problems. Some, for instance, know tax law from audit to withholding.

So in your first telephone discussion with a consultant, you'd better determine whether he's interested in tackling the kind of problems that are bugging you most. If he is, next check with colleagues who already use his firm's services. If the firm is worth its salt, it will give you a list of men to call. If you happen to employ one of the larger outfits, don't let it worry you if the man assigned to you seems a mite youthful. He has the resources of his firm behind him, and he's been told to draw on them.

If you agree to take regular service, expect your consultant to suggest that you adopt some business methods that may be a bit different from those you're used to—if only a little bit. He isn't suggesting change for change's sake. As soon as a management firm builds up a sizable roster of clients, it usually standardizes business methods in all the offices it services. Its men are expert in these methods. If it's ever necessary to switch from one of the firm's consultants to another, your new man will be taking over something with which he's thoroughly conversant.

Different firms favor different systems, of course. But no reputable concern can afford to install a system that won't work.

Office help service. There's one doctor of my acquaintance who has never had a typewriter in his office. He doesn't need to own one. And he doesn't need to pay a salary to a secretary.

Every day from 5 P.M. to 5:30 or thereabouts, he sits down with his phone and a stack of charts and correspondence. He dials a number—and reels off progress notes on patients, and answers to correspondence. He's talking to a recorder located 15 miles away.

Two days later, he gets a fat envelope with neatly typed, gummed-edge strips of notes to mount in his charts, plus his finished letters with carbons. Once a month he gets a bill.

Services as expert and reliable as the one he deals with aren't available everywhere—and probably won't be for several years to come. In many metropolitan areas, they're just starting to appear —because recording equipment equal to this kind of task has only recently come on the market. If there's a good electronic stenographic outfit anywhere near you, you'd be wise to establish friendly relations with it, if only for emergency use when your own girl is vacationing or sick.

If you don't yet have access to such a service, there probably is a temporary office help service in your area. Chances are, it can supply a girl who has worked for doctors. She won't cost you as much as a pile-up of untyped paper work or, worse, a missed month-end billing.

14

When the postman knocks

"If I shift some of this junk from my desk," a Philadelphia surgeon said to me, "you'll be able to spread out your papers." With that he shoved an unregimented pile of papers onto the floor: letters, X-ray and laboratory reports, advertising brochures, charity solicitations, and goodness knows what else.

"Quite a pile of mail you've accumulated," I said. "Doesn't it bother you to have so many papers around? And don't you get worried about unanswered letters?"

"I used to," he answered, "but I've found that if I leave 'em long enough, they answer themselves. If a letter writer is really anxious for a reply, he'll call me."

That surgeon isn't the only doctor I know with an overload of mail. Most doctors get more than they want. Few, though, have adopted his insouciant attitude, and it's just as well. The daily load of mail is not lightly ignored; it contains too many items of value.

To give you some idea of what a year's supply of mail contains, look at the findings of the New York mailing house that kept tab on a G.P.'s letter box for 12 months. He received no less than 4,800 pieces of second-class and third-class mail—including drug samples and medical journals. He also received 2,400 pieces of first-class mail—including some personal letters, reports from specialists, and patients' checks. His incoming mail averaged 24 envelopes or packages every office day. The estimated weight of the year's mountain of mail: just a little less than a ton.

Your mail won't amount to much less. If you open, read, and answer all your mail the day you get it, you're a wise and rare bird. To keep it from piling up on you, you probably don't open all of it yourself. You don't read all of it. And much of it that demands an answer isn't answered by you personally. But by being systematic, you can get the mountain leveled in a hurry and answer your correspondence promptly rather than let letters "answer themselves" the way my Philadelphia friend does.

To set up a workable system, first call in your aide and settle on a division of labor. Decide these three questions:

Who opens what? Lots of physicians authorize their aides to open all office mail. Explains one: "Family mail always goes to my home. I don't know of anything that would come to the office that my aide wouldn't see sooner or later. Why shouldn't she see it right away?" Another believes that people write "Personal" on their envelopes just to make sure their letters are shown to him. "They would be anyway," he says. Still another relates: "I used to open mail marked 'Personal' until I went straight from a vacation trip in Maine to a meeting in Chicago. Back at the office was a letter canceling the Chicago affair. If my aide had been authorized to open it, she could have phoned me in Maine and saved me a long journey."

Don't decide that because practice is slow at the start you can occupy idle time by opening the mail personally. Begin right. With or without a reservation on personal letters, hand over the mail-opening job to your aide. Give her these instructions:

¶ Knock down the contents of envelopes before using the letter opener—so you'll have to wrestle with fewer bisected sheets.

¶ If a letterhead doesn't carry the sender's return address, copy the address on it from the envelope without delay—or snip the address from the envelope and tape it to the letter.

¶ When a patient writes, check the return address with the one shown on the patient's office chart and ledger card. If they show an old address, update them.

¶ When a letter is about a patient's medical status or care, pull his chart and clip the letter to it. This procedure will help you guard against answering medical inquiries from memory—a dangerous practice.

¶ When a letter is in answer to one you wrote, attach the carbon copy of your letter, plus any other pertinent material.

Who reads what? You may think it's enough to tell your aide, "Let me see everything except checks, bills, and junk mail." Wait a moment.

All the mail that comes with your name and address on a stencil isn't necessarily junk. Drug houses tip you off to new products, and you ought to know about them. Publishers tell you when useful books are coming out, and you ought to buy some of them. Professional organizations notify you of meetings, and you ought to go to the ones you think will help you in your work.

On the other hand, you don't necessarily have to see all the first-class mail. Your aide can handle the letters from patients saying why they can't pay in full this month, the letters from insurance companies enclosing claim forms, and the routine acknowledgements of letters you've written. You needn't read such stuff. To settle who's responsible for what, take these steps:

¶ Have your aide save all the second-class and third-class mail for a whole month. Then go through it with her one quiet afternoon. Tell her what you want her to throw out in the future and what to save for your inspection.

¶ Classify first-class mail in two categories: yours and hers. Checks, invoices, insurance forms, collection correspondence, and other routine items are hers—unless they contain something unusual she judges you'll want to know about. All the rest is yours.

Who answers what? If your aide is a whiz at English, a spelling-bee champion, and highly skilled in medical terminology, she'll end up writing everything in the office except your charts and prescriptions. But such aides are scarce. So you'd better agree on a plan something like this:

¶ You write all letters to doctors, local bigwigs, and personal friends. You write all letters requiring a professional judgment.

¶ She prepares for your signature all letters to insurance companies, government agencies, etc., when the letter needs to convey only information that's already available in your office records.

¶ She prepares for your signature letters to go with charitable donations, notes of apology for inability to attend meetings, and similar communications.

¶ She writes in her own name to patients, suppliers, etc., on collection matters, invoice queries, and the like.

If you've recruited a competent aide, your share of the day's mail shouldn't amount to more than a few letters—always with relevant charts and prior correspondence attached—waiting on your blotter when you breeze in from the hospital. Don't start seeing patients until you've read the letters. Answer them the same day, if at all possible. The best time to answer is as soon as you've read the inquiry. The people who've written are hoping for a reply now, and it's discourteous to keep them waiting.

To answer rapidly, don't stand on ceremony. If a letter can be answered crisply with "Sure!" or "Sorry" or "I'll be there," answer it that way. Write such concise replies by hand on the incoming letters, and put them in your out tray. Your aide can then run them through the office copying machine and mail the copies to your correspondents. Also build a stock of form letters, form paragraphs, and form sentences. Compose them yourself or steal them from your correspondents. Keep a set handy in a folder and see that your aide also has them. You'll both make good use of them.

Here are some stock phrasings I've seen:

¶ "I appreciate your invitation to *[the Tennis Club banquet].* It sounds like great fun, but I won't be able to make it because of a long-standing previous engagement."

¶ "I received your letter asking for a donation to *[the church building fund].* I'm sure you'll understand that I have to plan my charitable contributions in advance. This year's budget, unfortunately, is all spoken for. I hope you won't be too disappointed that I'm not able to contribute."

¶ "I'll be happy to furnish the requested report on *[John*

110

Jones], if you'll be kind enough to send me the usual signed authorization from the patient. The charge for this report will be *[$5]."*

¶ "I was extremely interested in your paper on *[erythroblastosis],* and so I'd like a reprint for my file on the subject. Would you be good enough to send a copy to the above address?"

If you're *really* interested in saving your time, your aide's time, and your correspondents' time, junk all the flatulent flourishes that deform "business English." Thus, don't dictate, "I am in receipt of your inquiry under date June 15 concerning the probable date of return to full activity of my patient Mr. John Jones." Instead, say, "John Jones will not be fit for work for at least two weeks." And don't drag things out by adding, "If there is any additional information I can give you concerning the probable date of Mr. Jones's

---

Perennial mail problem: drug samples

Many a doctor in private practice receives thousands of drug samples each year. Here's what to do with them:

¶ When a sample of a new preparation arrives and you think you'll try it, keep it handy in your consultation room for one week. If the occasion to try it doesn't occur in that time, hand it to your aide for storage. Let her store all other samples routinely as they arrive.

¶ Have your aide store the samples in a cabinet reserved solely for them. See that she keeps them in boxes labeled by category— antibiotics, sedatives, stimulants, etc.

¶ Make sure she understands that no samples are to be given to a patient except on your specific instruction.

¶ Don't send samples round to the local hospital. Don't give them to a local pharmacist. Don't put them in the trash can.

¶ Once every month have your aide destroy all date-expired samples. Pour liquids down the drain. Run pills through a garbage disposer unit.

¶ When a box of samples is full, have your aide destroy half its contents. Don't worry about the waste.

return to work, please feel free to write again." If he wants to know more, you can *bet* he'll write again!

Maybe composition doesn't come easy to you. But there are ways around that problem. For instance, don't try to transliterate a chart if a photocopy or an excerpt will serve. Some doctors go to great lengths in their letters to paraphrase records they've already written. All that's needed is, "Here's an excerpt from my record on John Jones." The office copier or your aide takes care of the rest.

If you know your letters are stilted and stiff, stop trying to *write* —and switch to plain *talk*. Quit dreaming up sentences of the kind nobody uses in ordinary conversation. Try to write the way you speak. Don't write, *"I shall be grateful if you will . . ."* Say, *"Please . . ."* Don't write *". . . at this juncture."* Say *". . . now."* Don't write *". . . in the near future."* Say *". . . soon."*

Using ideas like those, you'll soon find that the mail *can* be coped with—even if it does arrive by the ton. I hope you already agree that my Philadelphia surgeon-friend was wrong when he said his letters answered themselves. His negligence finally cost him all referrals from a G.P. who objected violently to writing letters to him and getting no answers. You and I know that the surgeon could have prevented that loss if he'd bothered to find out that it takes only 15 minutes a day to read what must be read and to write what must be written.

One word more: If you're not sure whether a correspondent expects an answer, send him one. That way, he *can't* get mad at you!

15

Hospital privileges don't come gift-wrapped

If by any chance you've assumed that you have a right to admit patients to a hospital simply because you're licensed to practice medicine, disabuse yourself. You must first qualify for membership of the medical staff of the hospital—or hospitals, if you want to use more than one. And qualifying can be tough.

In big cities—New York, Chicago, Boston, for example—the G.P. who can walk into a voluntary hospital on any footing except that of an ordinary visitor is exceptional—and lucky. In some small-town hospitals, it's the specialist who hammers vainly against the closed door. And in scores of areas throughout the country where population growth has outrun hospital facilities, *any* new doctor has a hard time getting a staff appointment.

"We don't turn them down out of cussedness," a surgical chief in a metropolitan area says defensively. "We simply don't have the beds. Sure, the young fellows get mad at us, but what can we do? It was their idea to come here, not ours."

I'm not saying categorically that you'll find it impossible—or even difficult—to get privileges immediately at the hospital of your choice. Many doctors do—well over half of them, I'd say. I'm just warning you that a substantial minority is less fortunate. Here are some all-too-typical laments by young doctors who've run into trouble they didn't foresee:

¶ "I had to buck the only other man in my specialty. He was on all three local staffs and didn't welcome the competition. For two years, I had to admit my patients to out-of-town hospitals. But I kept on good terms with all the local men, and just recently I got the appointment I wanted most."

¶ "I can admit patients to only one of our local hospitals. At the others, I'm limited to consultations. I hope to get full privileges at one of these shortly."

¶ "There's an acute bed shortage here. It makes it hard for a new man to get privileges. Being in solo practice is also a handicap, since this is a town where two medical groups control a lot of voting power. I've waited a year now, and I'm keeping my fingers crossed."

¶ "The local G.P.s fought tooth and nail against me. I'm a board surgeon in a town where all the G.P.s do surgery. Fortunately, the hospital administrator went to bat for me, and in three months I got an appointment."

What can *you* do to improve your chances of getting an appointment in a tough area? In most states, a tax-supported hospital is bound to allow at least courtesy privileges to all local doctors of reasonable professional competence. Courtesy privileges, though, don't give you any claim on beds. The most they'll give you is a chance to fill a bed that's surplus to the staff's requirements at the time you ask for it. Proprietary hospitals, many of which are wholly or partly owned by M.D.s, are usually closed shops.

Typically, the by-laws of a voluntary general hospital—the kind you're interested in—require a staff member to be a graduate of a recognized medical school, to have a state license, and to meet all the state's legal requirements governing medical practice.

Beyond these minimal and easily met demands, though, the range of selectivity can be wide indeed. Most hospitals, for example, stipulate that staff members must belong to the local medical society. Many hospitals insist that the staffs of their specialist departments be board-certified, or at least board-eligible. Some hospitals restrict staff membership to holders of university teaching appointments. Some list no specific requirements, but choose between applicants according to undisclosed criteria.

The factor that most influences a hospital in adding to its staff is, as you'd expect, the law of supply and demand. If you're one of the specialists who hospitalizes a majority of his patients—a general surgeon, orthopedist, OBG man, or urologist, for example —you may easily find that staff appointments are at a premium, especially if the locality you've chosen has a good supply of men in your field and a poor supply of hospital beds. If you're an internist, a pediatrician, an ophthalmologist, a dermatologist, or a psychiatrist, you'll probably find the going easier. As a thoracic, neurological, or vascular surgeon, there's a good chance you'll find the welcome mat spread out; you'll bring in "prestige cases." If you're a G.P., your reception may depend on your town's size and its G.P.-specialist ratio. The rule of thumb is that the larger the city, the greater the likelihood that staff appointments are virtually monopolized by specialists. So the smaller the town, the better your chance of being allowed to hospitalize your medical cases, deliver your OB patients, and do at least run-of-the-mill surgery.

Whether you're a specialist *or* a G.P., you can't ever take acceptance for granted—even if you've located in a town that apparently needs more men in your field. The hospital may be holding a vacancy for someone. That was the obstacle encountered by a Michigan urologist whose wife persuaded him to move to her hometown in Georgia. Before he called the moving van, he made sure the hospital hadn't a single incumbent in his specialty. What nobody told him was that a former local G.P., then in the last year of a urological residency, had the job staked out. After a long battle, he returned to the Midwest, embittered and out of pocket.

You can't even assume that the hospital where you trained will grant you privileges. "We graduate two men a year in our program," explains a Texas OBG man. "Only one can stay."

Assuming there's an opening in your field in the hospital you're eyeing, what counts for and against your application? Says the head of a New England hospital's credentials committee: "Medical school grades aren't too important unless they indicate that the candidate consistently scraped through. We pay more attention to what we're told by doctors he's worked under. We ask them about his skills, personality, and ability to get along with people. If he was a chronic breaker of hospital rules during his internship or residency, it's a black mark. We've had some bad experiences with those stubborn types. One of them involved a Johns Hopkins graduate who'd got it into his head that only Hopkins men knew anything about surgery. We gave him a probationary staff appointment. He complained incessantly of the incompetence of the men proctoring him. When his probation ended, we gave our only vacancy to a less offensive young man."

Contacts, of course, are helpful in getting hospital privileges. For the man approaching the end of his residency, his own service chief is, by all odds, his most valuable contact. Why? Because *he* has contacts. Even if he can't arrange for the resident to stay on, he's usually well informed about openings at other hospitals.

Any physician already on the staff of the hospital you're aiming for is also a useful contact—unless he himself is held in low esteem by his peers. One surgeon who settled in a small Southern city went six months without hearing a word from the three hospitals he tried. When he finally—and discreetly—followed up his applications, he got three identical answers: "Your name's before the staff. We'll let you know." More time went by. Finally, an older doctor told him in confidence the reason for the delay. "So-and-so's pushing hard for you," he said. "But for a couple of years we've been trying to figure out a way of getting him off the staff. His work's so bad, we're afraid he's going to cost us our accreditation. There's a rumor that if he gets you privileges, you'll go into partnership with him."

Winning a place on a hospital staff through the good services of a nonmedical contact isn't unknown. But that kind of recommendation can backfire. It did for a surgeon who was voted to the staff of a Midwestern hospital because his uncle was chairman of the trustees. Soon after the appointment, the chairman died. At the end of the year, the surgeon wasn't reappointed.

If your pull comes through the distaff side, you could share the mortification of the internist whose socially prominent wife campaigned for him. She gave party after party, and at each of them she relentlessly turned the heat on staff members and trustees. Dutifully carrying cocktails one evening, the unhappy candidate heard a trustee's wife say to the chief of medicine, "When in the world are you going to let Mrs. Jones's husband on the staff?"

Personal factors that oughtn't to count at all actually do count heavily at times. Sometimes they're pro, as often con. Some staffs in the Midwest are closed clam-tight to foreign-born doctors. Sectarian hospitals everywhere tend to prefer men of their own faith. Inquiring sociologists have found that Protestant hospitals admit few Jews and fewer Catholics; that Jewish hospitals are rarely open to gentile physicians; and that in Catholic hospitals non-Catholic doctors are rare. And not even the U.S. Supreme Court has yet been able to guarantee any Negro physician an open shot at any randomly chosen Southern hospital.

How should you proceed if you have a decided preference for a particular hospital? Apply there—and also elsewhere. "A new doctor should apply to as many hospitals as he can," advises a savvy West Coast ophthalmologist. "He shouldn't wait to become successful at one hospital. By the time he gets around to the others, he's bound to have stirred up some professional jealousy, and he may find the no vacancy sign up."

Should you accept privileges at a hospital that other local doctors look down on? I'm inclined to think you should unless there's reason to suspect that medical hanky-panky's going on there. One reason for not scorning it: You could be instrumental in elevating the hospital's standards.

If you're in doubt about the standing of a hospital, find out if it's accredited by the Joint Commission on Accreditation of Hospitals. If the Commission's plaque isn't on view in the hospital lobby, and you're shy about asking the administrator about the hospital's status, consult the annual guide issue published by Hospitals, the journal of the American Hospital Association. You should find a copy on file in any medical school library.

How long should you wait before abandoning hope of obtaining a staff appointment at a given hospital? That's up to you. Rejections aren't necessarily permanent. That's proved by the experience of many young doctors, among them an OBG man who settled in a Midwest town short on beds and long on OBG men. He knew he'd have to wait and assumed he'd get courtesy privileges while waiting. To his dismay, he found that the hospital didn't grant such privileges. He hung on, though, and after two years he was elected to the staff. "We couldn't help but like him," says his service chief. "He kept in touch. He showed an unflagging interest in everything pertaining to the hospital. What counted most, though, was the way he kept his chin up."

If you reconnoiter thoroughly before committing yourself to the area you fancy, you probably won't have to wait that long. But if you do find yourself chafing at the bit because your staff appointment is slow in coming, guard against taking the bit between your teeth and prematurely bolting. Patience *can* move monuments.

16

How to win praise and encourage referrals

"The biggest mistake a new doctor makes in his relations with his colleagues," a Kentucky practitioner once said, "is simply to set up practice in that community." You *bet* there's a taint of truth in his wry overstatement! No matter how great the doctor shortage where you settle, you'll notice that your arrival arouses less than 100 per cent enthusiasm among your local colleagues. At least one of them may display a good deal more competitiveness toward you than the situation warrants—perhaps because he's never outgrown the memory and hurt of some initial anxious weeks in practice, when the bell on his office door seldom sounded except to announce the arrival of still another salesman.

Naturally, any such competitiveness will worry you. If you're a general practitioner, you'll be eager for an easy relationship with others of your kind. If you're a specialist, your livelihood will doubtless depend on other doctors' willingness to send you their patients.

What to do? First off, relax. If your community isn't overcrowded with men who supply your kind of services, you will indeed be asked to provide them. The competitiveness will turn out to be transient, limited, and rarely or never hurtful.

In a difficult case, even a competition-minded doctor realizes that two good heads may succeed where one may fail. In an impossible case, even a diehard finally recognizes that the patient or his family needs the reassurance a consultation can bring. And when a patient refuses to follow his orders, the diehard is smart enough to see that a prompt referral for temporary—even permanent—management is best for the patient and for him. Competitiveness doesn't rule the referral game.

What does? Quite often, a desire for peace of mind. That's my observation over the years, and it's also one finding of a Medical Economics survey of referrals published in 1966. "In a difficult case, the concurrence of another physician is of great value for the patient's peace of mind as well as my own," said one of the 3,000 practitioners questioned. Said another, "I prefer to split the liability when the patient's condition is fatal or the prognosis poor." A third said, "With all that's being published, I often suspect there's something new that I haven't read or heard about that pertains to a specific patient's problems."

Another common reason for referrals: hospital bylaws that insist on consultation in difficult cases. As one general practitioner noted, "Our hospital has made it mandatory to call in a pediatrician when a baby under a certain weight is delivered."

A third reason, and by far the most often mentioned in the survey, was referral for the good of the patient. "With more specialists in the community, a variety of therapeutic approaches and of consultants' personalities has become available," said one patient-minded survey respondent. "I try to match these to the individual patient's needs."

The study happened to be centered on G.P.-to-specialist referrals, but it did not overlook the referrals that G.P.s get. A reliable G.P. who's noted for the good care he gives to a large number of patients—whether because of long hours or a flair for efficiency—is apt to find plenty of colleagues depending on him to look after their patients when they want time off. "I'm available 9 A.M. to 9 P.M., Monday through Friday, and 9 A.M. to 3 P.M. Saturday," reported a Maryland G.P. "Many doctors, when they go out of town, put my name and phone number on their door."

When you get down to bedrock, practically all general practitioners owe their very livelihood to referrals. They come from loyal patients. The men who get most patient referrals, I've noticed, have agreeable personalities, are conscientious in their care of patients, and charge fees in line with going local rates.

Despite their own heavy reliance on referrals, many physicians do an incredibly poor job when they refer patients of their own to other doctors. One common blunder: They forget to tell the consultant *why* a patient is being referred. This problem is so rife that some hospitals are trying to solve it by demanding that referring doctors submit their hospital consultation requests in writing on special forms such as the one shown on page 123. In the cases I know, the adoption of this rule has worked well. At the least, the referring doctor is reminded to say whether the consultant is to take over the patient, give an opinion, or collaborate with him in treatment.

Let's assume you'll always remember to tell your consultants

Good ways to get referrals

These are the ways of attracting referrals used most often by practicing physicians. Each way is rated for its effectiveness. The percentages indicate the doctors who identified a method as being *most* effective. Source: Medical Economics Referrals Survey.

	Per cent
Report back promptly	33%
Be friendly with hospital colleagues	22
Do one's best to return patients	11
Give scientific talks	7
Offer the referring man an active role	5
Teach in a hospital	4
Teach in a medical school	3
Make one's availability known	2
Entertain colleagues	1
Publish scientific papers	1
Other	11
	100%

---

that much—with or without prompting by a request form. That's not all you should do, though. For your patients' good, I hope you'll send the consultant, without fail, a summary of your own diagnostic work and the therapy you've started. Include all pertinent laboratory and X-ray findings, and, where they'll be helpful, the actual X-ray films. No patient with, say, a lumbosacral problem should need to spend money for X-rays that duplicate those in your files, and no consultant should be forced to delay his study till a second set comes out of his own darkroom or the hospital's film processor.

When you're faced with the task of choosing just the right consultant for a patient, you may find that, unless your patient is willing to travel, your town has only one tip-top man in the field you're surveying. Making a selection in such a situation is no problem. But when you do have a selection problem, judgments like these can help you pick the right man from the list of those available:

¶ Are the consultant's training, experience, and ability sufficient to cope with the patient's problem?

¶ Is the consultant not too busy to give proper management?

¶ In his office, will the patient be handled with consideration, sympathy, and tact?

¶ Can you count on the consultant to keep you informed?

¶ Are his fees such as your patient can pay?

Usually, you'll be wise to mention a consultant's fees to your patient in advance, to relieve his anxiety about the bill. Don't describe the other doctor's fees as low or moderate unless you know they really are. If his bill turns out to be lots higher than the patient thought it would be, he may decline to pay it—and neither you nor the consultant may ever see him again, unless it's before your medical society's grievance committee.

Your best plan: Discuss the consultant's fee first with the consultant, *then* with the patient. When the patient knows in advance—to the dollar—what the fee will be, he's more likely to pay than if he's hit with an unexpectedly high demand. The consultant knows

Form 10492

622C SP.PAV. WMP 40-94-61
HALDER KENNETH 70-1
PHILA 19100 PA GL80376
MARY-W. GL80376
1-329LEVINSKY 12-22-67 522276

CONSULTATION TO:
(SERVICE OR PHYSICIAN)   *BARRY*

REQUESTED BY:
(SERVICE OR PHYSICIAN)   *LEVINSKY*

DATE OF REQUEST: *12/26/67*   TIME: *10 ⁰⁰ AM*

CHECK APPROPRIATE BOX: CONSULTATION ONLY: ☐   CONSULT AND FOLLOW ☒   ACCEPT FOR TRANSFER ☐

DIAGNOSIS AND INFORMATION DESIRED: *Prob. metastatic bone disease. Severe skeletal pain. Bone marrow desired   Ca? myeloma?*

UNIT CLERK TELEPHONED THE CONSULTANT, HIS SECRETARY OR ANSWERING SERVICE ON: *12/26/67*   TIME: *10¹⁰ A.M.*

REPORT OF CONSULTANT (PLEASE SIGN YOUR NAME, DATE AND TIME TO EACH CONSULTATION)

Sternal marrow aspirated with great difficulty. No blood or fragments obtained. The specimen consisted entirely of sheets of malignant cells of uncertain origin. Although there is a superficial resemblance to very primitive plasma cells, this is not a very serious consideration in my opinion. The cell type appears to be adenocarcinoma, but the primary site cannot be stated with any degree of certainty. In this patient the most likely possibility is a prostatic carcinoma, because of the clinical and radiologic picture.

Impression: Marrow specimen demonstrates metastatic malignant cells, probably of
              prostatic origin.

SIGNATURE OF
CONSULTANT: *William E. Barry*   SERVICE: Hematology   TIME: 2:00 pm   DATE: 12/27/67

PLACE ORIGINAL OF REPORT WITH MEDICAL RECORD
CONSULTANT MAY KEEP COPY

This consultation request form helps insure that a referring doctor tells his consultant what's wanted and that a consultant reports back to the referring doctor. As indicated in the upper right-hand corner, the form was developed for Temple University Hospital, Philadelphia. It's a three-sheet carbon snap-out form. Each doctor gets a copy, and the hospital files the original.

123

this. Just make sure he understands that you're not questioning the value of his services. And finally, make sure the patient understands that the quoted fee doesn't cover complications or other unforeseen difficulties that may require additional time and services.

What if the consultant quotes a fee that in your judgment the patient simply can't afford? Tread carefully. If you're not sure how the consultant might react to your suggestions of a fee reduction, *don't suggest one*. If you don't know each other any better than that, there's an odds-on chance that he'll consider you presumptuous—especially if he's much older than you. You'll do better to send the patient to a consultant with whom you have better rapport.

When a patient names a favored consultant, it's often wise to go along with his selection. Just as often, it's wise not to. Not long ago a Pennsylvania client of mine had to talk a local merchant out of bringing in an internist he joked with at Rotary. A consultation was needed, but not with the patient's doctor-friend. He hadn't been to a scientific session in 10 years, seldom glanced at a professional journal, and limited his practice to insurance physicals and the weight problems of suburban ladies.

In neighboring New Jersey, an OBG man had to persuade a patient with a possible herniated disk not to go to an orthopedist she saw regularly at church. He was, as she termed him, "a *nice man*." What she didn't know was that he had the fastest knife in the Garden State.

In upstate New York, a G.P. had to convince a family that their friendly neighborhood pediatrician couldn't handle their daughter's blood problem. It was so obscure that she needed extensive diagnostic studies at a university medical center.

You'd best be ready to face situations like these. When a patient names a consultant you're not sure of, stress the importance of teamwork between the referring doctor and the consultant. "I don't doubt that Dr. Jones is a fine physician," you can say, "but Dr. Smith is, too, and I know this because I've worked with him often. We're on the same hospital staffs and we see each other constantly."

Even if the patient names someone you're convinced is incompetent, start with the same approach. If it fails, stay with your positive arguments but add a little faint praise: "Well, Dr. Jones is certainly an adequate choice for many situations, but in this situation I think *I'd* want to rely on Dr. Smith. He *really* knows this kind of problem."

If the patient still doesn't get the message, you'll have to be negative. Choose your words carefully. Don't blast Jones. Take the blame yourself. One approach: "I'm sorry. I simply don't get along with Dr. Jones." If the patient still insists on calling him in, don't hesitate to withdraw from the case rather than get involved with a man whose work you mistrust. In time, you'll develop a list of reliable consultants to meet all the referral situations you commonly face in your practice. The list will necessarily be a result of trial and error.

If a consultant fails to report to you, you may easily find yourself red-faced because you can't give an intelligent answer to the patient's inevitable query about the consultant's findings. Have a face-saving stalling tactic ready, like this: "Dr. Jones probably tried to call me yesterday when I was in a meeting. Give me a minute, and I'll try to get him on the phone now." Better still, plan ahead. If it's a con-

---

Keeping tabs on doctors who refer to you

If your success as a specialist depends on referrals from colleagues, it's important that you spot any significant drop in referrals from any one man. It probably signals some misunderstanding that you'd better straighten out without delay.

So keep a special card file listing each referring doctor's name, address, and phone number. When a patient is referred to you, enter his name on the referring doctor's card under a yearly heading and a monthly subheading. Keep the cards in a rotary file.

Every month or so, your aide can pull the cards of doctors who haven't referred to you during the period. And you can follow up.

---

sultant you don't know well, arrange for the *patient* to phone you within 24 hours after he's been seen by the consultant. That way, you'll know the consultation actually took place. If the consultant hasn't given you a preliminary phone call about his findings by the time the patient calls you, the short time lapse gives you an automatic out for your lack of news.

Any time you're uncertain of a consultant's ability, don't be shy about checking up on him. Ask other doctors. Enlist the patient's aid, too. One Southern G.P. often invites referred patients back for a no-charge post-consultation visit—ostensibly just to review the consultant's findings. Through discreet questioning, he gets a pretty good idea of the consultant, his facilities, and his staff.

For many young physicians, I've noticed, a psychiatric referral is just about the toughest to engineer. Luckily for you, many patients today are outgrowing their old-fashioned fear of seeing a psychiatrist—thanks largely to TV and popular magazines. Many patients, though, still need to be educated. "I use tranquilizers to support a patient until he's willing to go to the psychiatrist," says one New York internist. "Meanwhile, I explain to him that I'm merely trying to alleviate his symptoms with stop-gap measures. I continually suggest that he think about a psychiatric consultation, because I can do only so much for him. Either this sinks in, and the patient finally goes to the psychiatrist, or he gets another doctor."

Another East Coast internist adds: "I think we physicians should be less apologetic about making a psychiatric referral. Sometimes we're inclined to make excuses, which makes us less than convincing. I get better results by calmly explaining the psychiatrist's function to the patient. I always come right out and use the word 'psychiatrist.' If you use euphemisms—such as 'specialist in emotional problems'—you're only going to make the patient suspicious. That doesn't mean you have to be brutal when you tell him you want to refer him. 'There's nothing physically wrong to explain your symptoms,' you might say. 'They're probably related to the depression and anxiety you say you sometimes feel. As a psychiatrist, Dr. X specializes in just this kind of emotional upset.' "

126

As a referring physician, you can feel assured of one thing: The patient *wants* you to refer him whenever you think a consultation would be helpful. You go up, not down, in his esteem when you suggest that his is a case for an expert. That was a significant finding of a Medical Economics study of patients' attitudes toward referrals. This statement by a patient about his doctor was typical: "If a problem is outside his training, he's not afraid to admit it and say a specialist is necessary. Such actions tend to increase my confidence in my regular physician."

As a consultant, you'll find you stand or fall largely according to how you follow these five rules:

¶ Report back promptly. "Sending along reports the same day—by telephone for fractures, suspected TB, and other cases where time is especially important—has resulted in a 50 per cent increase in my referrals in 18 months," says a North Carolina radiologist.

¶ Be a stickler for returning patients to their referring doctors. "I make it clear to a referred patient that I limit my practice strictly to my specialty," says a urologist I know. A psychiatrist adds: "I treat nothing outside my specialty and always return the patient. Every patient I see on referral is an example of how sound a policy this is. Before I came to town, most of the cases in my specialty were referred out of town."

¶ Make personal contact with potential referring doctors. Few physicians will send a case to a man they've never met, unless he's a celebrity in his field. "The new doctor should introduce himself, give a few details about his background, pass the time of day—and leave," advises one G.P. An internist suggests that the new doctor visit his colleagues "in a spirit of helpfulness. He might say, 'I don't want to muscle in on anyone's practice. But if I can help out, of course that will help me, too.' A specialist visiting a G.P. should add that he intends to treat only cases within his field, except in emergencies or when covering for another man."

¶ Whenever it's feasible to do so, offer the referring doctor an active role in the case. One confident general surgeon often asks a referring doctor to assist him in the O.R. because, he says, "It lets him see my surgical ability." Says an OBG man: "My best referral sources are delighted to participate in the care of their patients—and so they send me more of the same."

¶ Build up your reputation—ethically—among your colleagues. They can't refer patients to you if they don't know you exist, and they won't refer to you regularly till they're sure of your ability. Teaching in the hospital or a nearby medical school is a fine way to build up a reputation—if you're a good teacher. Publishing papers in professional journals is another—if they're good papers. I'll discuss ways to promote your image in the next chapter.

Of all the reasons why referring doctors choose one consultant over another, professional reputation ranks first, according to the Medical Economics referral study quoted earlier. Quality of training ranks second. The satisfaction of previously referred patients stands third. Lots of lesser reasons follow those three; chief among them is the consultant's promptness in keeping the referring doctor informed. So after you've seen a referred patient, make that preliminary phone report *statim,* even if it's only to say that your initial testing is inconclusive and that further studies must follow.

A New England urologist often phones a referring doctor with the patient still in front of him in the consultation room. "It's reassuring to the patient to know I'm not telling him one thing and telling his doctor another," he says. To avoid scaring a listening patient, he'll sometimes employ terminology the patient isn't likely to understand. " 'Neoplasm' isn't as familiar to the laity as 'malignancy,' " he notes. After every consultation, and with minimum delay, he does what every wise consultant always does: He follows up his express phone report with a *written* report. He considers a consultation incomplete till he's sent along his findings on paper.

"My reports aren't lengthy or elaborate," he explains. "They're concise. I don't pad them by including stuff the other man already knows." He has a good point there: A competent report writer gets to the point. He gives the information that's needed and skips the frills. Frequently, it's enough to run the patient's office record through a copier and send it on its way with a covering note.

128

Failure to return patients to referring doctors can kill a consultant's practice stone dead in a hurry. But what if you're a consultant and a referred patient says he *wants* you to manage the treatment you've recommended? Tell him firmly that the referring doctor is perfectly capable of managing it. If he simply turns up in your office for further care, encourage him as best as you can to return to the referring doctor. If he refuses, saying he feels the referring doctor isn't competent to see things through, you have a choice to make. If you know the other man is competent, say so —convincingly. But if you have any reason to suspect the patient is right, get out of a delicate situation with grace and honesty. The patient's welfare must come first; you owe him that. To the referring doctor you owe tact. So tell the patient the truth: Medical ethics guarantee him free choice of physician. Then call or write the other man and tell him what you said. If the patient then switches to you, you can—with the patient's written authority—request a transfer of the referring doctor's clinical record.

As a consultant, how should you react to requests for fee reductions? If you grant one yourself to a patient who convinces you he can't afford your usual charge, tell the referring doctor about it. He may have been asked to make a concession also, and knowledge of your action could help him decide his own answer. If it's the referring doctor who asks you to reduce or forgive a fee, grant it—if you value him as a referral source.

When, on the other hand, a referring doctor suggests that you charge more than you usually do, consult your conscience. He's asking you to practice Robin Hood medicine. And the lucrative pastime of soaking the rich received its comeuppance long ago. If your conscience tells you not to go along with him, you won't see any more of his patients. That'll be their loss.

It all adds up to this: Referrals—to and from—are best handled by putting the patient's interests first, by dealing with colleagues tactfully and considerately, and, when problems arise, by invoking the Golden Rule. If you'll put yourself in the other guy's place, be he doctor or patient, you can't go wrong.

17

There are ethical ways to get known

"This is a nation of promoters," a Texas internist once said to me at a cocktail party. "Not many Americans go out looking for something to buy; most of us expect to be *sold*. So it makes sense for a physician to promote himself all he can."

"That's the most cynical statement I've ever heard," said a surgeon standing near us. "Self-promotion is one of the things responsible for medicine's poor image. It's completely unethical. Besides," he added as an afterthought, "it doesn't pay."

Neither man was wholly right, neither was wholly wrong. Some publicity-bringing activities lead to practice growth and are ethical, too, while others are ethically dubious and not rewarding. What's certain is that the physician who launches a straight selling campaign in his own behalf will get more kicks than ha'pence, while increased practice often comes to the doctor who's widely known for some activity he'd engage in anyway.

"Publicity that came to me unsought brought me so many new patients I had to quit speechifying to lay audiences on heart disease," one New England physician told me. "The editor of our local paper attended a heart association luncheon and heard my talk. His write-up filled my office with cardiacs asking for 'the heart doctor.'"

It doesn't always work out that way, however. "I get plenty of publicity, but I'd go broke if I relied on it to bring me patients," reports a Pennsylvania G.P. "I do a weekly radio program that's

131

locally rated No. 1 in its time-slot. The fees I collect from listeners showing up at my office as patients wouldn't pay the parking charges on my car while I'm in the studio."

Granting that you're not interested in outright self-advertisement, are there any activities a physician can ethically engage in that might yield new patients as a by-product? There are indeed. I'll list half a dozen for you.

Communication with lay audiences via the lectern, the radio, television, and the press. It's said that half of all private physicians engage in one or more of these activities. And despite the Pennsylvania G.P.'s experience, most of them say they can trace new patients to their speeches or articles.

A Washington State OBG man, for example, tells how a lecture on cancer brought him "a rush of women for Pap smears." An Oklahoma neurologist says he got a burst of referrals after a series of talks on headache he gave to audiences that included laymen. "The overload," he adds, "forced me to stop the lectures."

Does it matter to the layman whether you're a G.P. or a specialist? Apparently not. You're a doctor talking about health, and that's enough.

You do, however, need to talk or write on a topic that's of general interest, in terms comprehensible to people with no clinical background. Do it well, and there's a good chance that some listeners or readers will want to hear more from you firsthand.

Activity in civic work and service clubs. I'm told that three out of five G.P.s and two out of five specialists belong to senior or junior chambers of commerce, parent-teacher associations, and service clubs such as Rotary and Kiwanis. But those I know didn't join such organizations merely to advance their professional interests. They like the fellowship and the chance to be useful in a field other than medicine. And they're careful to avoid even the shadow of self-promotion.

A Virginia surgeon puts the situation concisely: "A doctor who takes up civic work as a promotional gimmick will be found out quickly. Sure, I get patients from my Jaycee affiliation. And my medical friends in Rotary pick up patients there. But a doctor who'd make a pitch on his own behalf among the members of a civic club would be slapped down fast."

Is civic and service club work really a practice builder? Most doctors I know who engage in it say it is. Out-and-out politics, though, is quite another matter. "I wouldn't be mayor of my city again at any price," a Wisconsin surgeon once told me. "Many of my patients and some of my referring physicians resented my political activity."

A Missouri G.P. who served a term as his town's health commissioner rued it bitterly. "When I cracked down on some local eating places, my practice nose-dived," he mourned. "The owners had more friends than I had."

A Southern G.P. said: "My run for the State Assembly just about ruined me for a couple of years. You can't be a politician and a family doctor at the same time. Hundreds of people switched to other physicians while I was campaigning."

There's always the maverick, of course. One Ohio radiologist thinks being a doctor-politician is fine. "Why should I stay out of politics?" he demands. "Patients who agree with me politically gravitate to me. Those who disagree stay away. So I have a practice made up of people who have confidence in me."

So the consensus on public service—politics excepted—seems to be: If you go in for it, your practice probably will benefit without any active promotion on your part. But if your co-workers in voluntary service get the notion that you joined up with practice building in mind, you'll get nothing better than icy stares.

Speeches and articles beamed at your own profession. Most specialists seem convinced that publishing scientific papers and addressing professional audiences help promote their practices. General practitioners, in the main, say such activities do little to help.

Probably it couldn't be otherwise. As a Maryland proctologist puts it: "Any specialist who becomes known to his colleagues this way is bound to pick up referrals. He can only fail if the stuff he presents is no good, which in my experience is rarely the case.

When a man gets on a professional program it's because he has something worth sharing with others, and it's usually something specialized. What's more natural than that a listener should consult him with a problem he's heard the speaker discuss?"

A New England internist says that publishing papers has helped his practice enormously. "I've had referrals from cities 500 miles away as a result of reprints I've sent—on request—to doctors interested in the problems I've written about," he says. "But the man who expects floods of referrals from one paper on a hackneyed topic is going to be disillusioned. I happen to have published over 100 papers on a highly specialized subject."

On the G.P. front, a California doctor says mordantly: "Who's kidding whom? General practitioners don't get referrals from other physicians. The G.P. who publishes a paper does so because he wants to see his name in print. And when a G.P. makes a presentation to a medical meeting, it's always to the general practice section, isn't it? The audience makes plenty of notes—but the notes don't include the speaker's phone number."

Is reading—or publishing—a paper to other doctors on a medical subject truly classifiable as a promotional activity? "Definitely not," avers one doctor who prepares half-a-dozen papers a year. "It's a duty. If you know how to do something better than it's generally done, you owe it to the profession not to keep it a secret."

Promotional or not, a good paper never lacks a forum. Ask any program chairman or medical journal editor.

Taking an active role in organized medicine. Does it help to go to your state medical association's annual convention? Or to the meetings of your county medical society or specialty organization? Most doctors say it does. For many specialists, attending such meetings offers a chance to get acquainted with doctors they'd never otherwise meet. From these contacts, referrals often come.

"I'm convinced that attending medical meetings helps my practice," a Massachusetts psychiatrist tells me. "Time and again, I've met G.P.s there who've subsequently sent me patients. Many of them have been patients who wouldn't go to a psychiatrist in their own communities. If I hadn't frequented conventions, I'd never have made some of my most valuable professional contacts."

Is there any additional practice-building bonus to a man who holds office in a professional organization? For specialists, the indications are that it does—but only over the long haul. "My year as president of my state medical association cost me over $15,000 in work lost by attending over 100 meetings," a general surgeon reports. "Now, though, I'm busier than I've ever been. My term of office did more for my prestige among nonsurgeons in my home city than anything I could have thought up for myself."

It's contrariwise for G.P.s, according to an Indiana family doctor. "I was away so much my patients figured I'd retired," he said. "They got the habit of going elsewhere—and that's where most of them are still going. Take it from me, holding an office in organized medicine is the quickest way to wreck a general practice."

"That's all rot," said a former officer of the American Academy of General Practice. "I was away one-third of my time on official affairs. I just worked harder when I came back."

Take your pick of the views. But if you follow precedent, you'll go to more meetings and accept office more readily if you're a specialist than if you're a G.P.

Religious activities. Church work isn't too often cited by physicians as an influence on practice growth. Yet those who say it helps say it helps a lot. Typically, however, doctors bristle at the notion that religion can be "used" to promote practice. An Illinois pediatrician warns: "The doctor-churchworker risks being charged with 'professional piety.' He also risks a backwash from the suspicion that he rates publicity higher than prayer. I attend my church and I contribute generously to it. But I leave it at that. No one is going to accuse me of using my faith as a prop for my practice."

Church work, though, is one of the few areas where the G.P.s I know outnumber the specialists in saying it helps build—or at least solidify—their practices. "That's easily explainable," says a Montana G.P. who's also a Sunday-school teacher. "I live and worship right here among my patients. It's natural that a church-

135

goer, when he's sick, will turn to the man who shares his pew. Lots of specialists, however, live some distance from where they practice. Obviously, attending a church 20 miles away from your professional 'drawing area' isn't going to give you much exposure to potential patients, or to their family doctors, either. I think my church work aids my practice significantly. Of course, you have to be a churchgoer by desire. Any doctor who thinks he can invest in a church the way he invests in a glamour stock is in for a big disappointment."

If you ask me, he's said all there is to say on that subject.

Teaching. Only a minority of doctors can hope for the opportunity to teach medicine. But that minority—consisting almost exclusively of specialists—admits that it's the most potent practice builder of all. Referrals from former pupils virtually never stop.

"When you teach a man," says a Florida professor of ophthalmology, "you impress yourself on him indelibly. When he has a problem patient, he comes straight to you, just as a puzzled child goes to a parent."

A medical school dean says sagely: "We're well aware that when local specialists give up their time to teaching, for little or no financial recompense, they have a fringe benefit in mind. That benefit is reputation-building. We don't object. But if we suspect that the fringe benefit is his only motive, we object strongly. No doctor can teach residents, interns, or students anything if he's thinking of dollars. Fortunately, few doctors ever try it. Those who come here to teach do so compulsively; their professional consciences won't allow them not to."

Should you teach if you get the chance? Well, you heard what the professor said. And the dean's there to see that your conscience is really your guide.

Should you engage in *any* of the activities I've listed? My answer: If you're so inclined, engage in every last one—not because they're practice builders but because they're worthwhile. Afraid that, as a young doctor, you'll be frowned on as pushy? Bunk! Bright young men who are willing workers are needed everywhere.

18

An appointment system that works

H is name was Elmer Crump, but I always thought of him as Dr. Clump. That was because his patients didn't just visit his office: They agglutinated there. I thought at first I'd never seen such a busy G.P. The gilt-lettered words on his office door said, "Office hours 10 A.M. to noon, 1 to 5 P.M." At noon, the influx started. A patient arriving then stood a good chance of being out by three. Dr. Crump never honored the promise on his door. He'd breeze in any time between 1:30 and 2 P.M. He never carried out the threat on his door, either. He'd stay till he'd seen 'em all. Most evenings, he and his nurse got out around 7:30.

"I'm working like a horse, as you see," he said, "and I still have nothing to show for it. My income's just pathetic. And I mean my *gross* income, not just my net."

Around eight that evening, at Dr. Crump's home, I offered a suggestion. "Work by appointment," I proposed. "There were eight people who popped their heads into your waiting room this afternoon and popped 'em out again real fast. What they did reminded me of a barbershop: You take a quick look to see how many haircuts are ahead of you, and leave when you see it will be a good half-hour before it's your turn. If you *need* a haircut, you look for the next striped pole."

He didn't much like the image of his practice that I was raising. But his patients liked his way of practicing even less, so I continued: "I saw four people in your waiting room get up and leave without a word. A fifth asked your aide for an appointment to-morrow. She said she was sorry, but you didn't give appointments. He said he'd come back at 5 o'clock, but he didn't. Do you know how many patients you saw in your office today?"

"About 40, I guess," said Dr. Crump comfortably.

"Nope. By count, 28. But you could have seen more than 40—if you'd seen the eight who popped their heads in and the five who left."

"Lucky for me. I'd have been there now instead of here," said Dr. Crump.

"Oh no," I said. "You could have seen 40 patients and been home long since. Forty patients daily for you would be no big deal. Four of the patients you saw today were kids needing nothing but shots, two were old folks wanting their blood pressure checked, and four were OBs in the second trimester. You came in at 1:45 and left at 7:15. That's five and a half hours."

I reminded him how he'd spent some of that time: "You talked with me 20 minutes before you saw the first patient, and you were on the phone seven times for a total of 30 minutes. You talked with the mother of one youngster for 15 minutes after you'd given him his booster shot. You talked about Italy for 10 minutes with a man who came for vaccination because he's going there next month. That's the sort of afternoon it was."

"You've really got the book on me, haven't you?" said Dr. Crump. "Anything else?"

"Just this: Your old patients stick to you like glue, but you don't see many new ones. So your income suffers in two ways: People come to see you just for simple things—shots, blood pressure checks, and prescriptions for the sniffles—and you have one of the poorest collection records I've seen in a long time. The patients you need—those with the more serious ailments and those who pay—don't come to you. They won't stand for your hurry-up-and-wait way of running your practice."

"O.K.," said Dr. Crump. "Let's get a new system."

Dr. Crump does better financially these days. There are new

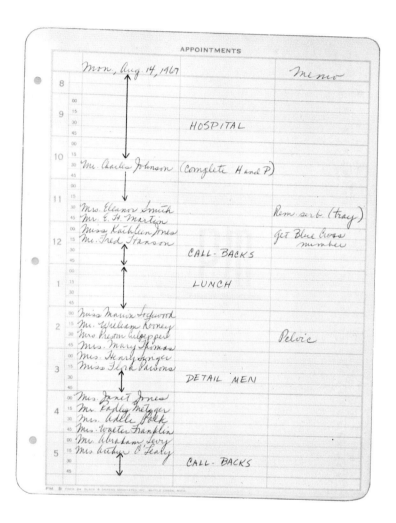

The best appointment book for a practice depends on the doctor's specialty and, more important, work pace. For many doctors, a standard form marked off in 15-minute segments, as here, is best. For others, a specially designed form works best. Even this, however, should include a column for noting the doctor's activities when not seeing patients (above, center) and another for showing reasons for patients' nonroutine visits (above, right).

139

faces in his reception room. Now that he works by appointment, the people in his community have found:

¶ They're not forced to waste hours in his reception room that they could put to better use elsewhere.

¶ They're not crowded by grumbling adults and fretful kids.

¶ They get a smile and a greeting from his aides, who formerly sighed at every new arrival.

Dr. Crump's wife likes the new system, too. She knows what time Dr. Crump will be home for dinner. And the Crump children enjoy having their dad play with them every evening before bed.

Dr. Crump and his two aides are counting some blessings, too. Their workweek is shorter. In fact, they usually lock the door behind them at 6 P.M. Many of the old patients who'd left Dr. Crump have returned, and there's a steady stream of newcomers. They're satisfied and therefore cooperative patients—who pay cheerfully.

If you're thinking of making do without an appointment system, or if the system you've instituted seems to have gone sour, try the recipe I gave Dr. Crump for an effective appointment system. It has these 10 ingredients:

Pick an appointment book that's right for you. Don't think any gift desk-diary will do.

Dr. Crump picked a loose-leaf, page-a-day book. Each page has three columns. One is marked off in five-minute intervals from 8 A.M. to 6 P.M. One is wide enough to take a patient's full name and phone number. The third has space for jotting down the reason for each patient's visit.

That page design suits some doctors. Another would suit you better? Then *that's* the kind to get. If you can't find a ready-made design that suits you, have one printed up specially. It will be worth its small extra cost.

Account for every hour of every working day. I had one of Dr. Crump's aides do some preparatory work on the appointment book. She blocked off all periods when the doctor did *not* see patients at the office.

For example, she drew a thick vertical line with a red pencil down each page from 8 A.M. to 10 A.M. and printed in the word "Hospital." Another red line disposed of the half-hour from 12:30 to 1 P.M. She marked this period: "Call-backs." The hour between 1 and 2 P.M. said "Lunch." The 5 to 5:30 half-hour was assigned for more call-backs.

Time left for seeing office patients: five-and-a-half hours.

If you're having a page of your own design printed, have the no-appointment periods shaded out.

Analyze your patient-handling capacity. Dr. Crump figured out how long he needed to take a history and examine a new patient, and how long, on the average, it took him to check the progress of an OB, a healthy baby, an aging cardiac, and several other patient categories.

His nurse figured out how much time she needed to weigh a patient, take his temperature and pulse, get an examining room ready for him, run a couple of routine lab tests, and give a shot.

His secretary calculated how long it normally took her to register a new patient, find the chart of an old one, make an appointment for another visit, give a receipt for cash, type up an insurance claim.

All of that helped to decide the daily office workload Dr. Crump could accept.

Designate specific days and hours for different types of patients. Dr. Crump now sets aside his first office hour each morning for the "I'm-sick-now-and-can't-wait" cases. The secretary's there at 8:30 to take their calls and assign them times.

New patients needing work-ups get the rest of each morning. Most days, the secretary can work in a quick recheck between two work-ups, if that's what is necessary to oblige a patient she knows won't waste the doctor's time.

The first hour each afternoon is set aside for the routine care of a specified category of "regular patient." Pregnant women are seen Mondays, well babies on Tuesdays, pimply teen-agers on Thursdays, old folks on Fridays. Dr. Crump finds he can schedule 10 or more patients per hour at these sessions.

The rest of the afternoon, he averages six "miscellaneous" visits per hour. Says his nurse with a twinkle: "That's when we see the puffers, primpers, and stuffers. We have a raft of regulars with emphysema, hypertension, and just plain obesity."

Dr. Crump saves Saturday mornings (after the "can't-waits") for desk work—"I'd never realized how much more efficient it is to dictate letters, sign forms, orders, and checks, and skim medical journals in silent solitude." Even so, his book seldom shows fewer than 200 office visits per week.

Let your aide give out all appointments. Dr. Crump tells his patients: "Come back in a week," or "I'd like to check you every month for awhile," or "We'll leave these stitches in till the end of the week." Exact days and times, though, are settled at the front desk. If, as rarely happens, the doctor does want to be more specific, he tells the secretary himself.

See that all patients receive an appointment slip on leaving. Dr. Crump's appointment slip says in bold print: "Please call this number if you have to cancel. We'll give your time to another patient and make a new appointment for you." It works fine. The few who cancel always call. And the secretary always knows someone who won't mind coming a day early to fill the vacated time slot.

Guard against running late. When Dr. Crump runs overtime on an appointment, his nurse rescues him. By pre-arrangement, she discreetly starts to tidy up the examining room, saying: "All ready next door, Doctor." If he gives her the patient's chart, she knows what to do. She leaves, returning almost immediately to say, "Dr. Williams is calling long distance, Doctor." Handing over the chart is Dr. Crump's SOS signal.

Don't see your patients twice at each visit. Dr. Crump used to have everyone shown first into his consultation room. He'd chat awhile, then turn the patient over to his nurse, who'd lead the way to an examining room. Now, only new patients get the two-room interview. On a revisit, a patient goes either into the consultation room or an examining room, depending on whether any undressing is necessary. Although there's no examining table in his consultation room, Dr. Crump keeps a basic examining kit there.

Don't work in any nonemergency patient while scheduled patients are waiting. If an emergency shows up in Dr. Crump's office, or if Dr. Crump has to dash out to a delivery, patients in the reception room at the time—and others as they arrive—are told what's going on. And they're given the option of making a new appointment. But outside these situations, no one jumps the appointment book. "I'm glad I finally made that rule," says Dr. Crump. "At first, I'd always give in to local bigwigs and to personal friends. Then my secretary told me that half of my callers told her they were one or the other."

Stay off the phone during appointment hours. Dr. Crump's secretary tells phone callers pleasantly: "The doctor's with a patient right now. If it's an emergency, I'll be glad to get him to the phone. Otherwise, I'll give him a message the minute he's free and call you back with his answer. If you'd rather speak with him personally, and you'll give me a number where he can reach you at 12:30 or at 5 o'clock, he'll call you at one of those times."

Result: Dr. Crump is hardly ever required to leave a patient to talk on the phone.

The last time I saw him, Dr. Crump told me: "I used to believe that appointments were invented by specialists who didn't like long hours. A G.P., I thought, was supposed to be on tap to all comers at all times. Now I can see that a G.P. needs an appointment system *more* than a specialist does."

Personally, I don't agree with Dr. Crump that a G.P. needs appointments more. Good management requires all doctors to work by appointment, with just enough leeway to accommodate people who are suddenly taken acutely ill.

See-'em-as-they-come is first aid, not modern medicine.

143

19

Time is your most valuable asset: Don't waste it

"I'd do fine if only there were 48 hours in a day." I'll bet you've said that, if you've been in private practice very long. If you're new to practice, I'll bet you'll say it before long. It's the plaint I hear constantly from physicians. That doesn't bother me. What does bother me is that some doctors never seem to accomplish all they want to in a day. Other doctors—just as busy—get their work done and have time left over for family, hobbies, and play.

The secret can be yours. It's this: Plan your day. I mean every working hour. Or even every waking hour.

The well-organized doctors I know carry no stopwatches, nor do they practice assembly-line medicine. They're damn good physicians. There's nothing superficial, for example, about the care received by the patients of a certain New England internist who often sees 125 patients in a single day. I've watched him at work, and I've marveled. And if you suspect something slipshod in the work of a certain small-town G.P. in Georgia who regularly sees 75 patients a day, ask the other doctors in his community about him—as I did. I got a unanimous answer: "He's an excellent doctor."

I'm not suggesting that you practice medicine at the same clip as the mind-like-a-steel-trap crowd, the supermen. I do suggest, though, that you *can* pack more work into your working day—if you've a mind to. It takes a few realistic calculations, plus the will to hit two targets you set up for yourself. The first is the income you

145

need to bring up and educate your family, pay off your mortgage and any other loans, insure prudently, and save modestly. Look for your target figure in the box on page 147. Target No. 2 is the number of hours per week you're willing to devote to achieving the income you want.

Watch for traps in figuring your working week. Chances are, you'll say you're working a 60-hour or 70-hour week—though you're not. Most doctors will give you those figures, but not all of the hours contribute to the attainment of income. You'll do well to put in 30 hours a week in your office and 15 hours a week in the hospital or at patients' homes. Sure, you'll put in another 15 hours or so at staff meetings, in charity work, in the reading of medical journals, and in professional travel. But none of those activities yields anything you can put in the bank. Your earning hours— your working weeks—are spent with patients.

How many working weeks in a year? If you're typical, your summer vacation, some odd weekends, and a few days at conventions will lop off several working weeks annually. To be on the safe side, figure 45 working weeks of 45 income-producing working hours each. That gives you paid working time of 2,000 hours a year. Now see, on page 147, what each hour must yield in cold cash if you're to end up with the income you're shooting for. If $1,000 a month net before income taxes is your modest goal, each of your 2,000 working hours must bring in $10. For a net of $2,000 a month, each hour must produce $20.

If your income target isn't frankly outrageous, I'll lay odds you can achieve it—if you'll organize your day properly. Here are six steps you can take to get the maximum mileage out of yourself:

Don't do other people's work. If you're starting out in practice, you'll have time to take down long histories in your own handwriting, give shots, change dressings, answer the phone, make appointments, collect fees, write checks, and look after books. You'll even gab with patients—because you're lonely. If you're aiming at take-home pay of $2,000 per month, you'll be wise not to start any of those bad habits. They're easy to acquire, hard to drop.

Right from the start, organize nonmedical work out of your professional day. Leave it to your help. If you can't afford an aide for a while, you can at least remind yourself that it's aide's work you're doing when you're doing it. It's important to keep your perspective.

On page 149, you'll find a list of eight of the jobs your aide can do as well or better than you. Let her do them. Save your time for doctoring.

Run an efficient appointment system. Stop thinking of the book on your aide's desk as just an appointment book: *It's your schedule.* You know best the pace at which you can work on different kinds of patients. You know best what your aide can and can't do for them. So design a work sheet that takes the capabilities of both into account.

Classify patients, if you can, according to their reasons for coming. A surgeon does so routinely. He spends his mornings in the operating room, and he groups patients needing operations. Later, in the office, he sees another group of patients—those for pre-

---

The hourly gross needed to produce the income you need

If you put in 2,000 productive hours per year and spend 40 per cent of your gross on practice-connected expenses—both figures are realistic—you'll need to use your time just as productively as the figures below indicate. They suggest: The more take-home pay you need, the less you can afford to horse around or to do work that an aide ought to do.

Desired net before taxes	Annual gross required to produce desired net	Average hourly gross required to produce desired annual gross
$12,000	$20,000	$10
18,000	30,000	15
24,000	40,000	20
30,000	50,000	25
36,000	60,000	30
42,000	70,000	35
48,000	80,000	40

147

operative or postoperative care. He'd go nuts if he had to operate on Patient A, clean up, dash to the office to see Patient B, and dash back to the O.R. to operate on Patient C.

If you're a nonsurgeon, take a leaf out of the surgeon's book. Classify your patients, and schedule them accordingly. For example, keep the first office quarter-hour for a conference with your aide. Have her brief you on the calls that have come in, summarize what's in the mail, run through the list of patients booked for the day. Don't start seeing patients until you've received this daily briefing.

Then see acutely sick people. Allot your first hour, after the daily briefing, to a sort of sick call.

Next schedule the nonacute new patients. These will include patients coming for more or less complete work-ups preceding a course of treatment. In between these patients, or while your aides are with them, slip into your consultation room and return urgent phone calls, dictate clinical notes and short letters, sign completed insurance forms.

Schedule all revisits, except the emergencies, for the afternoons. The internist, pediatrician, and G.P. will schedule the visits of patients under continuing care. The OBG man will schedule prenatal and postnatal visits. Most kinds of doctors will group patients by their ailments—so an aide can save time prepping and the doctor can save time examining.

I know G.P.s who save Monday afternoon for OB prenatals, Tuesday afternoon for children's shots, Thursday afternoon for cardiacs, hypertensives, and elderly patients in general, Friday afternoon for diabetics and ulcer patients.

Finally, fill out each afternoon's schedule with miscellaneous revisits after the "classifieds."

Now, don't say: "My patients wouldn't stand for such a system." Start it and see. You'll be amazed to find how many cheerful coteries form in your reception room every afternoon—all as cheerful as the golf foursome you'll be in every Wednesday, your afternoon off.

Schedule your interruptions. If you're really going to organize your day, you've got to schedule interruptions, too. It's not by accident that industry has long scheduled coffee breaks. The smart manager discovered years ago that indiscriminate pauses for cups of coffee and chit-chat break up the factory day. You, too, would be smart to schedule coffee breaks—10 minutes each morning and afternoon.

Detail men and other regular nonpatient callers are interruptions to be scheduled. They'll not object. In fact, they'll rejoice. Half-an-hour a week will take care of all of them. That's only two full hours a month.

Professional reading occasionally disrupts most doctors' schedules, so it's worth scheduling. Don't let an eye-catching title on the cover of a journal tempt you into taking a quick look at the article during appointment hours. Instead, schedule five minutes a day for title-scanning. Also schedule time to read your selections—say, on Saturday mornings after sick call.

A more significant threat to the doctor's day, though—need I

Work that an aide ought to do

Delegate to your aide as much work as possible—rather than as little as tradition seems to suggest. Delegate these jobs and more:

- ☐ Making appointments
- ☐ Starting case histories (nonclinical data)
- ☐ Explaining simple regimens to patients
- ☐ Operating diagnostic equipment—e.g., X-rays
- ☐ Performing minor clinical procedures—e.g., taking blood pressures
- ☐ Banking cash and checks
- ☐ Following up slow and delinquent accounts
- ☐ Filling out health insurance claims for signature

---

tell you?—is the phone. *Tame it.* If you put yourself at the mercy of every interrupter who has the savvy to use the phone instead of the front door, you won't get more than 45 minutes' work done in any hour of your day. So get this word out to all patients:

"I hold an open wire from 8:30 to 10 every morning. Try to phone for house calls before 9, for office appointments before 10. If you want to talk with me personally, leave a number at which I can reach you at noon or at the end of the day. If you'll cooperate, you'll help me, yourself, and all my other patients. In an emergency, call anytime."

Let your aide monitor the open morning wire and log the calls for you. At noon and again at 5:00, duck into your consultation room and get set for a half-hour of call-backs. She can dial one patient on Line 1 while you're talking with another on Line 2. As your phone skill develops, you'll find you can talk with 30 people, if need be, in 30 minutes. Yes, I know doctors who do it. Lots of them.

Be punctual. There's a small textile town in the South where the millhands going to work speed up if they see an old green sedan parked in the town square. Old Dr. Hobkins is in his office—so they know they're late. For 35 years Dr. Hobkins has risen at 6, reached the hospital at 7, and greeted his first office patient at 8 o'clock. The shift at the mill starts at 8, too.

The workers also know that precisely at noon Dr. Hobkins will leave for lunch. After a few house calls, he'll return to his office at 3. At 5, he'll depart again for the hospital and more house calls. Mrs. Hobkins knows that at 6:30 he'll be home for an hour's relaxation before dinner—and the emergency calls that always come in.

There's a reward in disciplining yourself to be punctual like Dr. Hobkins. Like him, you can see lots of patients every day and not develop ulcers. (He sees 40 or more a day.)

Cut your time losses. The practice of medicine being what it is, your schedule will get fouled up now and then. As a G.P., you may get a rush call to an old patient who's had a stroke while dressing.

As an OBG man, you may get a rush call to the labor room when your office is filled with prenatal patients. As a surgeon, you may get panic calls from the hospital's emergency room.

Don't try to make up all the lost time. Instead, estimate how long you'll be gone. Have your aide explain the nature of the problem to your waiting patients. And have her call and warn those who may not be already on their way. Many will settle for coming back another day rather than waiting it out.

That's as near as you can come to fending off the disruption caused by emergencies. You can, however, guard against letting your day creep off schedule. When you realize that Mrs. Jones's scheduled 10-minute visit isn't going to suffice, and that she isn't *in extremis,* don't plow ahead and dislocate the entire day. Tell her you want to see her again—tomorrow.

Finally, cut your time losses by searching periodically for errors in your schedule. If you need an hour to work up a new patient, don't stubbornly stick to 45 minutes just because other doctors tell you that's all the time they need. If you can't get through six routine office visits in an hour, don't try; settle for four. Can't finish with a detail man in five minutes? Well, give him 10 the next time. In short, be realistic.

Don't play in working time. There's a time and place for everything, so when the time's your working time and the place is your office, the hospital, or a patient's home, concentrate on only one thing—work! Give each job all you've got, and move on to the next—on schedule.

> "So many hours must I tend my flock;
> So many hours must I take my rest;
> So many hours must I contemplate;
> So many hours must I sport myself. . . ."

Your flock-tending hours number 2,000 a year. Don't waste 'em.

20

Practice by phone?
Most doctors do

"**D**o I treat patients over the phone? Why, of course I do. It's not the best way to practice medicine, but I've no choice in the matter." That's what a busy physician told me years ago, when I asked him if he ever gave significant medical advice by phone. Since then I've discovered that almost every doctor gives medical advice by phone—and more than just occasionally. Over half the G.P.s, internists, and OBG men do it up to 25 times a week. About 4 out of 10 general surgeons do it at least five times a week. Pediatricians do it all the time. Two out of five do it at least 40 times a week.

If you're new to private practice, you'd best know what's in and what's out in the world of medical care by phone. Here, in order of frequency, are the conditions doctors treat most over the wire: colds and minor respiratory complaints, nausea and vomiting, diarrhea, headaches. When a caller reports high fever or some other dangerous accompaniment, my clients tell me, they shy off from prescribing by phone; they want to examine the patient. Other symptoms most doctors I know won't *ever* treat by phone include abdominal pain, chest pain, high fever, bleeding, prolonged vomiting. When one of those problems is mentioned, they arrange to see the patient as quickly as possible.

Three out of four doctors I know unhesitatingly prescribe certain drugs—though not all drugs—on the basis of a phone talk with the patient, spouse, or a parent. Usually, the order is for a simple remedy or a refill of a prescription already given to a patient currently under care and seen recently. Most often prescribed: cold and cough relievers, non-narcotic analgesics, antibiotics, sedatives, laxatives, antidiarrheals, antinauseants, antiemetics, antacids.

Heading the list of preparations doctors say they *never* prescribe by phone: narcotics (codeine excepted), insulin, cardiac drugs, hormones. Some doctors never authorize antibiotics by phone. Others prescribe antibiotics only for patients they know well medically.

Do physicians ever make mistakes of judgment in treating by phone? They sure do. Nearly three out of each 100 doctors once surveyed by Medical Economics admitted they'd flubbed seriously at least once. About as you'd guessed? Then I know what you're wondering: Can you do anything to limit the risk of error? You can, my clients assure me. Their advice: Don't diagnose or treat by phone any patient—or any condition—you're unfamiliar with. Instruct patients to call back if the advice doesn't work a definite improvement in a given time. In some cases, you'll leave it up to the patient to call; in others, you'll check back yourself.

Such precautions, I'm told, should reduce the odds on errors such as these reported by the surveyed physicians:

¶ "A mother described a mild cold in her baby. She was one of those mothers who always minimize symptoms. Real illness: pneumonia. Got well, thank goodness."

¶ "A chronic asthmatic called after midnight saying he had trouble breathing. I told him to take another dose of the medicine I'd already prescribed for his asthma. But he'd had a myocardial infarction."

¶ "A child who'd been exposed to mumps developed what his mother said was 'a swollen face.' I prescribed for mumps. Soon the child had convulsions: He had acute nephritis. Yes, he recovered."

¶ "A woman seven months pregnant called late one night and described abdominal pain. She was very vague. I was tired out. I recommended aspirin. At 7 A.M. her appendix ruptured."

154

By and large, the consensus seems to be that advising by phone, though moderately risky, can be defended. "Of course, you can overlook something important," argue the defenders, "but you can do that with the patient right there under your hands." There's near-unanimity that treatment by phone can be safely undertaken if the physician knows the patient and his family well and his questions are understood and clearly answered.

The malpractice risk? "It's always there," says one Florida internist. "But it's there at the hospital, the office, and the patient's home, too."

It's natural to assume that if advice by phone is good medicine, it must also be good economics. That depends on how you look at it. It certainly doesn't line any medical pockets. Only one doctor in 10 ever charges for treatment by phone. Yet, as a spokesman for the few says forthrightly: "We doctors are paid for our knowledge and our time. They're the same whether we dispense them by phone or in the office. So why *not* charge?"

His view may be right, but only a few physicians—pediatricians mostly—charge for calls. And most of those charge only for calls made outside a regular daily telephone hour. Here and there, a physician will charge if a patient he knows well calls about a condition he's never had before. One or two of those surveyed doctors confess to masking charges for phone advice—i.e., they add a little extra to the normal fee the next time they see the patient. I know some men who charge if they're required to phone a drugstore—but not otherwise.

In that survey I mentioned, more than 90 per cent of the doctors said they never got paid for telephone advice. Why don't they? Here are some of their reasons:

Free phone advice is usual in the community. "My colleagues tell me they never charge. So how can I? Charges might damage my practice," says one doctor who'd like to charge but doesn't.

Charging might deter patients from calling when help is badly needed. One frequent statement: "I wouldn't want anyone not to call in an emergency just because I might send a bill." Another: "If

155

it kept patients from seeking advice early, I'd be against charging."

It's hard to know what to charge. Often all that's asked for is reassurance or an explanation of advice given at the office—or simple repetition. Says one G.P.: "Most of the time I advise on trivial complaints for which the patient's own common sense should suggest the treatment. But I'd rather he asked me than a neighbor." Most often, the plaint is: "How do you figure a charge for listening for three minutes and then saying 'I'll send something around'? Then you dial the druggist. Next morning, when the patient shows up at the office, you get paid, really, for the previous night's phoned advice."

Charging isn't worth the trouble. "It costs me at least 50 cents to send out a bill," an internist told me. "Am I to spend that much collecting a dollar? I wouldn't dare charge more for telling a patient to take the green pill before the red one."

Phone advice is part of normal medical service. "I feel I'm the patient's doctor and that I should answer questions on the phone just as I would in my office—even if they're nutty questions," said an OBG man. "Why, just this morning a pregnant girl called to ask if it would hurt the baby if she had her hair waved. I should have paid *her* for the lift her question gave me."

Advising by phone saves the doctor time and trouble. This is the clincher for most physicians. "I couldn't possibly see all the patients who phone me," is the view of a busy G.P. "I'm happy to take care of their minor complaints so easily. It lets me concentrate on the work that brings in my income."

As a layman, *I* can't say whether you should or shouldn't "treat" by phone. That's why I've taken refuge in quotations from doctors who do and doctors who don't. But as a management adviser to physicians, I'm clear in my own mind on whether or not you should *charge* for doing it. If you give any phone advice, I say, give it gratis and charge it off to public relations.

And keep in mind that it's easy to end a call with words like these: "Call my office tomorrow for an appointment." Seems to me that's good management of the case *and* the dilemma.

21

Take time off: It pays

Most employed Americans these days put in fewer than 40 hours a week at their jobs. For many, a 35-hour working week is the modern norm. Many executives and most self-employed persons work longer. Doctors work *lots* longer. In 1966, Medical Economics reported that physicians in private practice under age 65 work a median of 62 hours a week. True, that figure includes hours spent at professional meetings and in teaching, research, and the professional reading mandatory for the conscientious modern physician. Even without those inclusions, though, many a doctor's working week comes to 50 hours, which is 25 per cent longer than most other people's.

Is it good economics to work so hard? If money's the criterion, it apparently is. Every year the Medical Economics Continuing Survey finds a correlation between net earnings and hours worked. The 1966 report noted that the doctors who netted less than $10,000 a year worked a median of 53 or fewer hours a week. At the other end of the scale were the doctors who put in 65 or more hours a week—and netted $50,000 a year or more. The relationship between reward and effort couldn't be clearer.

"I can do without money at that price, though," said an internist-client of mine when I discussed these figures with him. "I want a private life, too. What's the point in earning big money and having no time to do anything with it?" When he said that, I told him about Dr. Finlan, a surgeon who practices solo in a Southern city

157

with a population of 26,000. Dr. Finlan's patients are millhands, shopkeepers, farmers. He doesn't charge fancy fees. Yet he nets $100,000 most years—from a 67-hour workweek. He puts in a few more hours a week than the average doctor, but more significantly he gets more accomplished in an average working hour. What's his approach to practice?

"I put the practice first," replies Dr. Finlan. "I spend 1,200 hours a year in the operating rooms of my hospital. I also put in 550 hours a year at the same hospital outside the operating rooms: about 450 hours on rounds and 100 in the emergency room. Then I put in 1,200 hours a year at my office seeing patients and 300 hours a year at two charity clinics. All that adds up to 3,250 working hours a year. For the 49 weeks I work, that averages a little more than 66 hours a week.

"But I live, too. I take two weeks' vacation every summer and one week in the winter. I spend at least a dozen weekends at my beach house. I go on brief hunting trips. Once a week I visit the farm I own for profit and pleasure. I'm president of our Little League and see lots of the games. Every Sunday afternoon when I'm home, I play golf with my doctor-son and two old buddies.

"I lunch at home four times a week and once a week with my pals in Rotary. I dine with my family almost every night of the year. After my second hospital round of the day—I slip out there after dinner—I play bridge at my own home or a friend's or watch TV with my wife. Or I talk coin collecting with some other coin nut, or clean my guns. Live? Of course I live."

Dr. Finlan gets warm on the subject of time off. "Too many doctors want time to *waste*," he snorts. "They think the factory worker's to be envied because his leisure time exceeds his working time. I don't. I'd be miserable with a 35-hour workweek. For me, the drawback of having a banker's hours is being a banker. I'm a surgeon; the job never palls. I'm over 50, but I hold out my hands for the rubber gloves as eagerly as any resident. I use my time off to fill up from the wellspring, to keep healthy. I don't want time off to be a slob."

Then, by way of contrast, I told my internist friend about Dr. Golliver, an OBG man who *did* want to be a slob. He's in a group, and his specialty is covered there in depth. For 24 hours, Dr. Golliver's on duty at the hospital, even sleeping there. He takes care of all the group's patients who deliver during his stint, operates, does rounds on all the group's OBG patients. The next 24 hours, he puts in a normal day at the office and is on call at home before and after office hours. Third shift, he's off the whole 24 hours; he doesn't exist as far as the group practice is concerned. I asked him what he did on his free days. "Nothing," said Dr. Golliver. "That —and a six-week vacation—is what I joined the group for."

There, it seems, is the rub. There are Finlans, and there are Gollivers. From knowing them and a few thousand other physicians, I've arrived at a few conclusions about time off for doctors. Some of them may help you toward a policy for yourself:

No formula for time off will suit everyone. As you've seen in the cases of Drs. Finlan and Golliver, time off has a different meaning to different men. In planning yours, there's a choice to be made: Do you want lots of work or lots of free time? And if you want lots of free time, will you settle for a smaller paycheck? Dr. Golliver did.

Bad working habits rob many doctors of time off. Does your working day begin at 8 A.M. and end at 10 P.M. most days? I know many doctors actually do work that way. They have evening hours every weekday except Wednesday, when they quit in midafternoon —if they're lucky. Some eventually realize that evening hours are a bad working habit. They discover that sick people aren't especially keen on nighttime office visits, and that the patients who are can just as easily come in the daytime—if that's the only time the office is open.

Staying longer than necessary at the hospital is also a bad working habit. "I get to the office at 9:30 instead of 10:30 these days," a busy internist told me not long ago. "It's no big deal to see your patients and get out promptly, if you make up your mind to it." A surgeon said, "I never realized how much time I spent yakking at the hospital until I started leaving as soon as I'd finished my work."

I've told many doctors what I'd already told him: "Staying around the hospital for a half-hour after your work's done is no more profitable than sitting for 30 minutes at the lunch table after your second cup of coffee. In both cases, time's a-wasting."

Scheduling office revisits the morning of your midweek half-day is a third bad working habit. "I'm on the first tee on time Wednesday afternoons now," a gleeful G.P. announced after he'd made the change I suggested. "I check the hospital, make the odd house call, and then see only new patients or old patients with new ailments. I'm out of my treatment area by 11:30 at the latest. I do paper work until 12:30 and then my phone goes on answering service."

The lesson: Remember "Murphy's Law," which says, "If anything can happen, it will." Don't pile up logs that will inevitably jam just before you're due to leave the office.

Some doctors don't know time off when they see it. I once asked nine solo specialists who were forming a group to keep track of what they did in their working hours for four weeks. The six internists averaged 28 hours a week in the presence of patients, the two pediatricians reported 30 and 20 hours, and the surgeon reported 36 hours. All put in a few extra hours a week doing paper work and attending meetings. And, sure enough, each man logged himself as being on call continuously at all other times. The facts: Not one was called out on his midweek half-day, they answered 28 night calls between them, and among the nine they reported 14 weekend turnouts. High man: the surgeon, with six weeknight and four weekend emergencies.

"I can't help it, but I *feel* I'm on duty all around the clock," said one of the internists. "That's why I'm keen to get into a group. I'm hoping to lose the compulsion to stay by my phone nights." It's easy to see how such a feeling of uneasy expectation takes the pleasure out of an evening of actual freedom. But it needn't if you'll adjust your thinking. The truth is that subconsciously you may be *wanting* to be called.

Try a switch: On your noncovered nights, do the calling yourself. Tell your answering service: "I'm giving you a number where I can be reached this evening. But don't call me unless it's an emergency. I'll call you during the evening for the other messages."

A weekend off is worth more than its weight in half-days. I've asked hundreds of physicians which time off they value most. They've voted overwhelmingly for weekends.

"I take 10 weekends off a year," says a high-load surgeon I know. "Fishing and duck hunting claim four. I take four more in the summer, and the whole family goes to the beach. My wife and I have two trips to ourselves every winter; we hop a plane to the big city and catch up on our culture. The secret: We map 'em all out in January. So I know in advance when I'll be away during the year, and later I move up or put back my heavy surgery to suit."

A pediatrician: "I don't worry too much if my weekly half-day is shot from under me, as it often is. But if I were to lose my weekends, I'd be real upset. I take every third weekend off, and my wife and I almost always go out of town. Her people live about 100 miles away, and mine are a bit nearer. We like visiting them. I have a deal with two other men. We've covered each other on weekends for two years now, and many of our patients know all three of us."

An internist: "I have two sons in college and five other children at home. A month's formal vacation for the whole crowd would just about break me. But I have a lakeside cottage 60 miles from home—nothing fancy—and the family spends every summer weekend there. Half of those weekends I'm there too. No, it doesn't do my practice any harm. I haven't personally admitted a hospital patient on a weekend for years. Who can get X-rays or lab work done in a hospital on Sunday anyway?"

Conventions are time off. On Dr. Tom Jefferson's office door there appears, the first Monday in May every year, a sign that reads: "Doctor is away. He is attending a professional meeting in your interest." His state medical association always convenes that first week in May. Dr. Jefferson puts in long hours at the scientific ses-

161

sions, filling his notebook in the eerie light from the color slides.

But it happens that the convention's four days provide one of the year's most enjoyable breaks for Dr. Jefferson and his wife, Mamie, with a bonus from Uncle Sam thrown in. The doctor's expenses are tax deductible. The lunches, the banquets, the president's ball are fine for Mamie, but what Tom likes best is the medical conversation he gets—four solid days of it.

I've never known a doctor who didn't like to talk shop. A professional convention offers the opportunity to indulge the passion to the limit. The banquets are, as they say in Louisiana, lagniappe.

Spend time off on shop-talk? "You bet!" says Dr. Jefferson.

Two vacations a year are better than one. I'm serious about this. For a medical man, two two-week absences from town beat one four-week absence. More expensive? Travel costs are higher, of course. But you lose fewer patients in the shorter absences. They're more willing to wait two weeks than a month. And you're less likely to need a hired vacation substitute, since it's easier to find two colleagues who'll cover gratis for two weeks each than one who'll cover for four.

If you feel that for the children's sake the summer vacation must be longer than two weeks, settle for three. Take a week in the winter. Giving the battery a fast charge in January or February does wonders for tired physicians. Adequate time off is good management. Ask the man who takes it.

162

22

Will your records stand up in court?

Your practice is coming along nicely. This day has been busy. The phone rings late in the afternoon, and it's Mrs. Brown on the line. Johnny's sick again—same thing he had before, only worse. Will you tell her what to do? You buzz for your record on Johnny Brown. You've seen a lot of kids since Johnny was last in the office. You flip through the sheets. You begin giving soothing advice. But Mrs. Brown says: "No, doctor, it's another attack like the one he had when you came to the house that night. You gave him the green pills, remember?"

Damn! That house call isn't in the record!

Well, you learned something—again. For your own sake legally and for your patients' protection, make this unbreakable rule: "My every contact with every patient will show on his record." You never can tell how grave an omission might turn out to be. You could inadvertently give a patient the wrong treatment. Or, lacking a reminder that you'd done it, you could do investigative work twice over.

And you could get into deep trouble in court. Imagine a suave attorney saying: "Mrs. Brown says you gave Johnny some green pills that night. You say that, if you did, it would be on your record. Your record doesn't even show the visit, Doctor. Only your bill shows that." Nasty, eh? Better get your aide to type this sentence on a slip of paper: *A malpractice suit may well be decided on the evidence of the record.* Slide that slip of paper under the glass top of your desk—now.

If records are vital in so many ways—and they are—it's worth taking pains to insure keeping good ones. What makes a good record, apart from what you write on it? Is there, for instance, a best size? Are typed records superior to handwritten ones? What's the best way to file them? How long should they be kept?

Here are some answers to those questions and others you've no doubt been asking yourself:

What's the best format for my medical records? Old Doc from

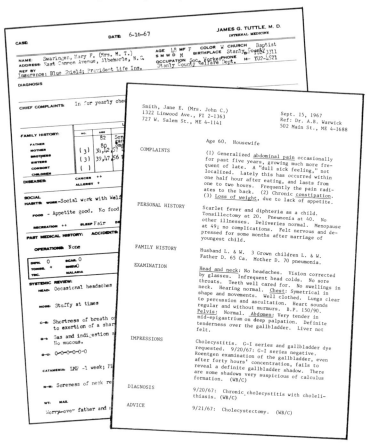

Chart entries can be made on either a preprinted form, like the form at left, or on plain paper, as at right. Medical stationers have some excellent stock forms available at reasonable cost. At extra cost, they'll be glad to prepare a custom-designed form for you.

the revered horse-and-buggy days used to jot a few hieroglyphs on an index card headed "Johnny Brown." In most modern practices, that won't work any more.

Start with a manila folder tabbed "Johnny Brown." You're going to need it. Today's medicine requires a dossier: history, examination findings, progress notes, incoming and outgoing reports, and correspondence.

Inside the folder, use loose letter-sized sheets, each headed "Johnny Brown." Don't use fasteners. Don't staple the sheets. Add

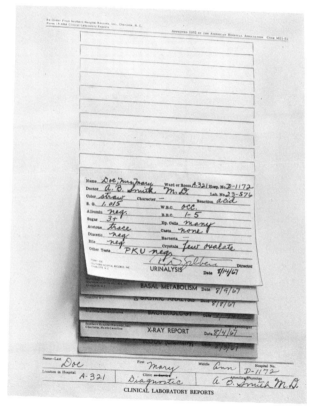

Keep undersized reports like these in order either by mounting them on a full-sized sheet of plain paper or, as has been done above, on a full-sized form that was designed for orderly record keeping.

Shelf filing, as here, requires less floor space than cabinet filing, since no space is needed for opening drawers. Also, shelf files can go higher. In cabinet filing, four drawers are the practical vertical limit.

new sheets in front or at the back as you prefer; just be consistent one way or the other.

You think you'll start with cards and maybe switch to folders later? Don't. I'm always having trouble with such switches— starting, usually, when about 10,000 old cards have already accumulated in the files.

Are preprinted records best, or will plain paper do? Plain paper will do. It's the favorite with most doctors. On page 164, you'll see a typed-up sample. Let your aide study it as a model for spacing and layout.

Preprinted forms are fine, though. The one shown on page 164 was designed by an internist to suit his own history-taking and examining routines. Many doctors have sheets custom-printed as he did, but you don't have to design your own. Standard forms— good ones—are obtainable from several firms that specialize in medical stationery. The A.M.A. has approved a series covering practically every specialty.

Rubber stamps save time when recording oft-repeated entries. And later the stamp marks can be quickly scanned, thus saving still more time.

167

If you're a plain-paper fan, I'd still recommend *one* preprinted front sheet carrying the nonmedical headings your aide uses regularly. The sheet has spaces for what statisticians call demographic data: name, address, phone number, sex, age, marital status, occupation, place of employment, insurance policy number, and what not. For your aide, a preprinted sheet like this is a time saver and memory jogger in one.

Whether or not your sheets are printed, make sure the patient's name appears in the top right-hand corner of every sheet exactly as it appears on the front sheet. If you don't, you'll find orphan sheets around the office before you know it.

How much of my record-making must I do myself? You're responsible, of course, for all of it. If you're typical, you write—or dictate—everything medical that goes into your records.

However, if your aide is sufficiently skilled, she can take over a good part of the record-making. A Virginia cardiologist, for ex-

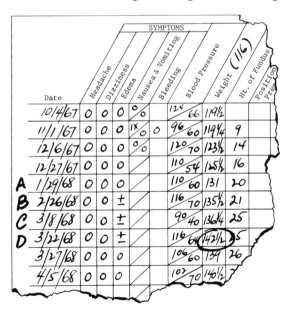

Code letters save time. One Southern physician uses them on the patient's record to indicate that he has given the patient one of his series of talks on weight control, marital relations, etc.

168

ample, says to every new patient, "Miss White will ask you a few questions while I'm examining another patient." Miss White—a former medical record librarian who's had extra training from my cardiologist client—then takes the patient's full medical history, family history, and the story of his current illness. The doctor may dig a little deeper later on, but Miss White is very experienced and usually comes up with the facts he needs.

Some physicians have the patient himself write part of his record. They ask him to fill out a health questionnaire—the Cornell Medical Index, for example—and the filled-out questionnaire goes right into the folder.

Everything you personally discover or do, of course, you must dictate or write yourself.

How much nonmedical information should go into my record? Every office chart (as I'll call it for short) should show at the top of the front sheet:

¶ The patient's first, last, and middle name, in that order, and

Columns save time when all entries in a patient's record are written by hand. A West Coast physician designed this form. He says that it helps him remember to touch all bases in an interview.

correctly spelled. If a name has a tricky pronunciation, it doesn't hurt to spell it phonetically, too. Patients like you to say their names right.

¶ The patient's correct title: Mr., Miss, or Mrs., and for a married woman her husband's first name and middle initial in parentheses after her last name—e.g., *Jane Weston Smith (Mrs. George A.).*

¶ The patient's full residence address, and business address if he has one, with the phone number of each. If someone else is responsible for the cost of his care, show that person's addresses and phone numbers, too.

¶ The name and address of whoever referred the patient to you. If this was a physician, you'll need his phone number; you may want to call him in a hurry.

¶ The patient's sex, date of birth, current marital status, occupation, and employer.

Several of those items will also go onto the ledger card your aide will keep on the same patient. Why, then, duplicate them in the chart? They'll help you revisualize the patient *as a person* each time you're slated to meet him. It helps if you're reminded that he

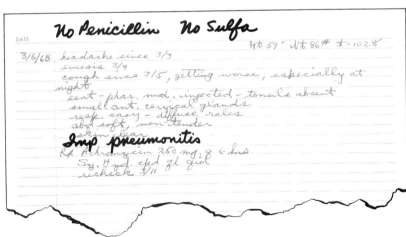

Colored ink saves time because it stands out and makes for easy scanning. Using it is a favored trick in many medical offices.

lives in that chi-chi new development, works for that firm that makes baby buggies, is the assistant sales manager, and came to you on the recommendation of his boss.

Should my charts be typed? Typing isn't vital, but it's a good idea. If your notes are at all lengthy, typed charts *are* best. If you're ever sick or out of town, the man covering for you will surely be happier with your typewritten notes than with your doctor's scrawl.

If you have more than one aide, you should be able to arrange at least for typewritten front sheets, case histories, and initial examination findings. For subsequent progress notes and medication details, handwriting may be acceptable.

If you opt for charts that are dictated and typed, watch these points:

¶ Dictate a date for every entry—month, day, and year. Your aide may not type up the chart for a day or so—and could easily misdate an important finding.

¶ Warn your aide against using nonmedical abbreviations. She

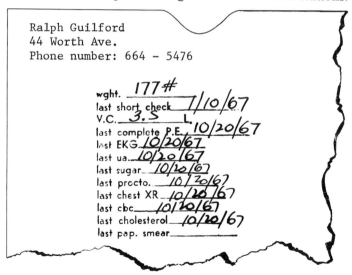

A list saves time. This list has been stamped on the cover of each patient's folder in a Southern internist's office, so that he can see at a glance whether or not a patient is due for a routine check.

171

saves time by typing *L&W* for "living and well," *Ca* for "carcinoma," *w/d, w/n, w/f* for "well-developed, well-nourished, white female." But you could lose a lot of time before finally discovering that to her *r.e.*—not *O.D.*—means "right eye."

¶ Spell out the medical terms you use regularly until she knows them thoroughly. Don't neglect this item on the ground that no one but you sees your charts. You won't be proud of the impression an ill-spelled chart will make on the jury if you have to take it to court some day.

Should incoming reports go into my charts? Yes. Abstracting them into the body of your own notes is poor practice. As court evidence, originals carry more weight. That goes for outside lab, X-ray, surgery, and consultants' reports, and even for the phone messages of medical import your aide takes for you.

If the incoming document is letter-sized, it goes into the chart as is. Small flimsy slips can get lost unless you anchor them. Best solution: Mount peewee-sized papers on full-size sheets with clear adhesive tape. The sample sheet of lab reports on page 165 gives you the idea.

Should my aide make carbons of the chart material I dictate?

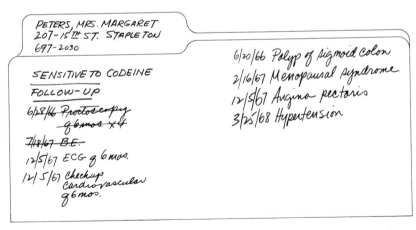

Key entries on the cover of a patient's folder save time for an East Coast internist. As indicated here, he lists any sensitivities for quick reference, along with a running history of diagnoses.

172

My answer to this question used to be, "Yes, if you're a specialist with a sizable referral practice or a lot of liability cases." I now say, "No, you can always run off a copy on your office copying machine."

Don't have an office copier? See Chapter 8.

What correspondence should I keep in my charts? The chart is the natural home for all papers of medical relevance—letters from other doctors, copies of your letters to them, hospital X-ray reports, laboratory reports, etc. If you get or send a letter that refers to more than one patient, have it run through the copier so that each chart can have one.

Don't use charts as repositories for copies of your collection letters, patients' replies to them, duplicates of insurance claims, or other financial papers. The financial records should be kept separate from the clinical records.

How much should my chart tell about a hospitalized patient? It should show the name of the hospital, the date of admission, the date of discharge, your admitting diagnosis, final diagnosis, the date and nature of any surgery you performed, and notations of any special therapy you ordered.

If the hospital will give you carbon copies or photocopies of your

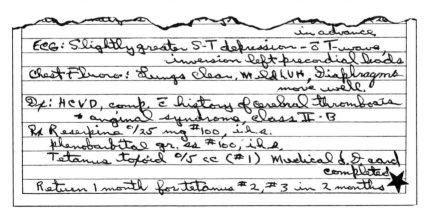

Colored stars within a record save time for a Western physician who uses them to call attention to summaries of examination findings. He says the stars make easy work of reviewing even an extensive history.

discharge summaries or operation reports, just add them to the patient's office chart and have your aide write "See hospital data" against the date of admission.

Will my charts get bulky if I put everything into them? They sure will. But you'll have everything that's clinically relevant in one folder. That's much better than distributing material around the office: your own notes over here, X-ray, hospital, and lab reports over there, ECG tracings some other place, and correspondence in a desk drawer. Any time you want the complete medical story on Johnny Green, there'll be only one place to look, and it won't take long to locate it.

How do I change an entry in a chart? Draw a line through the original entry so that what you mistakenly wrote is still readable. Don't obliterate it. Then write the correct entry above or below the wrong one, adding *Corr.* in the left-hand margin and your initials (with the date) on the right. If your aide flubs an entry—she could type a note on Johnny Brown into Billy Green's chart, for example —see that she corrects her error the same way, using her own initials.

Never, *never* erase a handwritten entry. An erasure makes your chart as legally worthless as an altered check.

How do I keep my charts from piling up on me? There's only one way to keep abreast of your charts. Assume you haven't finished with a patient until you've completed his chart.

If you dictate, dictate every day—even several times a day. Better still, take a minute to dictate each patient's chart entry as soon as you've finished with him. Many doctors say that's the very best way.

If you handwrite your entries, do it right there in the examining room or in the corridor outside. Useful tip: Write standing up. Time and again, doctors have told me that sitting down to write progress notes takes more time.

What's the best way to divide up my chart files? You have a choice between a unit system and a classified system. In a unit system, new charts and old are housed in one file. A classified system assigns them to separate files, usually "Active" and "Inactive" and "Closed." My vote goes to the unit system.

There is a third way, though I don't recommend it. It's the "chronological classified" system. As each new patient registers, his chart goes into a file labeled for the current year. Each year, a new file is started. If the patient turns up again years later, either he or your aide will have to remember the year he first came in. This system can cause more problems than it solves, but I know doctors who swear by it.

Should I file my charts alphabetically or numerically? If you have fewer than 5,000 charts, alphabetical filing is fine. For larger numbers—and even a one-man practice can soon have them—numerical filing makes sense. It's faster and more accurate.

If you settle for alphabetical filing, watch these points:

¶ Don't have handwritten folder tabs. They increase the misfiling risk because they're not always legible. Have your aide type the patients' names on gummed labels and stick these on the tabs. Half-a-dozen different colors for the labels—one color to a block of four or five initial letters—reduces the misfiling risk. A red label among the yellows announces itself as a misfile right away.

¶ Don't skimp on file guides—i.e., the hardboard separators that divide a file into sections. One guide for each letter of the alphabet isn't nearly enough. For 5,000 folders, you ought to have at least 200 guides—a guide to every 25 folders. Your office supply man can even get you a set of 2,500 guides if your files are really loaded.

If you decide on numerical filing, you'll need an alphabetical index as a key to the chart numbers. These come on cards or on strips, mounted on wheels or panels or stacked in drawers. There's even a motorized model. You can use your ledger-card file as your master index if you file the cards alphabetically. But watch out: If a ledger card is out of place, your aide won't be able to find its matching chart.

What filing equipment is best for my charts? You've already discovered that office space is expensive. Floor-based files for

10,000 charts, occupying 60 square feet at $5 per square foot per year, will cost you $3,000 in rent over a 10-year period. Walls come for free.

So the place for your charts is on the walls—on shelves. It's not unusual for shelf filing in a medical office to save 20 square feet of floor space. That saving, at $5 per square foot per year, represents a $1,000 economy over a 10-year office lease.

Space saving isn't the only advantage that shelf filing has to offer. It's easier on the girl who files and finds your charts. If you're a floor-filer, ask your aide what step in the filing process takes longest and tires her soonest. She'll tell you, "It's the opening and closing of those heavy file drawers." She's right: Half of her filing time is used up in just pulling and pushing. Even if you don't have a space problem, shelf filing will get her vote.

Neat, up-to-date medical records, shelf-filed by number, are a source of pride to the physician who owns them, and of pleasure to the aide who maintains them. Don't settle for less.

23

Fair fees are paid cheerfully

An ancient Yugoslav who'd worked half his lifetime in the United States made headline news not too long ago. He'd started back to his native land carrying with him his life's savings —$17,000 in cash. The newspapers featured his reason for taking the money to Belgrade: "I'm old. I might get sick. And then the doctors would get it all."

About the same time a woman led off a national television program by charging that a physician had reduced her to penury. "My husband had cancer," she said. "The doctor took all we had. And my husband died."

And did you ever hear of little Benny Hooper? He fell down a well. The entire nation turned purple at the news that a physician, summoned to the wellside, had sent a bill for his attendance. "His fee is outrageous," said Benny's parents. "We don't have that kind of money."

All three of those true stories illustrate the public's firmly held conviction that doctors charge too much. It's a belief hallowed by antiquity; physicians' fees have been criticized continuously down the ages. Yet here's an odd fact: Most patients seem to feel that doctors overcharge only *other* people. A short while back Medical Economics asked several thousand patients: What do you think of your own doctor's fees? Five patients out of every six questioned replied, "They're about right" or "I think they're low."

When discussing a physician's fees, the survey showed, people tend to speak in comparative terms. The many satisfied ones are apt to say, "Considering what other people pay their doctors, I've nothing to complain about." The gripers are likely to allege, "His fees are too high when you consider what others are charging."

Patients don't merely match the fees of one doctor against those of another, though. They also look for consistency in a doctor's charges from one visit to the next. They'll complain: "Sometimes he'll charge twice as much as he did the last time for the same service." Or: "He doesn't seem to remember from one month to the next what his charges are."

A third kind of complaint has to do with the time a doctor has spent on a service. "Sometimes you run into his office for just a minute to have him check something," people grumble, "and he charges the same as if he treated you for a cut." An occasional patient goes further: "For $5, I ought to get at least 15 minutes."

A fourth gripe lines up the fee for one procedure against that for another. Most often, surgical fees are involved: "I don't see why it should cost any more to have your gallbladder out than your appendix." Sometimes a complainant falls headlong into the apples-oranges trap: "The orthopedist charged more for setting my child's broken arm than our family doctor did for pulling me through a heart attack."

When a doctor is suspected of basing his fees on a comparison of the resources of one patient with those of another, all hell breaks loose. Typical: "What business is it of his if I have a little more money than someone else? He doesn't do any more for me."

With so many ways to be wrong in price-tagging the care you give your patients, can you hit on a way that'll please everyone? You can't. There's no all-American fee for any item of medical service that I know of. For any given service, your fee can be higher than anyone else's in the country and be right. It can be lower and still be right. It can be different for every patient and be right. It can change from day to day and be right. You don't need to consult a stopwatch, a slide rule, or even a management man to arrive at it.

178

The physicians I know who have the least trouble about fees, though, are the ones who set them with great care. Most of them recognize a ratio between money and services. They know a medical fee (price) is a compromise between the patient's resources (money) and the medical care (services) available to him. If *your* brand of medical care is unique, you needn't compromise at all; you have a monopoly. Conceivably, you do offer your patients unique care. You do, for example, if you're the only physician in the world who can perform a particular operation successfully. You're unique if, although other doctors do what you do, none does it as well. Either way, you can write your own ticket. Your appointment book or operating room schedule will always be full.

But let's orbit a little closer to earth. Let's say, for instance, you're the only local practitioner of your specialty. Obviously, for any procedure you specialize in, you can command a higher price than the local nonspecialists. How much higher? Not more than the price at which it would pay local people to travel to another community where the specialists charge less.

Now take another tack. Suppose that, although you're only one of several local specialists of your particular stripe, you're the acknowledged best. Can you charge more than the others do? You can. Locally, at least, you're offering care that's unique in quality. Be careful, though, about rating yourself as the nonpareil. It's just possible you're slightly biased. By definition, unusually skillful doctors are—well, *unusual*. And watch out that you don't overrate the things you do supremely well but infrequently.

If you're a G.P., pediatrician, or internist, I'll concede right now that at times you throw all your knowledge, skill, patience, and strength into the battle for life. But those cases don't make up your regular working day. Most of it's spent seeing patients with minor ailments at a four-per-hour clip or faster. They involve no more wear and tear on your neurons than the effort of choosing the right drug. You don't rate a premium price for *that* kind of work.

If you're a surgeon, I'll grant that late last night you walked wearily out of the operating room after four hours spent piecing together the victim of an auto wreck. I know you worked a minor miracle. I also know that you don't do it very often. Most of your time in the O.R., you're doing procedures you could almost do with your eyes shut. No premium price for *those* operations.

Get the point? Then you understand why, when I settle down to a fee discussion with a doctor and he begins by asking me what he should charge for a night-long hospital vigil, a day-long operation, or a 20-mile emergency trip in the wee small hours, I duck his question. Instead, I say: "Hard cases make bad law, Doctor. Let's start with the bread-and-butter items." Then, if he's a G.P., I'll ask, "What's your fee for a routine office visit?" To a pediatrician, I'll say: "What do you charge for a well-baby visit?" I ask an obstetrician what he gets for the complete care of a normal pregnancy. I ask a surgeon what he charges for an appendectomy. The unique can wait. It's outside Cotton's law of fee inversion.

Cotton's law is simple. It says: *Fees that ignore the going rates are self-defeating.* As I see it, a doctor who sets his fees way over the local going rates, hoping for a big income from a small practice, risks seeing his practice become too small. *Per contra,* the man who sets his prices way under the local going rates, hoping for a big income from a large practice, risks seeing his practice become too large to handle. "Then what in the name of Hammurabi," you're wondering, "are the going rates? Is there any way I can get a list of them for my specialty?" You can't. Going rates are something you find out for yourself.

Before we discuss ways to do so, we'd better pause long enough to define "going rates." Some years ago, in Medical Economics, the term was defined in a way that still seems to me as good as any I've seen:

The going rate for any given service is the specific fee that a majority of self-employed physicians in a specific region and a specific field of practice don't exceed.

Thus by definition no going rate is nationwide. Nor are there going rates for your state, county, or city. A going rate isn't a statistical mean, median, or mode that can be looked up in a book. It's simply the figure beyond which most doctors in your locality don't go when charging for a given service. It relates the quantity of money locally available to the quantity of goods and services locally available. A going rate is obviously acceptable to most patients; if it weren't, the patients would force it down. It's obviously acceptable to most doctors; if it weren't, the doctors would force it up. One test of the validity of a going rate is the legal test. It will usually stand up in court, while fees well wide of it, especially when based on the presumed ability of an individual patient to pay, are often knocked down.

Now, how do you find out what the going rates are where you practice? Fortunately, they're easier to discover than they used to be. Time was when physicians wouldn't even tell one another their fees. An elderly surgeon I know explained it this way: "Some men would tell you they charged more than they actually did. Some would tell you they charged less. Both had the same reason for not revealing their true fees—they were ashamed of 'em."

Concealment comes harder these days. Published fee studies abound. Hundreds of health insurance carriers keep tabs on the fees charged to their policyholders. Agencies of the city, county, state, and Federal governments collect data on doctors' charges. Inside the profession itself, the necessity to negotiate fee schedules with third parties has made the free exchange of fee data practically mandatory. In a growing number of states it's almost child's play to find the going rates for any given locality. These are the states in which the state medical societies have published relative value schedules to guide their members through the fee-setting maze.

The daddy of all relative value schedules is the California Medical Association's Relative Value Studies. It made its bow in the mid-1950s, and since then committees of doctors have almost continuously been busy improving and correcting it. You can consult it or another like it for the relative values of, say, an appendectomy and a removal of a dislocated lens. If an R.V.S. rates the eye operation as worth a fee almost twice that of the abdominal operation, it's assigned almost twice as many units of value. Similarly, an internist's full work-up of a new patient may rate a fee three times the fee for a brief interview with limited examination of the same new patient.

Dollar figures, though, do not appear in an R.V.S. manual. You fix the dollar amount yourself by pricing your own unit of value. You do so by pricing just one key procedure. As a general surgeon, for example, you may consider that an appendectomy as performed by you is worth $200. When you consult your relative-value schedule, you'll find that an appendectomy rates, say, 40 units. So if you value your unit at $5, your appendectomy will yield the $200 you want. If your colleague next door prices *his* appendectomy at $300, he'll price his unit at $7.50. And if most of the community's surgeons opted for a $5 unit, as you did, the man next door had better be good, because he's 50 per cent over what everyone else is charging locally for appendectomies—and for every other service he performs, too. Once a doctor establishes his own unit value, he applies it to *all* of the services he performs.

In like fashion, if an internist prices his diagnostic work-up at $30 and uses a relative value schedule that allots 6 units to that procedure, he'll price his unit at $5. If a neighboring doctor holds that *his* work-up is more properly compensated by a $40 fee, he'll price his unit at $6 and round off the resulting $42 to the $40 he wants. If the $5-a-unit doctor is in the minority locally, he'd better be good; patients may wonder whether his cut price is a survival tactic.

If there's a relative value schedule in your area, don't just adopt the same unit price as the man next door. Let's say you do eye surgery and the local schedule assigns 70 units to a dislocated lens removal. You note that 40 units are assigned to an appendectomy. Now you meet two general surgeons. One of them charges $300 ($7.50 per unit) for an appendectomy. The other charges $200 ($5 per unit). Problem: What's your lens removal worth—$525 or $350? Obviously it's worth nearly twice as much as an appendectomy. But an appendectomy by whom? Ask the other eye surgeons. You'll make the right choice if you interpret the going rate rule as follows:

The conversion factor to be applied by an individual physician to any relative value schedule is the one used by most of the self-employed physicians in his field in his area.

Will adherence to going rates eliminate patients' gripes about your fees? That's too much to expect, but it will minimize them. One common complaint, you'll recall, was, "He charges more than other doctors." Using going rates should help you handle that one. Another gripe was, "He varies his charges for the same service." That one disappears as soon as you follow any set schedule. Then there's the stopwatch theory: "He charges as much for 2 minutes as for 20." You'll find that all relative value schedules rate long visits as being worth more than short ones. Finally, the Big Gripe: "He charges what he thinks you can afford to pay." If you charge going rates, that one becomes a wild pitch.

I'm not through with fees yet. There's more about them in the next chapter. But before you read on, be sure you've got the message of this chapter: Going rates are no longer the coming thing. They *are* the thing—unless, as I said earlier, you're unique.

24

Don't just set fees: Make bargains

"**M**y first three years in practice, I never talked fees with my patients. I sent out bills that said: 'For professional services . . .' Just three little words, then a figure. One day it dawned on me that only four patients in five were paying the bills I sent them. I decided to ask some of the nonpayers why, straight out. And they told me straight out that I charged too much. Yet, in those three years, not a soul had said that. So I don't rely on the three little words any more."

The Michigan G.P. I've just quoted was answering a Medical Economics survey question: "What's the worst business mistake you ever made?" He's not the only doctor who'd confess that his biggest blooper was shirking mention of fees to his patients.

"Ever since then," the Michigan practitioner will tell you now, "I've taken the initiative. I discuss the fee before I get launched on a patient's treatment. Of course, I don't bring up the question at every routine office visit. That's not necessary. But once I realize that a new patient is going to be seen often or will have to be hospitalized, I talk to him about my charges.

"I say to him: 'Now that I've told you what's wrong with you and what I plan to do about it, I want to give you some idea of what you're in for financially.' Then I explain my fees. Almost without exception the patient says 'Go ahead, Doctor.' Now, only one out of 20 patients fails to pay my bill."

The lesson it took that G.P. three years to learn is one I never tire of preaching: *Patients keep bargains better than they pay bills.* The best-paying patient is the one who understands what he's being charged for and says, as the Michigan doctor's patients do, "Go ahead, Doctor." The bill that surprises the patient is most often the one that doesn't get paid.

A colleague of mine in the management field tells a story that illustrates my point. A man he knew complained to him about the fees charged by two physicians. A G.P., he said, had charged him $11 for an office visit and $30 for a house call. And an OBG man had charged his wife $20 "for a five-minute consultation." My colleague knew both doctors and checked on the complaints. The OB charge was one-tenth of the specialist's fee for full care of the wife through her pregnancy. By breaking down his fee into installments, he was trying to make payment easy for her. But neither the doctor nor his aide had told the patient—or told her that the full charge would be $200. When the complainant learned this, he said, "Why, that's lower than I expected!"

The $11 "office visit" for the husband comprised a $4 examination fee, a $4 injection, a $2 urinalysis, and a $1 hemoglobin estimation. Given that breakdown, the no-longer aggrieved patient conceded: "He charges less for his office time than my last doctor did. But that $30 house call still rankles." So my colleague reminded him: "You called the doctor out at 11 P.M. on a Sunday. He drove 18 miles, spent 25 minutes with you, gave you an injection and a supply of pills, then drove 18 miles home. The round trip took an hour and 15 minutes." Said the patient, writing the check: "I'm sorry I griped. But I wish he'd told me what to expect when I called him. I might have decided to wait till morning."

You can, of course, persist in trying to keep all mention of money out of medicine. But the subject will muscle its way in sooner or later. When it does, you'll suffer no less than if you'd grasped the nettle firmly in the first place. On the other hand, your practice may suffer measurably if you're totally unwilling to discuss money. I've known doctors who'd cancel bills rather than discuss them. "An argument with a patient over a fee ruins my whole day," said one of these. "If I fight it out, I stay mad till bed-time. If I put it off, I'm distracted till it's settled. So I avoid it. I tell 'em to forget the whole thing. True, *they don't come back.* But they don't ruin any more of my days, either."

If you think that's poor consolation, you share my opinion. That doctor did, though, own up to his weakness, while many doctors don't. In fact, there's quite a difference between what doctors say they do about fee discussions and what patients say they do. I remember a Medical Economics survey in which some 3,000 doctors across the country were asked: "Who discusses fees with patients?" Almost half the responding physicians said, "I do." Almost one in 10 said, "My aide does." One in 16 said, "No one does." To a second question, "At what point are your fees explained to patients?" almost two out of three of the doctors who said fees were discussed answered, "Before I render service."

What doctors say about fee discussions
—and what patients say

Physicians' answers [1]

	I do	*My aide does*	*We both do*	*No one does*
Who discusses fees with patients?	46%	9%	39%	6%

Patients' answers [2]

	The doctor	*His aide*	*I do*	*No one does*
Who usually brings up money matters in your doctor's office?	13%	12%	38%	37%

Patients' answers [2]

	The doctor	*His aide*	*No one*
With whom would you prefer to discuss money matters?	81%	12%	7%

Sources: [1] Medical Economics, Feb. 12, 1962, [2] Medical Economics, April 20, 1964.

187

Patients, though, tell a different story. In a nationwide survey of patients, Medical Economics asked, "Who usually brings up money matters in your doctor's office?" One patient in seven said, "The doctor does." One in eight said, "His aide does." That left three out of four offices where neither the doctor nor his aide mentioned money. The doctors, you'll recall, claimed 15 out of 16 the other way.

From my own experience, I'd say the patients were right. In most of my practice surveys I've had to prod my clients into giving patients advance information about the bills they'll receive.

Chances are, you'll ask: "How do I bring up this fee business without seeming to put money before medicine?" I'm ready for that question with a two-part answer:

Name small fees after rendering service but before the patient leaves the office. No patient wants to be greeted on arrival with the news that an office visit costs $5. Neither does he want to discover, after 30 days, that it costs $10. Typical reaction of a surprised patient: "I went four times and expected a bill for $20. When it came, it was for $40 and that really shook me. If he'd warned me, I could have changed doctors."

There are three easy ways to let a patient know what size bill to expect for office care. Method one: At the end of the visit, write the charge for each service you've rendered on an itemized charge slip. Hand the slip to the patient and say, "Please give this to Miss Smith at the front desk." Miss Smith can then answer any question the patient may have about the charges shown on the slip.

Method Two: Merely check off the services you've rendered on the charge slip. Leave it up to Miss Smith to fill in the charges in the patient's presence. If he queries any charge, she explains it.

Method Three: Just say, "Tell Miss Smith the charge for today is $10, please." If several services have been rendered, Miss Smith may have to break down the total to send the patient home satisfied.

With any of these three ways, the patient knows his liability before he leaves the office. Your bill at the end of the month will then be a confirmation of a charge he didn't cavil at when he had the chance to do so. Best of all, in many instances it won't even be necessary to send a bill; the patient will pay Miss Smith there and then.

Warn patients about big fees before starting treatment. Let's suppose a surgeon tells a patient that his recurrent pain comes from a gallbladder he'd be better off without. The first thing the patient may wonder is, "What will this do to my pocketbook?" But he won't necessarily ask the doctor.

So the doctor or his aide had better broach the subject, or the patient may be unable to put the forthcoming bill into perspective. No one keeps money in a savings account labeled "For the doctor." If there's any money in the account at all, it's tagged "New car," "New washing machine," "New shoes for kids," or "Vacation." Even your most modest fee was meant to be spent on something else. As a consequence, people want to feel sure that what they "buy" from you is worth at least as much as what they'd first planned to buy with the money. They know to a dollar what they meant to spend on the washing machine. They need to know the price of a gallbladder removal. If they don't, they can't make a *willing* choice between the two expenditures.

A plastic surgeon I know takes a direct approach to the problem. If a patient hesitates over the fee for a rhinoplasty, he'll ask, "What make of car do you drive?" The patient may say, "A Chevrolet." He'll then ask, "When do you plan to trade it in?" She says, perhaps, "In six months." "Well," says the surgeon, "it's simple. You can get a new Chevy in six months that you'll keep for a couple of years—or a new nose now that'll last you a lifetime."

Few doctors are as forthright as that. Yet most doctors do have to prove to patients that medical care is worth buying. The best way to prove it, I'm convinced, is to explain carefully what you've found, what you plan to do about it—and what it will cost. Don't put a man through 30 minutes of prodding, pinching, and puncturing, and then grunt, "Come back in two weeks." Sit with him long enough now to tell him what the prods and punctures were for.

189

Tell him what they showed. Tell him what needs to be done. And tell him the price of it.

If he's willing to pay it, he'll say so. If he hasn't a hope of raising that much money, he has the opportunity to ask you if you'll take less. If he isn't even willing to pay less, he has the option of backing out then and there. It's his health and his legal right to do with it as he will.

What words should you use when you're talking fees with patients? Don't fret yourself; the words will come. If you're one of the few who are genuinely tongue-tied when money is the topic, you may be able to use one or more easy-starting phrases such as these:

¶ *"My usual charge. . . ."* This opening implies service at regular prices. That's an important idea to get across. It dispels the suspicion that you're about to charge what you think the traffic will bear.

¶ *"The going rate around here. . . ."* This opening nips in the bud the patient's fear that he has landed in the office of the man with the local carriage trade. (If he *has*, though, you go on to explain why you don't charge the going rates.)

¶ *"The fee I'm going to suggest covers . . . ."* Examination, tests, diagnosis, and a course of treatment? Surgery and six months of follow-up care? Specify the coverage carefully. That way, you'll forestall a common complaint: "I didn't expect *that* to be extra."

¶ *"If you have insurance . . . ."* This opening can work, but I don't often recommend it. I think it's normally better to state your usual charge first, *then* explain that any insurance proceeds will be applied against it. By mentioning insurance first, you risk giving a patient the idea that you scale your charges to the insurance coverage he has. Still, I do know a surgeon who starts many amicable fee discussions with these words: "If you have insurance, it will be a big help to you. My regular fee for what we're planning. . . ."

With a good opening like one of those, you've got things under way. But it isn't enough to start a fee discussion; you have to end it, too. Get to the ending by being forthright. Ask the patient if the fee you've suggested is agreeable to him: "Will that be satisfactory?" If the patient says, "Yes, Doctor," he's made a bargain. And, as I've said, patients keep bargains better than they pay bills.

Skeptical? That wouldn't surprise me. Doctors don't invariably accept my advice about initiating fee discussions. Some grump: "I display a plaque in my reception room—I got it from the A.M.A. —inviting patients to discuss fees frankly with me. Isn't that enough?" My answer is always: "No." I've asked patients in many offices what they think that invitation means. The most frequent answer: "I guess it means I should tell him if I think he charges too much. But what's the good of that when it's all over? It's easier to change doctors."

So by all means display the A.M.A. plaque, but don't just leave matters there.

If you're still one of the diehards who don't believe in discussing fees, take a look at page 187. There you'll see proof that patients think you're wrong. Only one in 15 says, "I'd rather not discuss money in my doctor's office." When over 9 out of 10 patients want to know what your services will cost, I, as your business adviser, want you to tell 'em. It's good business. And because of the anxiety you'll be dispelling, it's probably good medicine, too.

25

*Fees can be
raised without making
enemies*

One Monday morning an elderly G.P. scribbled the numeral 5 on a charge slip. It made the slip read: "For office visit —$5." Then he handed the slip to the woman he'd just checked for hypertension and, with a farewell pleasantry, disappeared into the examining room next door. A few minutes later, the patient handed the charge slip and a $5 bill to the doctor's secretary, who smiled indulgently and substituted the numeral 4 for the doctor's 5. "That's the third time he's done that this morning," she said, handing the patient a dollar. Said the patient: "I just thought he'd gone up a dollar," and snapped her bag shut. "Oh dear, no," replied the secretary. "He's just preoccupied."

At the end of the office day, the secretary teased the doctor. "You must have had something on your mind today," she said. "I had to change 18 charge slips. Did you know you'd been charging $5 for office visits all day?" "Yes," said the doctor. "I've been thinking of raising the fee for some time. Last night I made up my mind."

Meanwhile, across town, a young pediatrician was frowning at a letter from a father of four. It read: "We received the announcement of your new fees. It's your privilege, of course, to charge more than other doctors do. We hope you'll agree it's our privilege to decide what we can pay. We're truly grateful for all you've done for our children, but I'm afraid that now we'll have to take them to another doctor."

193

You'll have noticed by now that many of my stories come in threes. The end of this triad concerns an internist who, after long consideration, decided that a fee hike could be put off no longer. He asked his secretary to type out a list of all his current fees. He told her what was in his mind and listened attentively to her comments and suggestions. Then he went down the list, changed the figures, and returned the paper to her. "It's important that we both know the reason for the increases," he said to her. "I'm so much below the other men here that people are wondering if my diploma's genuine. If any patients ask why I've raised fees, I'll tell them the truth. I want you to do the same."

A month later the doctor stopped by his secretary's desk. She was making up the day's bank deposit. Nodding at a pile of checks on her blotter, he said casually: "Nobody's said a word to me about the fee changes. You must have handled their questions very well." Said the secretary: "The only patient who's mentioned the subject is Mrs. Nussbaum. She said it was about time."

The doctors in those stories remind me of three military commanders, each assigned a battle objective. The elderly G.P. kept his battle plan a secret from everybody, including his own troops. The young pediatrician sent copies of his battle plan to everyone he could think of, including the opposition troops. The internist drew up his battle plan, briefed his troops, and kept resistance to the minimum by retaining the element of surprise. The third fared best—just as I'd expect.

What justifies a fee hike? Must your fees advance to keep pace with your spiraling costs? Not necessarily. Fees, after all, are only a means to an end. Your principal goal is to give good care to your patients. Obviously, as the cost of doing so goes up, more money is needed. A secondary goal is to earn a good living. Yet meeting your goals needn't automatically set off a fee explosion. There are other ways to put your income at a reasonable level.

Improving collections is one way. Many doctors have used this method effectively in recent years. In 1951, the typical private doctor felt he'd done a good job if he collected 85 per cent of what his patients owed him. Today's private practitioner collects 90 to 95 per cent of his bills.

Increasing productivity is another way. It's by no means unusual for a modern G.P. to see 40 patients a day. That's twice as many as his father saw. The income from the added work has slowed the rising fee curve.

It's illogical, of course, to expect those two factors to hold down fees permanently. What happens when a doctor has all the patients he can handle? Or when he's collecting as much as he can, short of putting up a no-tickee-no-washee sign? Many doctors—I'd say a majority—have been in just that fix in recent years, and they've had a hard time deciding what to do. They say things like this:

¶ "I've raised the pay of my three aides 27 per cent over the last five years. Now it's my turn for a raise. But I'm chicken."

¶ "I'm between the devil and the deep blue sea: I could practice better medicine if I saw fewer patients, but I can't cut down my work without charging more. How do you choose between bad work and a poor income?"

¶ "How can one doctor fight inflation? It's a national economic disease. I just paid $4,400 for my new professional car. Why, when I started up in practice a comparable car cost me less than a third of that. If I can't get a better return from my practice soon, I'll be in real trouble."

For many doctors, though, deciding to hike fees doesn't end the head scratching. They face another dilemma: "Shall I raise 'em now or wait? Am I a pathfinder or just one of the crowd?" I know what both kinds say:

¶ "The way I see it, it's dangerous to raise fees unless all the other local doctors do it, too. I'll follow, but I won't lead."

¶ "It's crazy to wait until everybody else is higher than you are. Who wants to be tagged as a cut-rate doctor? I'd rather charge 10 per cent more than 10 per cent less."

And there's always the let-well-enough-alone philosophy:

¶ "Sure, my fees are out of date. But I make a good living, and

I can't see making it a better one by charging more. There's such a thing as pricing yourself out of the market."

Is there any indicator, economic or social, to tip off doctors that the time is ripe for the new deal on fees? If there is, I haven't found it. Historically, physicians' fee hikes lag behind those of other professionals. They also trail, sometimes by a long way, the steady rise in the paychecks of their patients. Architects get extra money when construction costs zoom. Artisans get pay boosts under cost-of-living clauses in their union contracts. Manufacturers pass along rising costs to their customers in a hurry. But no surgeon can settle for a percentage of his patient's hospital bill. No internist can send out statements reading: "For complete physical examination, tests, chest film, and ECG, $55. Add 3.2% cost-of-living award. Total: $56.76." And it'd be curtains for any G.P. who tried to justify a higher house-call fee by quoting the price of his new-model automobile.

In fee raising, I believe, the watchword is caution. Unless you're a genuine trailblazer, do as you've always done: Stick with your fees till they hurt. When enough of your colleagues feel the fiscal pain, they'll compare symptoms with you. Then, by consensus, the right prescription will be written.

When the medicine is administered, you may be in for a surprise. Patients can be very understanding when fees go up. They've seen the price of everything else raised far oftener and far more, percentagewise, than the price of medical care. They don't relish higher medical fees any more than higher meat prices. But if the ticket is up all over town, they won't picket you—or change doctors.

26

Neglect third parties at your peril

Take 1,800 vendors of health insurance—about 1,000 insurance companies, about 75 Blue Cross plans, as many Blue Shield plans, and about 600 other independent organizations. Add one Federal Government, 50 state governments, and thousands of county and city governments. Stir briskly.

That's third-party pie, a staple in your professional diet.

You may not care much for it, but you can't send it back to the kitchen. About 150,000,000 Americans are insured for surgical care, 115,000,000 for nonsurgical health care. Physicians in private practice have in recent years received more than one-third of their gross practice income from health plans.

In years to come that figure may well rise to two-thirds or even more. The top men in the big labor unions want employers to go much further toward picking up their workers' entire health tab through insurance and prepayment plans. Medicare has hardly started; its expansion is inevitable and may prove to be staggering. And you can depend upon it that the various states, through the old plans like workmen's compensation and new plans like Medicaid, won't be shy about expanding their programs. Already New York State has a proposal in the legislative hopper that would, if enacted, compel all employed persons to have health insurance coverage.

So you might as well face it: A big chunk of your future income will come from checks signed by third parties.

If you're new to private practice, you may not yet be familiar with the way voluntary health insurance works. I'll run quickly through its main features:

¶ It's voluntary. No U.S. or state law *yet* requires any individual to insure himself against the cost of sickness. People insure themselves by choice—increasingly so. In 1950, the premiums paid by the public for health insurance coverage totaled $2 billion; in 1965, $12.1 billion.

¶ Most health insurance is issued to groups, not individuals. Better than two-thirds of the insurance issued by companies, and almost all that issued by the Blue Shield plans, is taken out by groups of persons linked by a common tie, usually a common employer. Some groups have as few as five members, while others have many thousands.

¶ Health insurance provides money, not service. It's the business of voluntary health plans and Medicare to pay for health care, not to furnish it. Commercial insurers ordinarily pay their money to the person who's insured; the only way a doctor can be paid directly is by obtaining an authorization, called *an assignment,* from the patient. Most nonprofit plans, on the other hand, pay doctors direct.

¶ You're not compelled to accept a voluntary health plan's benefits as full payment for your services, but you can agree to do so. Practically all private insurance companies limit what they'll pay towards a patient's medical costs. Often, the policy requires the patient to pay some initial costs (the "deductible portion") *plus* any costs over and above some limit stated in the policy. For physicians' bills, Medicare has an initial deductible and a 20 per cent "coinsurance" feature on the remainder, paying 80 per cent of the balance due—assuming that the fee is "reasonable and customary" by Medicare's standards. Blue Shield pays "participating doctors" a full fee that's been previously negotiated with them. A physician needn't participate; if he doesn't, he can accept the Blue Shield check as part payment and bill the patient for the difference between it and his regular charge.

¶ Some health plans offer "major-medical" benefits to their policy holders. Such policies generally do not limit the amounts payable for specific services beyond stipulating that charges shall be "reasonable." Total benefits, though, are usually subject to a high deductible and a ceiling.

¶ Benefits are paid only on submission of a claim which includes a signed statement by the physician. The statement usually includes a precise description of the patient's illness and details of the care he received, with relevant dates.

No one likes paper work, so you're normal if you curse insurance forms. But damn them as you do money in the bank, because that's just about what they are. You'll be less unhappy about handling them if you keep that in mind and if you and your aide have a firm grasp of these 10 essentials:

Know the policies you see most often. If you and your aide will make yourselves thoroughly conversant with the local Blue Shield coverage, you'll be taking one big step toward making the job of filing claims easier. The same is true if you'll familiarize yourselves with the main features of Medicare and the commercial policies that seem popular in your area.

Learn the benefits that matter to you. Study up on the allowances for the kinds of care you provide. For instance, if you're a general surgeon, memorize the allowances of the various plans for appendectomy, cholecystectomy, herniorrhaphy, hemorrhoidectomy, and a few other common procedures. Of if you're a G.P., internist, or pediatrician, learn the allowances for hospital care and office care. Most important, learn what the popular policies *don't* pay for. Then you can tell patients how they stand before you render service. If you can't spare the time to become an expert on the benefits that matter to you, be sure your aide does.

Use a standard claim form. Commercial insurers and the A.M.A. have collaborated to develop a set of standard forms acceptable to most such insurers—though not Medicare or Blue Shield. You can get a small supply of standard forms free and a list of printing firms which sell the forms from the Health Insurance Council, 750

Third Avenue, New York, N.Y. 10017. Use them instead of asking your aide to cope with the hodgepodge of forms your patients bring in. She'll be able to do her work faster.

Get the insurance details at the patient's first visit. Train your aide to get them down on paper while the patient is in your reception room waiting to see you that first time. Does he carry Blue Shield? A commercial policy? Does the policy he has cover the service he seeks? What's the policy number? Keep all such information on file.

When insurance falls short of your full fee, tell the patient—in advance. Remember: Most commercial policies and some Blue Shield contracts offer indemnity coverage only, and when your regular fee's higher than the listed benefit the patient is liable for the difference. Be sure he understands that. He may think he has bought better coverage than he actually has. If so, he may be shocked to be presented later with a bill—unless you've explained the facts about his health insurance beforehand.

Find out who'll get the money. Blue Shield pays you directly if you're a participating doctor, but most commercial companies and Medicare pay the patient—unless he says that you're to be paid direct. He says it by assigning the benefit to you—usually just by signing below an assignment clause printed right on the claim form. When you're faced with a form that doesn't include an assignment clause, have your aide type up one for the patient's signature and fasten it to the form with tape, not a staple or paper clip. Or have one made up in rubber-stamp form.

Use standard medical terminology in your claims. Checks arrive sooner and claims bounce less often when standard terminology is used in charts and claim forms. Loose terminology can cost you dearly. There are 12 ways to describe a cystoscopy—and 11 of them are wrong in any given case. In some areas, a term carelessly used could mean the difference between one Blue Shield payment of $15 and another of $150.

For diagnoses, I'd suggest you follow the "Handbook of Standard Nomenclature of Diseases and Operations," $1.50 (in paperback), McGraw-Hill Book Company, 330 West 42nd Street, New York, N.Y. 10036. For operations and other services, I suggest the names and code numbers in "1964 Relative Value Studies," or its most recently revised version, published for the California Medical Association. Get it for $1.50 from Six Ninety Three Sutter Publications, 693 Sutter Street, San Francisco, Calif. 94102.

Get claims in fast. Many policies put a time limit on claims. I know a doctor who accumulated a backlog of 90 unfiled insurance claims over a two-year stretch. Their face value: $7,000. He finally collected $4,800. The lesson: Out-of-date claims don't pay off. So it makes sense to file claims at least once a week. File daily if you have lots of them—say, 15 a week.

Follow up unpaid claims. There are slow-pay insurance companies as well as slow-pay patients. Some companies ignore assignment forms and send all their checks to their policyholders. Some claims you think will be good are denied—and though the patient may be notified, you may not be. When there's long delay in payment, write the company. Ask what's going on. If your inquiry isn't answered, say you're going to bill the patient direct. Then bill him direct. Let *him* tell the insurer to get cracking.

Make rules for special situations. For instance, do you charge anything for filling out claim forms? Some doctors do, some don't. Popular compromise: File one claim gratis, and charge $1 each for extras. It isn't a fee; it's a service charge. You won't make money on it, but you'll recoup your office costs.

I realize that in listing these 10 essentials for handling insurance forms I've given you a formidable task: Learn the policies, memorize the benefits, get claims in fast, and all the rest. Fortunately, help's available—at the other end of your office phone. Every Blue Shield plan and every insurance company operating in your vicinity, including the Medicare carrier, will gladly send a representative to brief you on every detail of coverage. All you need to do is ask.

27

Rx for the
professional courtesy
headache

At a state medical society meeting not long ago, I met an orthopedic surgeon who had a sizable problem. "It's the old professional courtesy headache," he confided. "It's getting out of hand. The way the other doctors and their families flock to me, you'd think I was the only orthopedist in town. I enjoy the popularity, and I can't help being flattered, but *damn!* I can't afford to give away so much."

Another time in another city, another doctor said: "I'm beginning to suspect that I'm the only internist hereabouts who accepts professional courtesy patients. In the past few months, half the doctors' families in town have had a representative in my waiting room. Ethics and local custom keep me from charging them. No wonder I've got money problems!"

When you start counting up the people who receive professional courtesy in doctors' offices, you begin to wonder if *lots* of doctors aren't faced with financial troubles because they give away too much. Other physicians and their families are by no means the only patients who get their medical care on the cuff. In some towns, medical students are traditionally counted in, along with R.N.s and often others from the paramedical group— L.P.N.s, druggists, hospital employes, other doctors' aides, and of course a doctor's own aides.

The list doesn't stop there. Many doctors also give free care to clergymen. In some towns, teachers, firemen, and policemen get it, too. So do many doctors' classmates and other old friends, neighbors, and lodge brothers. It's not unusual for even a doctor's landlord to get it.

On top of that, the privilege of receiving treatment on a professional courtesy basis is often extended to the various spouses, children, and aged parents of all those people.

To put all such free care into economic perspective, consider, too, the basic on-the-cuff group: the poor but honest patients who are supposed to pay but can't; the able and honest but scatterbrained patients who would pay but forget; and the 1 or 2 per cent of the population who aren't about to pay any bill they think they can beat. Whew!

It's no wonder I've been asked: Doesn't a doctor have more than enough economic problems without throwing professional courtesy on top of them? Well, believe me, some do. Some, like the orthopedist and the internist I just told you about, face economic difficulties mainly because of the professional courtesy load—*and know it.* But most doctors don't actually know whether or not professional courtesy is a problem to them. Who keeps score? In my experience, not one in 100 knows the actual dollar value of the services he gives away. After all, there's no bill for professional courtesy services, and so the appropriate dollar figures are seldom kept.

Yet keeping the score might reveal some startling figures that would lead to constructive action. Once, after some extensive checking, I had to shock the men in a small group practice by announcing that they were giving away at least $6,000 yearly in professional courtesy. Because of that experience and numerous others like it, I'm convinced that some doctors who gripe about their payroll spending might discover that they're giving away in professional courtesy just as much as they pay their aides—much of it needlessly.

The problem, I might add, is not merely sizable. It's also traditional. It's handed down from Hippocrates and the A.M.A. You know what Hippocrates said. The A.M.A. said that a physician "should cheerfully and without recompense give his professional services to physicians or their dependents."

Mind, now, you can't blame the A.M.A. for the professional courtesy you extend to druggists, firemen, and lodge brothers. That's a doctor's own doing—as though he didn't have enough of a problem just trying to take care of his colleagues and their families for free.

In many practices, that problem alone is so severe that professional courtesy is being thrown out the window, and Hippocratic tradition be damned. Many psychiatrists, for instance, give away just five visits and then start billing. Others charge their full fees from the first visit onward.

I know some surgeons and medical men—that orthopedist is one, and the internist is another—who have started limiting the number of professional courtesy appointments they'll book in any one week. They figure that when a doctor's wife is offered an appointment seven weeks off, she may then be more willing to admit that there *are* other orthopedists or internists (or whatever) in her community.

A New England practitioner has found his solution in what he calls a professional courtesy classification system. It, too, is worth considering. His Class I includes physicians and their immediate families. His aide knows she is to charge them nothing. In Class II are physicians' lesser kin, their grown children, and doctors who, bless 'em, insist on paying. They're charged no more than their health insurance covers. Class III includes working R.N.s and those who've left their careers only temporarily (as in pregnancy), chief hospital technicians, and clergymen. They're charged 60 per cent of the doctor's usual fees. Finally, there's Class IV—L.P.N.s, druggists, and other paramedical personnel. They're charged 80 per cent of usual fees.

At least one management colleague of mine advises this solution: Limit professional courtesy to physicians and their immediate families, and continue to give them your professional services without charge; but do charge them for the expenses you incur

205

in accepting them as patients. In most practices, about 40 per cent of each fee received is for overhead. "So give away the 60 per cent," my colleague recommends, "but bill for the 40 per cent." The A.M.A., it seems to me, supported his view in principle when it specifically approved of compensation for travel expenses and professional income lost when providing professional courtesy.

What's my own recommendation? I'll go along with my colleague, though I recognize that many doctors—especially any young doctor, new in town—would be wise to conform to local custom. They can rationalize the high cost of giving by considering the expenditure an investment in professional and public relations. That's worth paying for.

On the other hand, what do I recommend when you, your wife, or your child is the patient? Offer the doctor a full fee. If your offer is rejected, insist on paying 40 per cent of a full fee—to cover the expenses. If your colleague also refuses that offer, donate the amount in his name to his hospital's improvement fund.

28

Collections: the simple truth

A young Georgia G.P. buttonholed me one evening below the rostrum from which I'd just delivered a talk on medical economics. "You said up there that the doctor who collected less than 90 per cent of his fees had a faulty collection system," he said. "Then, when you began to describe the cure, I was called away. Would you repeat that part of your talk for me? I've been in practice one year, and so far I've collected less than two-thirds of what I've put on my books."

"That's a common occurrence in the first year of practice," I told him. "There are several reasons for it. The principal one is that a new practitioner puts more on the books toward the year's end than at its beginning and hasn't had time to collect as much as he'd like. So, if I were you, I wouldn't panic about a low collection percentage yet."

"*Yet?*"

"Well, the day may well come when you'll have good reason to be upset. The odds almost suggest it. Better than two out of five established G.P.s have trouble collecting 90 per cent of their charges. One in four collects less than 85 per cent, and one in nine doesn't even hit 80 per cent."

Of course, as I then pointed out to him, that still leaves nearly three out of five G.P.s who do collect 90 per cent or better. About four out of five specialists do, too. Indeed, nearly one-quarter of all G.P.s and over one-third of all specialists haul in about 95 per cent of their charges. And it's always been my contention that what some can do, others can do also.

My Georgia questioner had no doubts as to what he wanted. "I'd like to be one of the 95-per-centers," he said. "If there's a secret, let me in on it."

"There's a secret all right," I told him. "But you'll find it hard to believe. Sit over here and listen."

Most doctors look on asking people to pay, I explained, as the most disagreeable necessity in medicine. What they don't always realize is that, often, they feel worse about wanting to be paid than their patients feel about paying. Even medicine's fiercest critics don't claim that a doctor shouldn't be paid. They may think someone else should write the check, but they don't dispute his right to get one.

The secret of collecting medical fees? It's simply this: Ask people to pay.

Many fees can be collected *without delay* just by asking, since many fees are small. G.P.s, internists, and pediatricians, for instance, do their work mainly in the office at fees under $10. The most effective way to collect such small charges is to ask for them there and then in cash. Incredulous? Don't be. Believe me, it works. If you'll make asking the custom in your office, you'll find that most patients will fall into the routine of paying as automatically as they pay their lunchroom checks at the cashier's desk. Others—even some who've previously paid doctors only when billed—will come through simply because they've noticed that paying right away is now the routine.

Notice that I'm suggesting you institute a custom, not an iron rule. Don't, for example, put up a notice saying, "All charges up to $10 must be paid in cash." Nor need you personally do the asking. All you need to do is to station your aide where every departing patient must pass in front of her, and see that she gives every one of them an opportunity to square small accounts there and then.

How do you give a patient the opportunity to pay cash without bluntly demanding it? That's simple. Introduce the lunchroom check's ethical professional equivalent: the charge slip. This little piece of paper has, to my personal knowledge, improved collections in thousands of medical offices in recent years. You'll notice, in due course, that charge slips are built into the write-it-once income-recording system described in Chapter 30. They're in the system for a collecting reason as well as a recording reason.

Charge slips are easy to use. When Mr. Jones arrives in your office—or before, if he comes by appointment—your aide writes his name and the date on a numbered slip and clips it to his chart. Mr. Jones, his chart, and the slip all come in to you. At the end of your consultation, examination, or treatment, you check off —on the slip—what you've done. Mr. Jones takes the slip to your aide. She figures the amount due, in his presence. Don't write in a figure yourself, unless you want her to collect more or less than your usual charge.

Brevity is the key to effective collection letters

These letters will help you draft your own requests for payment of past-due accounts. Note that they're all short. They appeal successively to the delinquent's honor, pride, and fear.

Letter No. 1. "We're sure there's some good reason why we haven't heard from you in response to our previous statements. If our enclosed account is wrong, we'll be happy to check it for you. If it's correct, may we hear from you soon?"

Letter No. 2. "We're disappointed not to have heard from you in response to our statements and our letter. At the same time we know that medical costs often unexpectedly strain the budget. Please let us know during the next few days when you think you'll be able to take care of the enclosed account."

Letter No. 3. "In trying not to press your overdue account, we've evidently failed to make it clear that we expected full payment long before now. Much as we regret it, we'll be compelled to resort to another course of action if we don't hear from you about the enclosed statement."

If, on learning the amount he's to pay, Mr. Jones reaches for his wallet or his checkbook, your aide writes a receipt—and that's the end of it. He may, though, drop the slip on her desk and keep moving. She then has an amiable but swift question for him. She says: "Would you like to take care of this now?" If he seems to be a slow study, she adds, "Most of our patients like to stay current with these small charges." He can still reply, "Will you send me a bill?" Unless his account is already a problem, she can say: "Surely, Mr. Jones. At the end of the month."

What she should never say, unasked, is, *"Would you like me to send you a bill, Mr. Jones?"*

When larger office charges are involved, cash payment is obviously less probable. If the service is rendered outside the office—at a hospital, for example—it's hardly possible. You're still going to ask for your money, though—by means of a bill, usually sent through the mail. And here's the good word: Mr. Jones will pay you more readily if he knows in advance what your bill will be than if you take him unawares.

There are still doctors—surgeons, mostly—who'll genially tell an anxious patient: "Now, whatever else you do, I don't want you to worry about my bill. It won't be more than you can pay." Some of their patients take the injunction literally. They don't worry—*ever*. Others worry awhile, then relax and turn the worrying over to the doctor.

For any physician who hopes to achieve an acceptable collection percentage, naming the fee before rendering a substantial service is a must. And, if he's wise, he doesn't quote fees by the inch—that is, he doesn't try to soften the blow by doling out the bad news in bite-sized bits. He tells the patient the full amount he plans to charge for all the care the case requires. Here, for example, is what you should do:

¶ If you're a surgeon, name an inclusive fee that covers the preoperative consultation, the operation itself, the hospital visits you'll make, and the final office checkup.

¶ If you do OB, quote mothers-to-be a fee that covers all prenatal care and tests, the delivery, the postpartum hospital care, and the postnatal office visits.

¶ As an internist recommending a full diagnostic workup, tot up the prices of all its ingredients: the history and physical examination, the chest film, the ECG, and the lab tests. Tell the patient the total.

¶ As a pediatrician taking over the care of a preemie, tell the parents your charge *by the week*. If you can, estimate how many weeks.

In all cases, make it clear that the fee you quote assumes that the case requires the exercise of normal skill and will occupy you the normal amount of time—and that complications, if they develop, will come extra.

There'll be many patients who'll wince when you tell them what it will cost to get well. But if they say they'll pay, they mostly will. You'll do lots better telling them now than by surprising them later.

Some of them, it's true, may eventually need to be nudged be-

---

How long should you try to collect $5?

Many physicians' books show hundreds of unpaid accounts ranging from $2 to $5. Problem: What's the best way to handle them without spending more on the collection effort than the accounts are worth?

Counting postage, stationery, and labor, and making some allowance for a doctor's investment in office equipment and floor space, it costs at least 20 cents to send out a medical bill; in fact, recent estimates have ranged up to 75 cents or so. It costs even more to send a letter. So if you send three statements and three letters in pursuit of a $5 debt, you run a risk of spending lots more than the debt warrants.

It's better economics to turn over the chickenfeed bills to a medical collector after sending just two statements and one warning letter.

---

fore they come through. There are lots of improvident people around. They take fiscal chances. They chance having enough money to buy food, fuel, and clothing after paying the mortgage company, the finance company, and the auto dealer—and they chance having enough left to pay the doctor after meeting all their other expenses. Most people budget big outlays by the month, and by hallowed business custom their largest payments fall due during the first week. Thus, if any money is likely to be left over for unbudgeted expenses, the family treasurer decides early in the month who will get it.

Make sure your claim to it is in his hands when the decision is made. Get your bills out in time for the whom-shall-we-pay-this-month session. Your aide needs time to get the bills ready, so have her close out your patients' ledgers around the 25th. Have these words printed on your statement forms: *"This statement includes all charges through the 25th of this month. Later charges will be shown on next month's statement."* See that the bills leave your office not later than the last day of the month, and see that they're addressed—correctly—to the person from whom you expect payment.

You can expect one-half of your patients to pay the first bill you send them. A second bill, sent at billing time the following month, will usually bring checks from about one-third of the patients who didn't pay the first time. And about one-third of the remainder will reach for their pens in response to Bill No. 3. Now, approximately 80 per cent of your patients have paid you for the work you did three months ago. Your collection problem: 20 per cent of your patients haven't come through. And, unfortunately, they include a good many whose bills are substantial.

What to do? When your next billing day rolls around, write each slowpoke a letter. Not just any old letter, and certainly not a hectoring why-don't-you-pay-me-what-you-owe-me-you-dirty-rat letter. It would just elicit a resentful reaction like: "Let him damn well wait. I'll pay him when I'm good and ready." Instead, just ask the slowpoke if the bill he received was wrong. Your implication:

William A. Brown
NAME
123 Main Street N⁰ 7625

SERVICE:	CHARGE
✓ Office Call	5 —
House Call	
Surgery	
Injection	
Laboratory	
X-Ray	
Pap Smears	
Other	
Drugs	
Total	5 —

RECEIPT · STATEMENT · APPOINTMENT

John E. Doe, M.D.
MIDTOWN CLINIC   ANYTOWN, MO

William A. Brown N⁰ 7625
NAME

OLD BALANCE	TODAY'S CHARGE	TODAY'S PAYMENT	NEW BALANCE
10	5	15	—

10/18/67   *Sally Green*
DATE   SIGNED

YOUR NEXT APPOINTMENT *2 p.m. Nov. 1*

An itemized charge slip gives detailed fee information to a patient, thus encouraging him to pay before leaving the office—or preparing him for the balance due that will appear on his month's end statement. This well-designed charge slip includes a receipt and an appointment reminder. It's consecutively machine-numbered to help discourage embezzlement.

A guy as smart as he is isn't going to dash off a check in payment of an incorrect bill.

That mild letter of inquiry brings in more payments from slow-pokes than any other collection letter I've seen. But it doesn't bring checks from all the people who get it, of course. So, next billing day, write again. This time, mingle reproach with magnanimity. Let Slowpoke see you feel let down. Then suggest that maybe your bill hit him at a fiscally disastrous time. If it did, are things likely to look up soon? If so, you'll gladly wait a while longer. Letter No. 2 will bring in a trickle of checks. It'll also bring some more or less believable promises.

The toughies, though, will still keep mum. You've asked them for your money five times now, and so come next billing day ask them one last time, in letter No. 3. In two terse sentences tell the holdout that the jig's up. If he doesn't answer this time, you'll blow the whistle; you'll send the account to a collection agency.

Ten days after you've given that warning, turn the account over to a medical collector. He'll charge you nothing if he collects nothing. If he does collect, he'll be scoring where you struck out for six solid months. More important to you, though, is the good chance that the delinquent will, as a result of his brush with the collector, learn to take his medical bills, and perhaps even his health, more seriously.

It's odd how some people won't pay a doctor but hurry to pay a bill collector—people who could just as easily have paid the doctor in the first place. They get their checks off to the collector in the next mail. Some who *can't* pay will dash off valid explanations to a collector posthaste, although it has never occurred to them to let *you* know of their troubles. And even some hardshell debtors who've ignored you for months will call a collector after the first contact and fix up an agreement to pay in installments. Him, they take seriously.

If, like many beginning doctors, you don't relish the idea of setting a collector on to your patients, relax. A good medical collector isn't hard on people who genuinely can't pay. He won't hesitate to advise you to wipe their accounts off your books. He, not you, foots the bill for all hopeless quests, and he doesn't want to waste *his* money dunning penniless widows and orphans. Besides, he's not at all the heartless wretch his public image suggests. If he were, he wouldn't be specializing in medical collections; he'd be out repossessing refrigerators for discount houses.

"Let's do a fast recap," said the young Georgia doctor to whom I told all this. "According to you, it's easy for a doctor to collect 90 per cent of his charges. All he does is train his patients to pay small charges in cash, name larger fees before starting in on the case, send three bills, and write three letters. It all sounds too simple."

It's simple—almost too simple to be believed. The doctors who can never quite believe the simplicity are the ones who've never tried it. And, as you might expect, they're usually the ones with the biggest collection problems.

29

Watch your money or you won't see it go

A hundred years ago a witty Frenchman said: "Business is easy. It's just other people's money." Well and good, but business is also knowing what to do with other people's money after it becomes *your* money.

If all goes well with you, enough greenbacks and checks will pass through your office ($3,000 to $4,000 a month) to make it essential that you know how to protect the money and yourself—the money from theft, yourself from the Internal Revenue Service. Don't be like some doctors I've known who seemed to be almost begging for the wrath of the I.R.S.

A certain Southern surgeon comes immediately to mind, though he's really not so atypical. "This is a small town and I don't want our two bankers to know all my business," he told me. "So I take the currency home and mail all the checks to my brother who owns a store 50 miles away. He banks them in his account and sends me two checks in return. I cash one of them at one local bank, one at the other. Say, do you make out tax returns for doctors?"

"I'd rather not make out *yours*," I said, "and I'd hate to make out your brother's."

Keeping the money straight and yourself out of tax trouble isn't impossible, despite the tales of tax woes you've heard. It isn't even difficult. I've worked out six simple rules for my clients to follow in handling money. Follow them:

Bank all your practice receipts. If your daybook shows that last month you took in $3,000, I expect your aide to show me duplicate deposit slips certifying that she's banked $3,000 in your office checking account.

If her deposit slips don't add up to that much, I'm going to ask her some questions. For instance, I'll ask if you gave her all the cash you collected on house calls. I'll ask if you grabbed any loose sawbucks out of the cash drawer the day your old professor was in town to lunch with you. I'll ask her if she paid cash to the janitor, the window washer, the florist.

She'll probably remember all the details eventually. But why put us both to all that trouble? *Let her bank every nickel.* Any other way, believe me, you're vulnerable. And so is she, poor girl. You're dead wrong if you airily assume that it's all right to put the cash in your wallet and send the checks to the bank. Some doctors do just that. Wish them good luck (they'll need it), but don't emulate them.

CONTROL OF ACCOUNTS RECEIVABLE

Outstanding accounts at end of preceding month $8,400

Month of December 19 67

(1) Day	(2) Services rendered (less discounts)	(3) Receipts from practice	(4) Rent, dividends, other income	(5) Total receipts and other income	(6) Increase (col. 2 over col. 5)	(7) Decrease (col. 5 over col. 2)	(8) Outstanding accts.
1	$325.00	$125.00	$25.00	$150.00	$175.00	--	$8,575.00
2	125.00	300.00	25.00	325.00	--	$200.00	8,375.00
3							
4							
5							
6							

A daily control of accounts receivable (↑) helps keep the records straight. It's also a good idea to do an occasional spot check (→). Simply pick a few patients' ledger cards at random and check the entries against the entries in the daybook.

Make a deposit every day. Even if there's a safe in your office —as there should be if substantial amounts in cash or checks are around—it's best not to keep incoming receipts there overnight. Doctors' offices aren't burglarized as often as supermarkets, but I have records of plenty of break-ins. In one case, the burglars took the safe. In another, in their rage at finding less than $20 in folding money, they tore up $300 worth of checks, and did the tearing in a field 10 miles away.

Give your aide a routine to follow. "First chance you get every morning," tell her, "go through the mail for cash and checks. Slap the backs of the checks with that rubber stamp that says: '*For deposit to the account of. . . .*' Then if someone snitches one while you're busy in another room, he won't be able to cash it at a grocery store at the other end of town."

Tell her to list all incoming checks in the "Paid" column of your daybook. If the signature on a check isn't that of the patient the

---

MONDAY					NOVEMBER 20
Hour	NAME	SERVICES RENDERED	CHARGE	CASH	REC'D ON ACCOUNT
1 PM	Harold Gates	OC	4		
1:15	Lucy Lampert	OC		4	
1:30	Frances Sterling	OC Lab	2		
2:00	George Appleby	OC	4		
2:15	William Aletti	OC WIT		9	
2:30	Grace S		19		
3	Panton				
3:30	Mary R				10

GEOFFREY R. PLANDOME, M.D.
103 HALSEY TERRACE
WINTERLEDGE, NORTH DAKOTA

NORTH 1-8300

Mr. George Appleby
21 Woodlawn Avenue
Winterledge, N.D.

DATE	PROFESSIONAL SERVICE	CHARGE	PAID	BALANCE	CASE NO. M 2-031
10/3	Wife HCD	7	7		
10/12	Self HCD	7		14	
11/6	Self OC			18	
11/20	Self OC	4		22	
12/5	Wife OC Lab	14		36	
12/19	Wife OC	4		40	

219

payment's made for, she's to write the patient's name in parentheses after the name of the check-writer this way: *S. E. Stimson (for Mrs. Barbara J.), $10.*

Caution her to stow cash and checks in the office cashbox right away. You don't have a cashbox? Phone the stationery store for one today. Specify a metal lockbox to fit her desk drawer, with a removable tray divided into compartments for coins and bills. The checks go under the tray.

As the normal day wears on, your aide will receive more cash and more checks. She lists the checks in the daybook as before, and she adds them to the others in the cashbox. When a patient pays in greenbacks, she enters the payment in the daybook, puts it in the box, and gives the patient a numbered receipt. If you've installed a write-it-once pegboard system, the daybook entry and the receipt writing will of course be done simultaneously. If you've elected to use a write-it-twice system, insist that she enter cash payments in the daybook first. Warn her against writing up the daybook from her duplicate receipts. That's a short cut she should never take.

At closing time, she compares the day's cash and checks with the daybook total, and the cash with the duplicate receipts. Then she gets the bank deposit ready. Your bank will supply pads of deposit slips with carbons and tissues.

Tell her to list the cash total on the deposit slip first, then to double-check her count by noting the number of bills of each denomination, e.g., two $20 bills—$40, 17 $10 bills—$170, 7 $5 bills—$35, 11 $1 bills—$11, total—$256.

With a write-it-once system, she need only list the total of all the checks she's holding. But with a write-it-twice system, she should list the checks individually. See that she writes the bank's routing number—that's the hyphenated figure printed above a bold line in the top right-hand corner of every check—the signer's name, and the amount of the check, e.g., *55-680, Henry L. Thompson, $5.* She'd better turn each check face down after listing it, to make sure she didn't forget to use your endorsement

220

stamp earlier. The bank will return any that aren't endorsed, and that means more paper work.

Finally, when she's sure the deposit slip total agrees with the "Paid" column in her daybook, she brings you the daybook, the deposit slip, the receipt book, the cash, and the checks. Why should she bring them to you? Well, it's your money, isn't it? Maybe you don't know if she's done things all according to Hoyle. Then the least you can do is look at everything knowingly. But do have her bring everything in.

If the day's collection is small, you can let her leave it overnight in the locked cashbox in her locked desk if you don't have an office safe. If the deposit's large, though, one of you had better drop it in the bank's night depository on the way home. The bank provides special locking bags for night-safe users.

Whether the deposit is left in the office or dumped in the bank slot, the duplicate deposit slip shouldn't be left in the office overnight. Should the deposit be lost, stolen, or burned (people have been known to drop explosives into a night safe), the duplicate may be the only clue you have to the extent of your loss. Either you or your aide should hold it personally just in case.

Next morning, send your aide to the bank to make the deposit or claim the night-deposit bag. If everything checks out, she'll bring back the duplicate deposit slip with the bank's stamp certifying that the deposit was made.

Be suspicious of checks. This is an important rule that's too often broken. A check isn't money until it has cleared the bank on which it's drawn. Not all checks manage to do that. When a check comes in the mail, all you can do is deposit it and hope for the best.

But when a check is handed in at your aide's desk, there are some precautions she can take against the bad-check artist.

Tell her not to cash personal checks for people she doesn't know, if she can possibly avoid doing so. Under no circumstances should she cash a personal check from such a person for a large sum without your express authorization. Neither should she cash a paycheck, unless as a special favor to a patient she knows well. Bad-check artists specialize in faking payroll checks.

She should refuse any check that's made out to a third party and endorsed over to you—even if the third party is the patient himself. If the check bounces, it's more trouble than a no-good personal check signed by the patient.

She should flatly refuse to cash Government checks for people she doesn't know. U.S. mailboxes are robbed of them every day, especially of Social Security checks—and Uncle Sam recovers the money from the foolish people who cash them for the robbers.

She should never take a check for more than the amount due you and hand out your cash in change. If she does that, you're liable to lose not only your fee but your shirt. You can lose even if the patient's honest. An elderly man paying a $500 fee by installments wrote numerous checks for larger amounts, taking the change in cash each time. He died still owing the doctor $300. The lawyer for the estate wrote: "We hold canceled checks for $400. Please send us a corrected bill for $100." Obliging the old gentleman cost the doctor $200 and a lot of unpleasantness.

Set up a petty cash fund. Your aide has to make numerous piffling payments for postage due, freight charges on drugs, office coffee, and other such nickel-and-dime expenses. Don't let her pay them out of the cashbox. If she does, her bank deposit won't jibe with her daybook total as it must.

Sign a check for $25 made out to "Petty Cash." That should cover at least a month's small outlays. Let her put this cash in a safe place—not the regular cashbox. Every time she makes a payment out of this fund, she puts in a signed voucher for the amount paid. Once a month, sign a check for whatever amount's necessary to restore the fund to the $25 level—after you've examined the vouchers.

Don't authorize her to pay any but trivial sums out of petty cash. And *never* pay wages out of it, not even to a casual employe who works only on odd half days.

Set up a change fund. Your aide tells you a patient wants to pay

$4 but has only a $20 bill. The cashbox holds nothing smaller than a ten. You give her a five and a one out of your wallet. She comes twice more with the same problem. You get good and mad.

The answer: Sign a check to "Cash" for $50. See that the stub is marked "Change Fund." Tell your aide to cash the check at the bank and specify two tens, three fives, twelve ones, and $3 in coins. Tell her to put the money in a third cache, *not* in the cashbox or the petty cash fund.

Here comes a patient, now, with a double sawbuck and a $4 charge slip. Your aide swaps a ten or a twenty from the cashbox for smaller bills from the change box. Now she can break the patient's twenty. At day's end, she may be able to exchange the big bills in the change box for the original assortment of small bills and coins from the cashbox. If not, she can get the change she needs at the bank next day.

If you take any cash from the cashbox, leave a personal check in its place. I'd rather you take no cash—ever—from the office cashbox, but I know there are times when that's the only way to get some in a hurry. Well, at least try not to take $1,000 a year from it, as some doctors do.

One of them once told me in New York City: "I take $20 a week for cab fares now. You can't give a hackie a check—and last year I forgot about the deductible cab fares when tax-return time came around." I gave him the advice I'm now giving you. Any time you raid the cashbox, put in your personal check for the amount you take out. Then your aide's bank deposit won't have a hole in it.

If it's lunch money you need, go ahead and borrow from petty cash—and pay it back.

You've noticed, I suppose, that in all I've said about the care of money, your aide figures more prominently than you do. That's because she's the one who actually watches the cash and checks. But who watches her? Don't be scared. The great majority of physicians' aides are utterly trustworthy. Nonetheless, every management man's files hold reports of thefts from physicians by their aides. I've personally investigated embezzlements of $30,000, $20,000, $16,000, $11,000, and a dozen smaller sums. I know of cases involving much larger amounts.

One estimate I've heard is that the doctor in private practice runs a one in 20 risk of employing a white-coated thief during his professional career. A long shot? Maybe, but not long enough to justify neglecting some simple precautions. Don't, please, say to yourself: "Not *my* aide. I'd trust her with my last dollar." Almost every doctor who's been robbed has said that—before the theft. And why not? You wouldn't expect a doctor to say: "I've hired a girl who'll probably rob me."

No system of financial control is proof against embezzlement since an intelligent and determined thief can outfox any system for a while. What you *can* do is minimize the risk of hiring a dishonest aide, limit the amount she can steal once she's hired, and cut down the length of time her thefts can continue without discovery.

To begin with, check a new aide's references thoroughly. Don't be hesitant about asking a former employer: "Is she honest?" That's the kind of information former employers are shy of volunteering; they're afraid of lawsuits for character assassination. But if you ask, they won't give a flat Yes if the answer's really No. They'll hedge—and that, to you, is the red light.

Secondly, have your aide bonded. The cost is low, and the bonding company's investigation is searching. If your aide says she isn't willing to be bonded, that should be enough warning for you.

Third, never get so busy you can't find time to keep track of what goes on in the front office. It's your money. You *can't* be too busy to keep an eye on it. If you do, it may dawn on you one day that you're working harder than your colleagues in the same field, with less to show for it. Sure, there can be many reasons. One may be that you're not getting all that your patients are paying. At any rate, that was the explanation in the case of a woman G.P. who couldn't understand why, when she was so busy, she netted less than nearby doctors with much smaller practices. Her aide, we

224

found, was holding on to no less than $100 a week. Moral: When you suspect you smell something bad in the front office, it's time to call for an audit.

Don't, though, wait till then to bring your auditor in. Even with a well-vouched-for bonded aide, it's bad management to leave her entirely unsupervised. Have an accountant or a medical management consultant spot-check your financial records at intervals —monthly or quarterly, as he recommends—without advance notice to your aide. The psychological value of such checks is immense.

Some years ago I was in a client's office and told his aide I'd like to check a few accounts as a matter of routine. To my surprise and distress, she began to weep. "I'd better tell you, since you're going to find it out anyway," she said. "I've been taking $40 a month to pay off my car." Would I actually have discovered this from a spot check? Honestly, I can't say I would have, since a spot check is lots less than an audit. But she felt sure I'd latch on to it. So she confessed.

Another precaution: When your aide is away for at least a week, have your accountant or consultant make a more extensive check than usual. If she refuses to take a vacation, don't be too sure this is a proof of devotion.

Still another precaution: Keep your accounts receivable in balance. Accounts receivable are the amounts your patients owe you. Their total should appear in your daybook—adjusted daily. And that total should agree with the total of the outstanding balances of individual patients as shown on their ledger cards. If those totals don't agree, something's wrong. The disagreement *may* be the result of honest error. But if the error can't be traced, someone may have some tough explaining to do.

If you haven't already set up an accounts receivable control system, here's how to go about it:

¶ Round up all your patients' ledger cards. Make sure none are missing. Make sure they're all posted up to date.

¶ List on an adding machine every unpaid balance on the cards and take a total. The resulting figure is your starting accounts receivable. Enter the figure at the foot of today's page in your daybook or in the right-hand top corner of the control form shown on page 218. (If you're using a write-it-once pegboard system you'll find that provision is made in it for recording your accounts receivable every day.)

¶ Tomorrow, if you decide to use the control form, give it to your aide. Every day, tell her, she's to enter the total charges and the total payments for that day. She *adds* the charges to your starting receivables and *subtracts* the payments. In the last column, she enters the resulting current receivables figure. If you don't use the form, have her write the figures at the foot of each day's daybook page.

¶ The current accounts receivable figure on the form or in the daybook must agree *at all times* with the total of the outstanding balances shown on your ledger cards. So run an adding-machine tape on the cards three or four times a year, and compare the total with the figure on the control sheet or daybook. If they don't agree, one or the other is wrong, and the disagreement is due either to accident or design. If it's accidental, it's honest. If not—that's just what you wanted to know.

You needn't give your receivables the full treatment very often. But there's a lot to be said for spot-checking them fairly frequently. That's no big deal. Check the arithmetic of 20 control sheet entries taken at random. Check your aide's additions and subtractions through three pages of her daybook. Pick 10 or 20 individual daybook entries and check them against her postings to the ledger cards of the patients concerned.

Do I seriously think you're going to do all this—scrutinize the bank deposits like a hawk, be cautious about the checks you accept, ride herd on your accounts receivable? Seriously, I do not. I've no reason to think you'll be any different from all the other doctors I know who find such activities boring and unacceptable.

So I'll ask you instead to do this: Hire someone—an accountant or a management consultant—to do it for you.

30

Keep track of what's due and from whom

D r. Strafaci's phone rang just as we were getting ready to leave his office. He grabbed it up and listened, pencil poised over his scratch pad. Reading his scribble upside down, I saw he'd jotted down, "Mrs. Hampton—$35—paid last Friday, has receipt."

"My secretary isn't here at the moment, Mrs. Hampton," he finally said. "But I'll see that the record's corrected. Tear up the bill she sent you."

After hanging up, he looked at me in despair. "That's the third time this week I've been cussed out for sending bills to patients who owe me nothing," he said. "I'll have to fire Miss Broom if she can't keep better track of patients' accounts."

En route to the golf club, I told Dr. Strafaci he needn't fire his overworked secretary. "The real fault lies in her method of posting your patients' ledgers," I said. "She's still using a write-it-twice system."

"Whatever it's called, it's the same system that's used in other offices," said Dr. Strafaci. "My accountant set it up, and he's installed it in several other doctors' offices."

"Smart doctors have switched to a write-it-once system," I told him. "I'll be glad to tell you why."

"I'll be glad to hear," said Dr. Strafaci, "but not now. Let's get down to that locker room."

The following week I was at Dr. Strafaci's office half an hour early. He was waiting for me—with a question. "You said I needed a different method of handling my patients' ledgers," he began. "That word bugs me. I thought my accountant kept my ledgers. What does Miss Broom have to do with them?"

I explained: "Your accountant keeps all your ledgers except those of individual patients. They're the cards on which Miss Broom writes who owes what. Every day she has to pull 30 or 40 of them to post payments or charges. At the end of the month, she types up your patients' bills from them."

"All right," said Dr. Strafaci, "spell out what's wrong, and tell me what to do about it."

"Miss Broom notes down each new charge and each incoming payment in her daybook," I said. "Later—usually the next day, but sometimes not for several days—she copies each daybook entry onto the appropriate ledger card. Each time she does this, she figures out the patient's new balance—how much he still owes— and writes that down, too.

"Remember Mrs. Hampton, who complained that she'd been billed for a $35 charge she'd already paid? The charge had been posted to Mrs. Hampton's ledger. But when billing day rolled around Miss Broom hadn't yet posted Mrs. Hampton's payment. So Mrs. Hampton's card showed that she owed $35, and Miss Broom billed her for it."

"But that's not the fault of the system," said Dr. Stafaci. "If Miss Broom had done her posting promptly, the mistake wouldn't have happened."

"True," I agreed, "but in an office as busy as yours it's always hard and often impossible to keep postings current. Since systems exist that guarantee current postings, it makes sense to use one. Your system demands that Miss Broom write everything twice, once in the daybook and again on the card; if she'd use a write-it-once system, she'd post the daybook and the card simultaneously. She'd gain in three ways. First, she'd cut out half the labor she now expends on posting her daybook and cards separately. Second, she'd cut out the time lag—sometimes considerable—between the daybook entry and the card entry. Third, she'd have built-in protection against a common error—copying a figure wrongly from book to card."

"If there are more than one of these write-it-once systems," said Dr. Strafaci, "you'd better tell me how they differ."

Here, condensed, is what I told him:

Machine posting. This way requires the use of what's popularly called a bookkeeping machine. Using a source document such as a charge slip, the doctor's aide can in a single operation post a transaction to the daybook and the ledger card—and also make out the patient's bill ready for mailing. At closing time, the machine totals the day's charges and payments at the touch of a key, giving

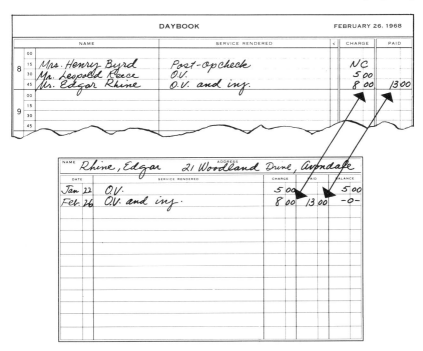

The write-it-twice system requires that transactions be recorded by making one entry in the daybook and another on the patient's ledger card, as indicated here. It's easy to keep the daybook entries current—but even easier to delay copying them onto ledger cards. The problem: End-of-month billing errors are inevitable when ledger cards aren't kept current.

her the figures she needs for her cash receipts journal. The arithmetic required to arrive at each card's new balance is done by the machine. At billing time, the aide mails out all statements that show balances due.

Some doctors, I added, like machines that produce several copies of each patient's statement. "The copies are often in different colors. They're mailed in successive months. If the first statement —white, perhaps—doesn't bring a payment, the second—yellow —may do the trick. If not, the patient gets number three—the green one. A fourth copy—pink, let's say—doesn't go to the patient at all. It goes to a collection agency as a delinquent account."

"Sounds great. Where do I get this machine?" Dr. Strafaci asked.

"Several firms market them," I told him. "Your office equipment salesman will be glad to give you a list. They come in various models at different prices. If you want, you can get a machine that will list and total charges and payments for different kinds of service. That's useful if you want to know how much of your income comes from office visits, how much from house calls, how much from X-rays and lab tests, and so on. Clinics use machines that list the 'production' of each doctor in the clinic, broken down by the types of service they've rendered. The more sophisticated the machine, of course, the higher its cost."

"I wouldn't want any elaborate breakdowns," said Dr. Strafaci. "I just want the accounts kept current—and correct."

"Then we're talking about a capital outlay of up to $1,500," I said.

"Sounds like lots of money," said Dr. Strafaci, "but, then, I guess we *need* that machine."

"Hold on," I said. "I'm as machine-minded as anyone. But while there are pros, there are also cons—and maybe you'd better hear them, too. To start with, the machine needs an operator. Miss Broom could easily learn to work it. But when she's on vacation or out sick, could Mrs. Brush, your nurse, operate it? You shake your head. Then who would?

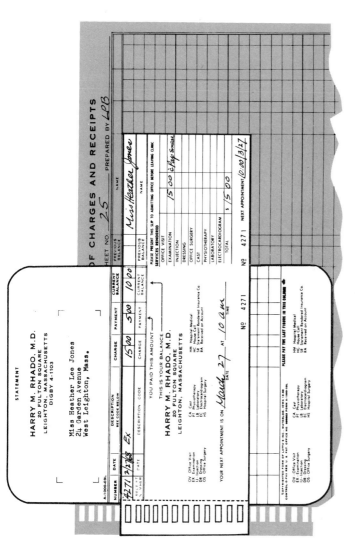

The write-it-once system puts the necessary information on three documents at one writing. A pegboard helps line up the forms properly, so that information written on the uppermost form will appear in the right places on the forms underneath. Some suppliers use carbonless paper; others spot the carbon strategically. Either way, nothing is left for the aide to do but put the forms on the pegs and write. Notice that the uppermost form here, a charge slip, includes a receipt for payment and an appointment reminder as well.

"Next, your office has about 1,000 ledger postings a month. The first two weeks, when the checks are rolling in, you average 60 or 70 postings a day. The second two weeks, the figure drops to 35 or 40. Measured against the machine's capacity, such numbers are piffling. Your machine would have more idle hours than working hours—a lot more. Those idle hours would cost you plenty in depreciation.

"Third, there'd still be a time lag in posting, although it would probably be short. An operator with other work to do, as Miss Broom has, usually accumulates her postings until she has, say, a couple of hours' work to do. She figures, and rightly, that there's no sense dashing to the keyboard every five minutes."

"You're leading up to something, I can see," said Dr. Strafaci, "—another system, I suppose."

I nodded affirmatively.

Pegboard posting. There's a write-it-once system, I told Dr. Strafaci, that uses a device called a pegboard rather than a machine. A pegboard is nothing more exciting than a clipboard fitted with pegs down one edge rather than a spring clip at the top. The pegs hold the forms the system uses "in register"—lines them up.

The three basic forms are a daybook sheet, a ledger card, and a charge slip. But the charge slip tells more than the fee. It also serves as a receipt and a reminder of the patient's next appointment. A typical design is shown on page 231.

To do her posting, an aide uses a ballpoint pen or hard pencil. She strikes a new balance and arrives at her daily totals with the help of an adding machine. For month-end billing, she can use a pen, a typewriter, or an office copier. But the patient gets his first bill right there in the office. His card is posted in his presence. There's no time lag, no accumulation of postings.

"Maybe I was in too much of a hurry about that $1,500 machine," said Dr. Strafaci. "If Miss Broom weren't here one day to run it, Mrs. Brush would shy away from it. And I don't like the idea of the machine's being idle so much of the time. I'll settle for a pegboard."

"In this office, it will do the job adequately," I said. "And I should mention that there's one more advantage possessed by machine and pegboard alike. An identical entry automatically appears on both the daybook and the ledger card because they're carbon copies of the original entry on the charge slips. An aide can't get these two entries to show up differently unless she alters one of them—and they're pretty hard to alter without detection. That's a deterrent to a girl who's tempted to book a payment on the card and leave it off the daybook—the embezzler's favorite maneuver."

"That's exactly what Miss Broom's predecessor did," said Dr. Strafaci.

If you are planning to keep your patients' accounts on a write-it-twice system, I'd advise that you give the matter further consideration. Choose between a machine or a pegboard on the twin basis of your monthly postings and the ability of your aide to operate the system you favor. Just don't let her write things twice. That isn't good management.

233

31

Plug those
cash leaks

All the money that goes into your office account goes out again. If you're typical, something more than 60 per cent of it doesn't travel very far. It shifts over to your personal account. The rest goes to other people: your office landlord, aides, the electric company, phone company, gas station, and various suppliers of goods and services ranging all the way from drugs to income tax advice. The exit door for all those practice-connected expenses is your office checkbook. If it isn't, it should be. Paying your business bills with folding money, aside from petty cash items, is definitely out.

Note that I said: "Your *office* checkbook." Do I mean you should have two bank accounts, one for the office and one for home? I do. Your practice has a fiscal identity separate from your own. Don't merge them.

You're not, I take it, planning to write your business checks yourself. Your aide can do that for you. But you'll sign them—every one. For the woman with authority to sign checks, stealing through the checkbook is a breeze; much, much simpler and safer than poking sticky fingers into the cashbox. As I've said many times, not many aides steal—but those few who do can clean their employers thoroughly.

So give the checkbook to your aide and tell her: "You write the checks. I'll sign them." Before she writes the first check, see that she enters at the top of its stub the amount currently standing to your credit in your office account. That's her *opening balance*. Now she's ready to write the check. Here's her best procedure:

¶ She writes the stub first.

¶ She notes briefly—but in sufficient detail—on the stub the reason for the payment. If the payment is for more than one kind of expense, she shows the breakdown on the stub.

¶ She writes the check in ink, not pencil, unless she types it. And typing is preferable. Best of all, provide her with a check protector—the pint-size gadget that embosses, in words, the amount the check's for. The person receiving an embossed check can't alter any figure on it.

¶ She dates the check the day she writes it.

¶ She writes the payee's name in full, or as indicated on the invoice, if there is one. In making out a check to an official of a firm, or of a government agency, she adds his title so that the check can't be deposited in his personal account by mistake. Example: *S. L. Jones, Postmaster.* She verifies that the dollar amount is the same in both places on the check and also on the stub.

¶ She never corrects an error when writing a check by erasing and rewriting (or by crossing out and writing over). Instead, she voids the check and writes another. She does so by writing the word *"Void"* across the check and also across the stub. She preserves the check since your auditor will want to see it.

¶ She writes most of her checks on one regular day each month —the 10th, for instance, which is a good date. Your bank balance should be fairly plump at that time, with collections received in response to the bills sent out to patients about 12 days earlier. But when your aide can pick up a discount for paying early, she should write *that* check before the regular check-writing day, naturally.

¶ She goes to the adding machine at the end of check-writing day. She tallies the face amounts of the checks and takes a total. She subtracts the total from her opening balance—it's on the first stub, remember—and enters the result at the top of the next unused stub. That's her new checkbook balance.

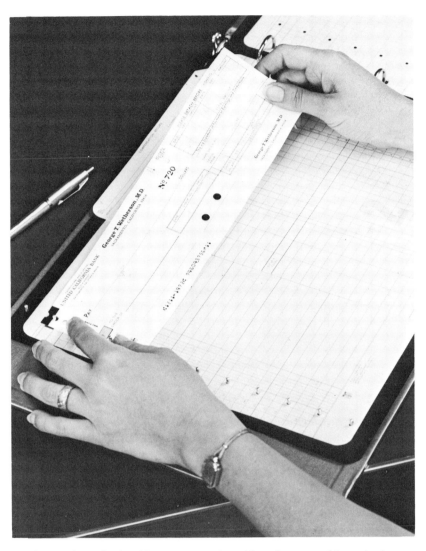

A time-saving checkwriting system. An aide who uses this write-it-once disbursements stationery can pay the month's bills in jigtime. The checks, specially designed, have carbon strips on their backs—so there's no need for stubs. Entries are made on the disbursement journal through the carbon strips, eliminating a big posting chore. Payroll data slips explain deductions and eliminate the posting of separate earnings records. Finally, a ring binder with built-in guide pins holds checks and journal sheets in register.

¶ She records the amount of a deposit on the next unused check stub.

¶ Finally, she brings you the checkbook with the checks still in it, along with all invoices, premium notices, and other supporting documents. You verify that the checks agree with these and with the stubs, and sign. Next in line: the mailman.

As you'd guess from those recommendations, I advise never signing a blank check. If you're going on a trip and know that certain payments will fall due while you're away—your aide's pay, for example—have the checks made out before you leave, with the actual amounts written in. Sign them, and tell your aide to hold them for issue on the proper dates.

Once each month your bank will report to you on the status of your account. It will also return to you, duly canceled, all the checks it has cleared against your account since the last report. As soon as this *bank statement* arrives, it should be reconciled with your checkbook. That means you should verify that your *bank balance* agrees with your *checkbook balance.* Here's the simplest way to do that:

1. Arrange the canceled checks in numerical order.

2. Note, from the gaps in the numbering, which ones are missing. These haven't cleared the bank. The money they represent is still in your account. From your checkbook stubs jot down the amounts of the uncleared checks and total them.

3. Verify, from the canceled checks, that the bank has correctly recorded the amount of each cleared check and that it hasn't thrown in one drawn by some other customer. Verify, from your aide's duplicate deposit slips, that the bank has all your deposits down correctly. *Banks do goof.*

4. Subtract the total of the uncleared checks from the stated bank balance. This is your *adjusted bank balance.*

5. Note, from the bank statement, any service charges or other withdrawals from your account not represented by a check. You might, for example, have signed a standing draft for your rent, or your aide may have ordered a new checkbook and told the bank to

Check No. 1

JOHN FRANKLIN MACDERMOTT, M.D.
13071 SOUTH STREET
SOUTHBROOK, N.H.

No. 1
SOUTHBROOK, N.H. October 27, 19 67

PAY TO THE ORDER OF ————MARY R. HAWES———— $ 123.31

————ONE HUNDRED TWENTY THREE & 31/100 only———— DOLLARS

For: Salary $150.00
Less Soc. Sec. 4.69
Fed. WH 22.00   26.69

THE CITIZENS BANK AND TRUST COMPANY
SOUTHBROOK, N.H.   66-439
66-439   ⑈⑈⑈⑈⑈

J.F. MacDermott, M.D.

Check No. 2

JOHN FRANKLIN MACDERMOTT, M.D.
13071 SOUTH STREET
SOUTHBROOK, N.H.

No. 2
SOUTHBROOK, N.H. October 27, 19 67

PAY TO THE ORDER OF ————NINETY SEVEN & 16/100 only———— $ 97.16

DOLLARS
ETHLCOS DRUG COMPANY

For: As per statement for Drugs and Supplies

THE CITIZENS BANK AND TRUST COMPANY
SOUTHBROOK, N.H.   66-439

J.F. MacDermott, M.D.

Check No. 3

JOHN FRANKLIN MACDERMOTT, M.D.
13071 SOUTH STREET
SOUTHBROOK, N.H.

No. 3
SOUTHBROOK, N.H. October 27, 19 67

PAY TO THE ORDER OF ————RUSHINGTON COUNTY MEDICAL SOCIETY———— $ 125.00

————ONE HUNDRED TWENTY FIVE & NO/100 only———— DOLLARS

For: Annual dues for 1967

THE CITIZENS BANK AND TRUST COMPANY
SOUTHBROOK, N.H.   66-439

J.F. MacDermott, M.D.

Register

DEPOSITS	NUMBER	DATE			CHECKS
123 45	1	October 27 1967			
		ORDER OF Mary R. Hawes	150.00		
		For Salary	Less Soc. Sec. 4.69 Fed. WH 22.00	26.69	123 31
		Detail Deposit October 27 1967	393 50		
393 50	TOTAL DEPOSIT		393 50		
	2	October 27 1967			
		ORDER OF Ethicos Drug Company			97 16
		For Drugs + Supplies			
		Detail Deposit ___ 19			
	TOTAL DEPOSIT				
	3	October 27 1967			
		ORDER OF Rushington County Medical Sc.			125 00
		For Annual Dues for 1967			
		Convention, Dues + Journals	345 47		
		TOTAL CHECKS	345 47		
	TOTAL DEPOSITS 516 95		345.47		
		Bank Balance 171 48			

A good, standard checkbook is this three-to-a-page book. It serves most practices well, and any bank can supply it. Ask that the numbers be printed serially. To help spot forgeries, make sure the name printed on the checks differs slightly from the signature you'll actually sign. Here, Dr. MacDermott's full name is printed on the check, but he customarily uses only his initials in the signature.

debit the account. Subtract these no-check withdrawals from your checkbook balance. Now you have the figure for your *adjusted checkbook balance.*

6. Compare the two adjusted balances. They should tally. If not, don't panic. You might have done your sums wrong. Do it over, looking for mistakes in your arithmetic. If the balances are still different, check your aide's arithmetic. If it looks right, but the balances don't, call your aide in. If she can't explain the difference, pick up the phone. Your accountant is the next man up.

Do I hear you saying: "I'm not going to do all that?" Well, I know only a dozen or so doctors who score a perfect mark. The others cross their fingers and leave the whole business of check writing and bank statement reconciliation to their aides.

I'll go along with that—*if* you'll have your accountant check closely at least twice a year. Leaving your money-exit wide open and uninspected for more than six months is bad, bad management indeed.

32

*Balanced books
will keep you steady*

Down in the Kentucky bluegrass country there's a crusty old general practitioner who has some pretty strong views on bookkeeping. He rates it the way Henry Ford rated history. "It's bunk," he snorts. He goes on to explain that he doesn't need "any damned fancy books to tell me where I stand. I know what I'm worth—down to the dime." He does, too. But I can't recommend his all-in-my-own-head system of fiscal control. I think it's better to keep books. And I think double entry bookkeeping's the best way to keep books.

Justifying that opinion isn't the easiest of tasks, since there are management men and accountants who'll tell you that double entry bookkeeping isn't needed in a medical practice. Even the Internal Revenue Service, they'll point out, is satisfied with single entry books, and I've got to admit that's so. But I still hope *you* will adopt the double entry system of bookkeeping for your office, because I think you ought to keep books that will enable you to know more than just where your money comes from and where it goes. I think you should also know what you own, what you owe, and what you're worth.

That's what double entry bookkeeping is all about. As its name indicates, each financial transaction is recorded twice. One entry indicates how the transaction affects what you own; the other, how it affects what you owe. The difference between what you own and what you owe is what you're worth. Single entry bookkeeping calls

241

for only one entry per transaction, and it doesn't tell you what you're worth.

To grasp the principle of double entry, you need to know the meaning of three words: assets, capital, and liabilities. Your assets consist of all the things of monetary value that belong to you, whether or not you have fully paid for them. Those you own free and clear are your capital. Those you haven't yet paid for are your liabilities. And the difference between these figures is your net worth.

When your aide keeps double entry books for you, she'll need a cash receipts journal, a disbursements journal, income and expense

	DATE 19 68	EXPLANATION	PROF. BUSINESS DONE	PROF. CASH RECEIPTS	MISC. CASH RECEIPTS	BANK DEPOSITS	MISC. CASH EXPENDITURES	CREDITS TO PATIENTS ACCTS	
1	Apr. 1	Rent - Apt.	78 -	85 -	100 -	50 -	100 -	SAVINGS A/C# 574567	1
2									2
3	1	Int. S.N.B.	155 -	100 -		795	85 -	795 " "	3
4	1	Dividends	93 -	91 -	365 -	100 -	365 -	BROKERS A/C	4
5	5		210 -	340 -		340 -			5
6	6		205 -	565 -		565 -			6
7									7
8	8		198 50	410 -		410 -			8
9	9		89 -	50 -		50 -			9
10	10		213 50	155 50					10
11	11		197 -	167 -		155 50			11
12	12		154 50	160 -		167 -			12
13	13		235 -	135 -		160 -			13
14									14
15	15		201 50	198 -		135 -			15
16	16		77 50	98 -		198 -			16
17	17		310	219 50		99 -			17
18	18		177	189 50		219 50			18
19	19		185 -	176 -		176 -			19
20	20		219 50	212 50		212 50			20
21									21
22	22		140 -	77 50		189 50			22
23	23		94 -	69 -					23
24	24		229 -	169 -		146 50			24
25	25		197 50	143 -		169 -			25
26	26		167	139 -		143 -			26
27	27		159 -	104 -		139 -			27
28									28
29	29		210	69 -		104 -			29
30	30		63	87 -		69 -			30
31									31
		TOTAL	4257 50	4210 50	472 95	4173 50	472 95		

A cash receipts journal shows the daily totals of the money that comes into the office. It also shows what happened to the money. The column "Prof. Business Done" serves as a memo of the day's total dollar value of services performed—useful in comparing charges with collections.

242

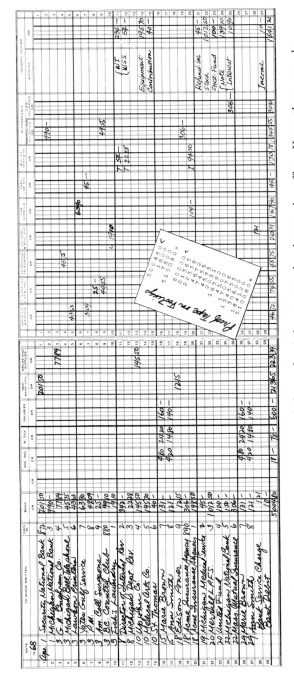

A cash disbursements journal shows the daily totals of the money that leaves the office. Here, there are also columns showing the amounts deposited for Social Security and withholding taxes, as well as the deposits to the office accounts. Keeping this journal and the cash receipts journal is aide's work.

243

What a balance sheet looks like

Its purpose is to sum up how much you're worth, and it's a product of double entry bookkeeping. The form may vary slightly from one accounting firm to another, but this is a reasonably typical appearance:

A. B. CEDY, M.D.

BALANCE SHEET, DECEMBER 31

ASSETS:

Cash on hand		$ 210.00
Petty cash		30.00
Cash in banks		
Office account		7,615.15
Savings account		2,513.83
Personal account		1,000.00
Government securities at cost		1,875.00
Other securities at cost		12,617.50
Broker's account		317.16
Office equipment at cost	$5,718.10	
Less depreciation	2,307.05	3,411.05
Office leasehold improvements		
At cost	$790.00	
Less depreciation	507.50	282.50
Automobiles at cost	$4,916.10	
Less depreciation	2,409.12	2,506.98
Residence plus improvements at cost		25,709.78
Other real estate (building lot)		3,500.00
		$61,588.95

LIABILITIES:

Accrued payroll taxes		
Withholding and Social Security	$ 256.10	
Federal and state income taxes	1,500.00	
Mortgage payable (residence)	7,618.10	
Note payable (automobile)	1,217.94	10,592.14
CAPITAL (Net Worth)		50,996.81
TOTAL LIABILITIES AND CAPITAL		$61,588.95

244

ledgers, and ledgers for assets and liabilities. The cash receipts journal is a blow-by-blow record of what comes in; the disbursements journal, of what goes out. The income and expense ledgers classify these incomings and outgoings in categories, ready for recording their effect on what you own and what you owe. Finally, the ledgers for assets and liabilities taken together produce what is known as a balance sheet. The balance sheet shows you what you're worth.

The aide who knows her bookkeeping realizes that every finan-

---

Where expenses go in the disbursements journal

The journal can contain only a limited number of columns, so the disbursements must be grouped under general headings. Many accounting and professional management firms supply their clients with a list of uniform classifications as an office reference. This condensed list contains the more common items of expense.

Salaries. All amounts subject to withholding and Social Security taxes and all other amounts paid to persons performing services other than bona fide contractors.

Rent. Office rent, utilities, minor repairs, painting.

Drugs and supplies. Drugs, medical supplies, small instruments, repairs to professional equipment.

Stationery and postage. Stationery, printing, office supplies, stamps.

Conventions, dues, and journals. Travel and other convention expenses, professional dues, professional books and journals, magazines for patients, promotional expenses.

Car expense. Fuel, lubrication, washing, repairs, tires, license, insurance, garage, parking.

Business interest, taxes, and insurance. Interest on business loans, Social Security, taxes, state unemployment taxes, state business taxes, real-estate and personal property taxes on professional property, premium payments on professional liability and office insurances.

General ledger. Refunds to patients, withheld taxes remitted to government agencies, new depreciable equipment, contributions, stock purchases, interest payments on personal loans, payments of principal on business loans and mortgages.

---

cial transaction she records affects equally both sides of the book-keeping equation, own versus owe. And since every entry does affect both sides of the equation, it requires two ledger entries—double entry.

There's no need, however, for your aide to keep double entry books all by herself. It's a sensible division of labor to have her keep the journals while your accountant keeps the ledgers. You needn't make any of the entries yourself. But you should be sufficiently familiar with them to be sure that your books are being properly kept. For a start, you should make it your business to know whether your income's being correctly recorded. Thus you should know at least this much:

¶ Your daybook should show the date, source, and amount of every dollar that comes in.

¶ Every day, your aide should post the daybook totals to her cash receipts journal. The journal sheet shown on page 242 shows you what a month's entries should look like.

¶ Your aide should show your income from fees separately from other income.

¶ The source of nonfee income needs to be identified. If you rent out some rooms over your office as an apartment, for instance, your aide should isolate the tenant's payments from your patients' payments.

¶ The cash receipts journal should show how the receipts are disposed of—i.e., how much your aide deposits in your office bank account each day and how much she hands to you for current use.

Next, you should know at least this much about the recording of office expenses:

¶ Your outlays on practice expenses should be recorded by your aide in her cash disbursements journal daily. The specimen sheet on page 243 shows you what this journal looks like. In it, she records every check she writes. You pay *all* your business bills by check, remember.

When your accountant is satisfied that the figures in your aide's

246

journals are accurate, he can post the month's totals to his ledgers and get out a balance sheet—a listing of your assets, capital, and liabilities, telling you how much you're worth. There's a specimen balance sheet on page 244.

Is it really so important to know how much you're worth? It is if your retirement planning and, for that matter, your short-term financial planning are to make good sense. It is if your lawyer is to have a chance of heading off some very expensive estate problems before they develop. And it is if you're to have any assurance that your practice finances are being handled properly.

Remember the old Kentucky G.P. I mentioned at the beginning of this chapter—the one who crustily told me he knew what he was worth, down to the dime? What he didn't know, I discovered, was that he should have been worth a lot more. For five years, out of every dime that came in, he'd gotten just nine cents. The 10 per cent had gone to an embezzling aide. If he'd kept "fancy" double entry books, his accountant could easily have spotted her surprisingly clumsy ways of stealing—and he could have done so very early in her career as a thief.

Now you know the reasons why I recommend double entry bookkeeping. Still feel that your understanding of the process is pretty foggy? Well, you needn't knock yourself out trying to understand it. Just ask your accountant to read through this chapter and fill you in on any details he thinks you need to digest. He's the man to teach you; bookkeeping is *his* subject. Mine is management, and I'm only saying here that it's good management to keep double entry books.

33

Overhead:
index to management
success

Let's face it: It costs plenty to be a private physician. Overhead takes about 40 cents of each dollar collected by most practitioners. That means a busy solo G.P., for instance, can expect to pay out at least $17,000 a year for professional expenses.

Is so much overhead good practice? It seems to be. Physicians have been spending at a similar clip for a long time. Medical Economics magazine has for years surveyed doctors' finances and the overhead percentages haven't changed much. Six of the 10 major groupings of M.D.s spend in the range of 38-42 per cent. The G.P. is at the top of that range, followed by the orthopedic surgeon, pediatrician, internist, OBG man, and ophthalmologist. General surgeons and radiologists spend a little less—about 35 per cent of gross practice income. The lowest percentages are reported, as you'd suspect, by psychiatrists (about 25 per cent) and anesthesiologists (about 20).

In calculating your own overhead, watch out you don't confuse expenses with payments. Management consultants' files are full of case histories of physicians who do so. For example, Dr. Neil Sandeman, a G.P. in a small Midwestern town, once told me that practice-connected expenses had eaten up $31,000 out of his previous year's $53,000 gross. That figured out as a whopping 59 per cent overhead. "How can I get it down to $20,000?" he asked me. "That would be around 40 per cent. I need to clip my spending by $10,000 a year at least."

I dug into the details. Trimming off expense fat in a half-dozen places, I showed him where he could cut $5,000 from his annual payout.

"Where do we look for the other $5,000 or so?" he asked.

"No problem," I told him. "You really didn't spend that much more for expenses last year. What you actually did was put $6,000 into an X-ray machine. But the machine is an asset; in fact, today it's worth $5,400, or nine-tenths of what you paid for it. Only the $600 loss in value is expense. I figure that, with the savings you've just agreed to, your outlay for the next 12 months will be $20,600, near enough to your 40 per cent."

Cutting expenses happened to make sense for him, but not for many other practitioners—the ones who could earn more by spending more. Some years ago, for instance, I persuaded Dr. Sam Blackmon, a Georgia internist, that he needed to double his practice costs—yes, *double*. Dr. Blackmon had cheese-pared his way to a take-home of $18,000 out of a $24,000 gross. But after 12 months of higher spending—a bigger office, an extra nurse, more equipment, new medical and business records—he took home $24,000, or the exact amount of his previous gross. A year later his net went to $30,000, a jump of two-thirds over the reward of his cheese-paring days. "I was proud of my 25 per cent overhead," he says today. "But I soon found out that I'd carried my scrimping too far."

Dr. Blackmon is hardly the only doctor to have discovered that it doesn't pay to pare costs too closely. I remember one who wrote in Medical Economics about how he slashed his spending to the bone. By switching to the smallest imported auto on the market, he halved his annual professional car costs. After firing his accountant, he turned his bookkeeping over to his wife. After recalling all his past-due accounts from a collection agency, he divided the dunning chores between his wife and a friendly attorney. He was his own janitor. And he laundered the office linen himself. His stop-the-waste drive netted $2,500 in reduced overhead the first year.

Keeping tabs on your monthly operating expenses

Young Dr. Green, a general practitioner, has been in private practice a little less than two years, yet financially he's already doing just fine. But his overhead percentage (36.7%) is below average for solo G.P.s. (42%), so if he's to do much better he may need to start reinvesting more money in his practice—for instance, by taking on a full-time medical assistant. Right now he has only part-time help. Compare your figures with Dr. Green's:

	Dr. Green's figures		Your figures	
	Latest month	*Last 12 months*	*Latest month*	*Last 12 months*
Total charges	$3,145.00	$32,693.30	___	___
Percentage collected		95.8%		___
Gross practice income	$3,397.40	$31,320.18	___	___
Practice expenses:				
Payroll	$200.00	$2,400.00	___	___
Rent, maintenance, utilities	150.00	1,800.00	___	___
Drugs and supplies	53.76	1,174.72	___	___
Office supplies and postage	42.17	530.64	___	___
Conventions, dues, journals	45.00	327.29	___	___
Telephone	39.69	461.82	___	___
Laundry and miscellaneous	20.33	225.86	___	___
Professional car	57.84	714.00	___	___
Fees, lab., etc.	35.00	413.88	___	___
Depreciation on equipment	133.00	1,600.00	___	___
Business interest, taxes and insurance	150.79	1,840.50	___	___
Total professional expense	$927.58	$11,488.71	___	___
Net practice income	$2,469.82	$19,831.47	___	___
Overhead percentage		36.7%		___

251

There's a sequel to his story, though. In another article three years later, he reported that he'd backslid. Once more he had a big car, a collection agency, a janitor, and a laundry service. He confessed he'd found some "splendid ways to save money. If you can afford to. I no longer can. My time has become too valuable."

Other economy-minded physicians have asked me about the feasibility of analyzing their practice costs in detail in the hope of identifying some sensible ways to save. Internist Melvin Cutler, for one, showed me this line on a brochure plugging a dictating machine: "Do you know that in a modern business office it costs $2 to write even a short letter?"

"I wonder what it costs *me* to write a letter," said Dr. Cutler. "Or to take a patient's history, do a physical examination, write a prescription, give an injection. If business firms can figure out their exact costs, we doctors ought to be able to do it."

It's all but impossible to figure such costs exactly, I told him, but I did give him a formula for estimating the cost of each minute his office was open. "Start with your professional expenses for a full year, as shown on your last income tax return," I said. "Add a minimum salary for yourself. Then add some interest on the cost of your medical education—say, 6 per cent. Divide the resulting total by the time—in minutes—your office is open in a typical year. The answer is your office cost-per-minute." Dr. Cutler's cost worked out at 28 cents. His office cost-per-hour was $16.66. His is a fairly typical internal medicine practice.

"Interesting," he said after we'd done all the arithmetic, "but I guess what I really need to know is: How do I go about keeping costs down?" I suspect that's your question, too. Well, being your own janitor and washerwoman is false economy, as we've seen. Here are three ways to achieve true economy:

Keep informed. Make sure your aide—or your accountant or management consultant—gives you, at the end of each month, an operating statement showing your expenses in detail for the month and the year to date. There's a specimen of such a statement on page 251.

252

Don't be content merely to compare this month's outgo with last month's. Check it against the corresponding month last year. Then compare the year-to-date with the previous year-to-date—and with the year before that. If any figure has taken a leap that surprises you, dig out the reason for the jump.

Watch the payroll. Out of every dollar of the typical physician's practice expenses, the payroll takes 40 to 50 cents. So test your payroll two ways: If it adds up to more than 50 per cent of your total overhead, or more than 20 per cent of your gross income from practice, there's a case for review.

I'm speaking, of course, about an established practice. For a beginning doctor, the payroll will almost certainly go over both of those marks for a while. That's as it should be.

Watch the "small" expenses, too. "A wheen o' mickles mak's a muckle," says the Scottish proverb, and truer words were never spoken. The principal expenses of medical practice—payroll, rent, medical supplies, auto costs, and insurance—aren't easy to cut. But about one-fourth of all practice costs are for small supplies for the office, magazine subscriptions, organization dues, convention expenses, long distance phone calls, and the like. It's in this miscellaneous area that unnecessary expense is most liable to occur.

To get your money's worth, use more than one office supply firm; for competitive pricing, pit them against each other for typewriter ribbons, adding machine tape, etc., and buy such items in quantity. Subscribe to magazines for three years rather than one year at a time. Drop out of professional organizations in which you have no real interest. Don't stay three days at a convention if the section for your specialty meets on only one day. Don't talk four minutes when you're paying for a phone call if you can say what you have to say in three minutes; the extra minute can double the cost of the call.

Keeping a wary eye on such seemingly trifling expenses can put $500 to $1,000 a year back in the net income column of your operating statement. True economy, however, isn't achieved merely by not spending. It's the result of *wise* spending. For example:

¶ A Michigan internist's net jumped $6,000 in a single year when he moved from a cramped $200-a-month office to spacious quarters costing $500 a month.

¶ A North Carolina G.P. showed a net gain of $4,000 the first year he hired a part-time technician to do work he and his nurse had previously done between them.

¶ An Illinois two-man partnership switched from permanent to' disposable supplies of various kinds—linens, syringes, etc. They paid more for the throwaway items, but the resulting savings in time enabled them to recoup the extra cost several times over.

Sum it up this way: The only guarantee that overhead will stay *down* percentagewise is to keep gross income *up*. Thus the key question to ask when considering an addition to your overhead is: What will this do for my gross? If, with an existing 40 per cent overhead, you can see $2.50 of added income for each $1 of contemplated new expense, you can go ahead knowing your overhead will remain pegged at the same level.

34

Raising the wherewithal

You're looking at the floor plan of your new office. Beside you is a pile of equipment catalogs and furniture brochures, with check marks in the margins. "With this much space and all this equipment," you tell yourself, "I'll really have myself a practice!" Then a thought strikes you, and everything clouds over. *"Where'll I get the money?"*

If you have as much nerve as five medical students in Washington, D.C., displayed some years ago, the clouds won't stay around long. "When we're through with this grind," they promised each other, "we'll go in practice together in our own clinic." Their dream came true. Two years after making their vow, the five moved into a 45-room, fully equipped clinic. All it took was $170,000—of which only $2,000 was their own. They borrowed the remaining $168,000.

Few doctors start anywhere near that big. At the other extreme is the North Carolina anesthesiologist who invested just $30. He spent it on a second-hand desk and a card file. An Oregon G.P. joining a partnership spent $50—on a bag. Most beginning doctors spend more than that to get started in private practice. The table on page 257 indicates that the typical amount needed these days by young doctors is in the neighborhood of $9,000. Naturally, a young solo doctor keeps adding to his equipment as his earnings make the improvements feasible. So for an older established physician, an investment of between $10,000 and $20,000 is run-of-the-mill.

A doctor who eventually builds an office, alone or with others, may end up with an investment of $50,000 or even $100,000.

Much of the capital, for a young doctor or old, must come from borrowed funds. It's often possible for a doctor's family to do some of the lending. In fact, about half of all young physicians get some financial aid from their relatives. If that other half includes you, remember that partly because of medical ethics, these three standard methods of raising business funds are *not* available to you and your medical practice:

¶ You can't form a company and offer shares in yourself to the general public.

¶ You can't go partners with an investor who shares the profits without doing any of the work.

¶ You can't raise money on your expectation of future profits.

How, then, do you get the capital you need? You borrow it, with or without security.

Fortunately, lenders will tend to consider you a good personal credit risk. In a university survey a few years ago, doctors were rated 89.3 per cent likely to repay a loan. If you used a charge account in the past few years and paid the bills promptly, your local credit bureau (there are more than 2,000 bureaus in the U.S.) will rate you even higher than that. And with a good credit bureau rating, you can shop around for your loan. After all, lenders are looking for good risks all the time.

Let's say you need exactly the $8,641 listed in the table on page 257. Of that amount, you need $5,425 in cash to support your practice and your family till the practice can support both. Start by taking a risk; cut down your cash requirement to an even $5,000.

Now, aside from relatives or friends, where can you go to borrow that much money? Let's review the more likely possibilities:

A commercial bank. There are about 14,000 commercial banks in the U.S., and they all lend money. They prefer, of course, to lend against adequate security. But many commercial banks will make character loans to a good risk. As we've seen already, doctors—even new doctors—are rated as good risks. Some commercial

How much cash will you need to start practice?

The figures listed below are my own current estimates, based on the experiences of doctors I know who recently entered private practice. Not included: the costs of a medical license and a professional car.

	Typical expenses	Your expenses
Equipment and furnishings:		
10% down payment	$ 400	_____
12 monthly payments totaling	1,416	_____
Subtotal	$1,816	_____
Incidental cash expenditures:		
Medical and office supplies, stationery, bag, shingle, etc.	$300	_____
Moving	250	_____
Medical society dues	125	_____
Business insurance (including professional and personal liability, auto, fire, theft)	350	_____
Redecorating office (including special electrical and plumbing work)	500	_____
New clothing	300	_____
Subtotal	$1,825	_____
Professional expenses:		
Figure three months' worth totaling	1,500	_____
Living expenses:		
Figure six months' worth totaling	3,000	_____
Emergency and miscellaneous	500	_____
GRAND TOTAL	$8,641	_____

banks make character loans only to their regular customers. So go first to the bank where you keep or intend to keep your account.

An industrial bank. There are about 200 industrial banks in the U.S. There used to be more, but most have turned themselves into commercial banks. Traditionally, the industrial bank's specialty is lending to customers against future deposits; when the customer's deposits equal his loan, he's all square. Today, though, many such banks require no "thrift accounts"; they lend much the same as the commercial banks do. For instance, the industrial banks make character loans to selected risks. They'd probably classify you as a good risk. But, as you can see, there aren't many industrial banks around.

An industrial loan company. State laws allow these companies to lend more money for longer periods than small loan companies in the same states may lend. In consequence, many companies wear two hats: They're chartered as industrial loan *and* small loan companies. Practically all their loans are character loans. But they cost plenty, interestwise.

A small loan company. More than 2,000 of these companies conduct their lending business through more than 20,000 offices. As their name implies, they lend small sums only. Also, they lend their money for short periods of time. The amount of money they're permitted to lend varies from state to state. In some, they may lend one individual only $1,000 or $1,500; in others, $5,000 or $7,500. Small loan companies specialize in lending amounts that banks don't want to bother with, to borrowers banks don't want to be bothered with. And their prices can be astronomical.

The Small Business Administration. This Government agency will lend money to a physician who can meet its somewhat stringent requirements. One of them is that you'll have to try every reasonable commercial source first, and fail. If you're accepted by the S.B.A., you'll have to put up collateral. However, the S.B.A. is one lender that might let you have more cash than your collateral's worth, if you can make a strong character impression on the department's loan officer.

All in all, your best bet for a loan is a commercial bank. Don't be discouraged by the first turndown you get. "There are 15 banks in my city," says a North Carolina G.P. who refused to take No for an answer. "The first 14 turned me down, but the 15th came through."

A commercial bank will invariably make the loan you're seeking if you can put up acceptable collateral or if you bring along someone who'll put up collateral for you. If you can't meet the collateral requirements, your chances of getting the full $5,000 will dwindle. That doesn't mean they'll vanish. The banker might consider a smaller loan against what he calls "low-grade collateral." For example:

¶ On a clear title to an automobile under two years old, a commercial banker will normally lend up to two-thirds of the car's current resale value. On an older car, he'll offer less.

¶ The commercial banker might accept a chattel mortgage on your home furnishings. Usually, though, he won't volunteer to do so. He knows from experience that the goods, if you forfeit them, will be virtually unsalable. But if *you* make the suggestion, he just might take the risk.

Generally speaking, commercial banks try to keep a character loan smaller then the full amount the borrower wants. And they almost always fix an early repayment date. Bank examiners are highly critical of loan officers who lend substantial sums for long terms without security.

What does a commercial bank regard as adequate collateral for a loan? The loan officer will cheerfully dust off a chair for you if you can offer him:

¶ A savings account held with his bank, equal in amount to your loan. Don't assume, as some doctors do, that this amounts to borrowing your own money. *Your* money is still right there in the savings account, earning interest. True, it doesn't earn enough to pay the loan interest. But, somehow, money taken out of a savings account has a habit of staying out. A loan *has* to be repaid.

¶ A life insurance policy with a cash surrender value slightly

259

above the amount you want to borrow. You may wonder, "Why shouldn't I simply cash in the policy?" Borrowing against it is definitely better. If you surrender it, you'll also surrender some valuable rights, chief of which is the right to the premium rate that applied to your age when you bought the policy. You can buy new insurance when your financial squeeze is over, of course—but you won't get it at the old low price. So hold onto your policy, even though you pledge it for everything it's worth.

The catch in a cash-value loan is that you'll never be pressed to repay it. If you make one, set up a repayment schedule and stick to it. Banks, of course, aren't the only institutions that will lend money against life insurance policies. Any insurance company will lend up to 95 per cent of the full cash surrender value of any policy it has issued. And if your G.I. policy has a cash value, the Government will lend you money on it.

¶ Stocks or bonds. Many commercial banks will lend 30 to 50 per cent of the current market value of over-the-counter stocks; up to 70 per cent on stocks listed on a major exchange; 70 to 90 per cent on well-rated bonds. Bear in mind that if, while your loan is still outstanding, their market value takes a dive, the bank will call for more collateral.

¶ Real estate to which you hold a clear title, provided its appraised value is substantially more than the amount of the loan.

Can you get loans from a bank and from another lender simultaneously? You can. Having other loans outstanding is no bar to a loan request. Example: Dr. Sparco's bank loaned him $3,000 on a life insurance policy. He needed $2,000 more, but he had no more high-grade collateral. In his state, the maximum small loan is $1,000. One small loan company accepted another doctor as co-maker of Dr. Sparco's $1,000 note. Another company advanced Dr. Sparco $1,000, taking a chattel mortgage on his home furnishings.

When you turn to a second or third lender, though, you must disclose the loans you've already obtained. However, you don't have to go back to an earlier lender to report additional borrowings. (Not that they won't learn about them; the local credit reporting system takes care of that.)

How much will it cost to borrow $5,000? That depends in part on the kind of loan you get. These are the four main kinds:

1. Simple interest loan. Figuring the cost of such a loan is relatively easy, since simple interest is true interest. It's a percentage of the amount you borrow, expressed as an annual rate. If you borrow $5,000 from a bank at 6 per cent simple interest, you pay the bank $300 a year for the loan as long as you retain the principal sum.

Here's a handy formula for figuring the cost of any simple interest loan:

$$R \times A \times P = I$$

R is the percentage you agree to pay for each period you keep the money. A is the money itself. P is the number of periods you keep it. I is what you want to know—the total amount of interest you pay over the entire term of the loan.

Thus, borrowing $1,000 at 6 per cent for three years, you pay a total of $180 in interest. At 5 per cent, you pay $150. It's worth wearing out some shoe leather to get this best type of loan at the best price you can find. But be sure you have your collateral with you.

2. Add-on installment loan. Here the lender applies a simple interest rate to the loan, but he doesn't let you keep all the money for the full term. You must repay in installments, the last installment falling due at the end of the term. If the installments fall due monthly, the true annual interest rate is nearly twice the simple interest rate he quotes you.

Figure the true interest rate on an add-on installment loan this way:

$$\frac{2\,PC}{A\,(N+1)} = R$$

P is the number of payments you make in one year. C is the quoted interest rate. A is the amount of the loan. N is the total number of payments you'll make. R is the true interest rate.

Borrowing $1,000 for 12 months at 6 per cent add-on, and re-paying in monthly installments, the true interest rate is 11 per cent. Next to simple interest, this is the cheapest way of borrowing cash —but don't keep it any longer than you must. Two years is the sensible limit.

3. Discount loan. Here the lender deducts the simple interest from the sum you're borrowing, and he gives you the change. You'll repay by installments. A 6 per cent discount loan of $1,000, though, isn't the same thing as a 6 per cent add-on loan of $940. To borrow $1,000 for 12 months at 6 per cent discount, repaying in monthly installments, costs 11.8 per cent in true interest. The lender also makes an extra smidgen by having your $60 interest payment in his possession for the entire period. If you can't get a simple interest or an add-on loan, this is one you can live with if the term's short—say, two years.

4. Unpaid balance installment loan. Small loan companies use the unpaid-balance method. The interest charge for each upcoming period is figured on what you owe after paying the previous install-ment. Since each payment reduces the outstanding principal, you pay interest on a smaller amount each time. Don't look for a 6 per cent annual rate on unpaid-balance loans. Indeed, don't expect to be quoted an annual rate at all. It's the custom to quote such loans by the month. To get the true annual rate, multiply the monthly rate by 12. Thus 1 per cent per month is 12 per cent per year, 2 per cent per month is 24 per cent per year, and so on.

State laws fix the interest rates chargeable on unpaid-balance loans. In one state, for example, 3½ per cent per month can be charged on the first $150 of an unpaid-balance loan repayable in 12 monthly installments. That's a true annual rate of 42 per cent. So steer clear of these monthly interest loans if you possibly can; their price, as you see, can be prohibitive. It takes a special set of circumstances to make them worthwhile.

"I paid 2 per cent per month on a $1,000 loan for a year," a South Carolina doctor who had the special circumstances once told me, "and I came out ahead. I pledged everything I had on other loans, except one stock I was afraid to hock in case the bank sold me out. During the year, the stock hit a low that might have forced the bank to sell. Then it staged a comeback. By the end of the year, it had gained many times the amount of interest I paid on my loan."

You can borrow to buy things without handling any actual cash. How? Buy now and pay later. In the table on page 257, you'll see the figure $1,816. It represents borrowed goods. It's the first-year cost to a young doctor of $4,000 worth of furnishings and equipment for his office. His suppliers, in effect, lent him the money to buy their goods. Almost all suppliers willingly do so. By doing it, they sell more goods than they otherwise could. Sometimes their profit from extending credit exceeds the mark-up on the actual goods. According to The Wall Street Journal, 60 per cent of the per-car profit made by new-car dealers in the first three months of one recent year came from credit charges—and only 40 per cent from the sale of the cars!

It's understandable that doctors, especially new doctors, should be heavy users of credit buying plans. As I've explained, cash lenders take a poor view of goods as collateral. In credit buying, the goods are the *only* collateral.

A special loan plan to consider

The National Association of Residents and Interns, Inc., of New York City, offers its members an all-in plan for borrowing and buying all it takes to start a private practice in any of the 50 states—and to feed the family while waiting for paying patients to appear.

Says a N.A.R.I. spokesman: "The plan offers a young physician cash to use for office equipment and furnishings, a home, an automobile, office operating expenses, and domestic living expenses. Cash advances go as high as $5,000 for up to five years. Equipment (at 20 per cent off list prices) is financed up to $20,000 for up to seven years. There's no ceiling on the cost of office and home improvements, and they're financed on a long-term basis."

Goods are bought on credit in these four principal ways:

1. The charge account. Generally, a conventional charge account gives you one month's free credit.

2. The short-term credit account. This is merely an extension of the conventional charge account. Instead of getting one month's free credit, you get it for three months. In most instances, though, the price of goods bought that way is higher, though the extra cost may not be obvious.

3. The installment credit contract. More people—including doctors—buy goods this way than any other. You sign an agreement to pay for the goods, plus a credit charge, by a specified number of equal installments, usually monthly. The agreement is actually a promissory note; returning the goods won't cancel it. Since a promissory note is a negotiable instrument, the supplier of the goods can sell it, and he usually does. So you may end up owing the money to a finance company you never heard of.

An equipment firm's credit buying plan

Credit buying plans are many and varied. But to give you an idea of what to expect, here's a rundown on what one leading equipment firm offers:

Goods available: Professional equipment and office furniture of any make, provided one major item from the equipment firm's own catalog is included.

Credit limit: $5,000 if one major item of the firm's equipment is included in the purchase; higher if the firm's goods make up 70 per cent of purchase.

Down payment: None.

Credit charge: 6 per cent per year, add-on.

Payment period: Up to six years.

Payments: Under six years, in equal monthly installments. For six-year contracts only, lower payments (totaling 10 per cent of the contract) for the first year, higher payments (totaling 18 per cent of the contract) for each of the following five years.

Fire and life insurance: Free, subject to a physical examination for life insurance on a physician aged 61 or over.

---

4. The revolving credit account. This type of credit plan bids fair to oust all rivals. It includes a charge account feature: Pay your bill in 30 days, and there's no charge for the credit. After that, your revolving credit takes over. If you plan to spend, say, $600, on reception room furnishings, the furniture store may agree to accept six monthly payments of $100, plus interest. In three months you'll have paid $300 off the principal and still owe $300. But your revolving credit ceiling is $600, so now you can buy another $300 worth of goods.

Is credit buying more expensive than borrowing cash? Except for small loan company loans, Yes. Your biggest headache is finding out how much more. The interest you pay on credit purchases is often disguised. It's called a service charge, a carrying charge, a recording fee. Under any name, it's always interest.

To find out the true cost of a credit purchase, find out the cash price of what you're buying. You'll have to ask for it. The price tag on the article may be the credit price. To know the full cost of the credit, count everything above the cash price, regardless of the name the vendor gives to any extra charge. Then deduct your down payment from the credit price. Now use this formula:

$$\frac{2\,PC}{A\,(N+1)} = R$$

P is the number of payments in one year. C is the difference between the credit price and cash price, less your down payment. A is the credit price, less your down payment. N is the total number of payments you'll make. R, the answer, is the true interest rate.

For revolving credit, the true interest rate is the quoted monthly rate multiplied by 12. The commonest monthly rate is 1½ per cent, which works out to 18 per cent per year.

The price of borrowed cash is almost invariably cheaper than the cost of borrowed goods. But either way, don't hesitate to borrow what you're sure you can repay. Just don't pay more for it than you have to.

Section

II

Sizing up your practice

The main purpose of this book is to steer a doctor up the road toward better practice management. The book's main section, just completed, does that.

But let's not stop there. I'd like to accompany you along that road—with ideas and guidance meant to serve you well into your career as a private practitioner. Naturally, I'll address you not as a youngster but as an experienced practitioner—a busy doctor with a thriving practice who, if he's typical, has let some harmful practice-management problems creep up on him. That kind of a physician usually needs competent management help even more than he knows.

If you've just started out in private practice, the chances are that before long you'll be in the same fix yourself. So go ahead and read the pages that follow now. They'll serve as a useful review of the material you covered in Section I of this book, and they may help you head off some problems that are as yet only threatening.

If on the other hand, you've been in practice awhile, you probably suspect *or know* that you could use some management help—or you wouldn't be taking time out to read this book. So pick up a pencil, turn the page, and read on. For you, Section II should be even more useful than Section I.

35

Sizing up your rate of practice growth

As far as I've been able to discover, not more than one physician in 10 has ever submitted his practice to the critical inspection of a management consultant. For one thing, consultants are scarce. For another, many doctors still don't seem fully aware that they're actually managing a fair-sized business as well as practicing medicine. This basic lack of understanding is commonest among solo doctors and doctors practicing in small partnerships. Big groups usually hire full-time managers to run the business end of things. So it's the smaller practices that, in my experience, gain most from outside appraisal and advice.

In these nine short chapters that follow, I'll try to show you how to size up your own practice the way a management consultant would. Remember, I'll be talking with the solo and small partnership practices in mind. And I'll talk just as though I were seated on the other side of the desk from you. Much of what I'll be saying will be what you'd be told by any other experienced man in my field. We tend to think pretty much alike on the fundamentals of good practice management.

If you were to invite me to run an economic tape measure over your practice, I'd start by asking you a lot of questions. Then, with your permission, I'd ask your aides even more. More than 100 of my questions would come from an eight-page quiz sheet you would never see. I'd have it with me, but I wouldn't walk around your office with it in one hand and a ballpoint pen in the other, taking notes as I go. I know all the questions by heart, and I'd fill in the answers when you weren't around, perhaps in the plane on my way home. The intensive interrogation, plus an inspection of your entire setup, is what we management consultants call a practice survey.

In these chapters, I'll reproduce some key questions from my survey form. If you'll answer them as you read, you may never have to seek out a management consultant's phone number. I'll lead off with six questions that go to the heart of an important matter: the *kind* of practice you have.

Each question comes with six possible answers, drawn from an analysis of actual replies I've received from other doctors. Next to each set of replies is some interpretive comment—and the answer I got from an internist I'll call Dr. Longstreet. He told me, by the way, that he was anxious to build up his subspecialty: gastroenterology.

Circle your answers; they'll stimulate your thinking about possible weaknesses in your own practice. And keep an eye on Dr. Longstreet's answers. Your verdict on his practice may fit your own. Now let's go:

1. How long have you been in your present practice?

(A)'Started up this past year. (B) 1 to 3 years. (C) 3 to 5 years. (D) 5 to 10 years. (E) 10 to 20 years. (F) Over 20 years.

"Your present practice" in this question doesn't necessarily mean "at your present address." Dr. Longstreet, my internist friend, had just moved to a new professional building two miles from the older one in which he had rented space for six years. Correctly, he circled D.

If you're an A or B man and worried about the amount of white space in your appointment book, don't fret unduly. It's true that some new doctors get off to a flying start. I know a pediatrician who built up a full schedule in less than three months. He met a baby boom head on at a space center bristling with young scientists and technicians. But by and large, it still takes two to three years to launch a practice solidly.

If you're a C man whose practice is stubbornly sluggish, it's possible that your initial choice of location was less than perfect. Maybe you elected to buck some unusually stiff competition. Or perhaps the local people aren't yet educated to using service of the quality you're offering. One thing is sure: The longer you stay, the harder it will be for you to move. A well-timed decision to start over has bailed out many a physician.

Something's radically wrong, I'd say, with a lagging D practice. You ought to be firmly based after five years. An OBG man, for example, should be getting "repeats" by now. A general surgeon should be operating at least three mornings a week. An internist should be seeing familiar faces regularly. And a G.P., after five years of family doctoring, should be a little rushed.

E and F practices are more often too big than too small. The most common complaint I hear from these doctors is, "My practice runs me ragged." Often, the cure is to get more help. An extra secretary, nurse, or technician—or sometimes all three—can be the answer. Sometimes relinquishing a segment of the practice is the best solution. Many G.P.s, for example, have made their practices manageable by giving up OB work.

To sum up: If you're new in practice, be patient. If after five years you're doing badly, take a hard look at your location. If things look black after 10 years, go over every detail of your practice with a critical eye. And if your long-established practice has grown to be more than you can handle, choose between getting extra help and narrowing your field.

2. What's the growth record of your practice?

(A) Hardly noticeable. (B) Slow and steady. (C) Sporadic gains. (D) Fast, steady climb. (E) Good growth until recently; static now. (F) On the slide.

B is the answer I like best. There's something wrong with a medi-

269

cal practice that doesn't get bigger. But don't measure growth by your rising income tax bracket. Instead, count your new patients. You should see more new faces each year than you saw the year before—and most of the old faces should still be around.

If you circled A, ask yourself whether there's really enough work for you in the community—and try to answer honestly. You may be pitting yourself against a tough obstacle: a surplus of men in your field. Five years ago, I advised two internist-partners in a Southern city to break up and relocate separately. They broke up, but only one of them relocated. Today he's flourishing. His ex-partner, still at the old stand, is way behind.

If you're sure your problem isn't one of supply and demand, put *yourself* under the microscope. You must be doing *something* wrong. If you marked C, for instance, you may be getting new patients while too many old ones are leaving you—a situation that can often be remedied. A case-by-case analysis of the losses can reveal why patients drop a doctor. I'm thinking, for example, of a surgeon whose patients never sent their friends to him. As a surgeon, he was legendary. As a man, he was as cold as February. His aide recalled patient after patient who'd admired him for his skill and detested him for his iciness. It wasn't easy, but I told him. He still doesn't have a June disposition, but it has improved —and so have his patient referrals.

How much growth rates a D? In the early years, a 20 to 30 per cent increment isn't too much to expect; anything above that is abnormally fast. Later, a steady 5 to 10 per cent is more like the norm. As for the remaining answers, E is obviously a danger sign; and F—if undesired and due to unknown causes—is a disaster.

Internist Longstreet gave himself a B on this question. "But," he told me, "it should probably be a small b. I doubt whether my practice grew as much as 3 per cent last year."

3. How's your patient load as of now?

(A) Disappointingly small. (B) I'm busyish. (C) I could take

on more work, but not much. (D) I'm as busy as I want to be. (E) Too heavy; it bothers me. (F) If I don't get some help soon, I'll break down.

You'll probably think that D is the best answer. If you're a D man with less income than you'd like, it may not be. You'd better want to be busier, unless your low income is due to inadequate fees, poor collections, or sky-high expenses.

Answer A is obviously a sign of trouble, B only slightly less obviously so. C may well be the best answer; circle it if you're busy but not rushed, satisfied but not complacent.

If you circled E or F, ask yourself whether you're really giving your patients a fair deal. Most of the doctors I've met who had too many patients weren't doing a good enough job for any of them. So either get the help you need in your practice or start referring more patients to other physicians.

Dr. Longstreet chose B. But he felt that, after seven years in practice, he should have been able to answer C or D. So did I.

4. Who sends patients to you?

(A) Other patients, mostly. (B) Other physicians, mostly. (C) I take only patients referred by other doctors. (D) They drop in; mine is a neighborhood practice. (E) It used to be other physicians, but now it's other patients. (F) I've never really thought about it.

If you circled F, you'd better start thinking about it. Not long ago an ophthalmologist I know noticed a steep decline in the number of children coming to his office. He didn't know that his town's doctors were sending them to a new man 30 miles away. The new man's specialty: pediatric ophthalmology.

If you're a highly specialized surgeon, I hope you circled B. If you circled C and put in a full week's work, my hat's off to you. Answer A is good for a G.P.; D less good. A is all right for an internist, too, unless he prefers to subspecialize in hearts, chests, G.I. tracts, or whatnot. In that case, a fair number of his phone calls should come from professional brethren.

If you depend a lot on physician referrals and have reluctantly circled E, the cause is more likely traceable to something you haven't done than to something you have done. Most frequent offense: failing to keep up to date professionally. Next: neglecting to report back to your referring doctors.

Are you wondering about internist Longstreet? He circled A. And remember, he wanted to subspecialize in gastroenterology. His trouble: skimpy, delayed reports to physicians sending patients for diagnosis.

5. *How far do your patients come to see you?*

(A) From the immediate neighborhood. (B) From the neighborhood and its fringes. (C) From all over town. (D) Some old patients who have moved come a long way. (E) In my specialty, I draw from a large area. (F) I haven't studied up on this.

F is a big black mark. You're passing up an illuminating sidelight on your practice. If you're an E man, you're probably in one of the more arcane specialties. I have a neurologist-friend who gets referrals from doctors in seven states. A suggests to me that you're fairly new in town. For a five-year or ten-year man, A doesn't look too good. You should rate a B or a C.

D is fine. It speaks well for a doctor when old patients who have moved are willing to drive extra miles rather than switch to a new man.

Dr. Longstreet circled B. I asked him if he lost many patients via change of address. "Quite a few," he told me. "The people around here seem to move about a lot."

6. *What income groups do your patients belong to?*

(A) "Carriage trade." (B) Mostly well-fixed. (C) Middle-income people. (D) The low-income group predominates. (E) They come from all income groups. (F) Wait a minute, I'll ask my secretary.

The answer I get most often is E. To me, that's the same as F. You ought to have a more specific idea of the income group you serve. You can cater to it in some special ways. By gearing your practice to suit a particular group, you can make it easier for its members to choose you. This can cause you to lose patients from other groups, but that's a choice you'll have to make.

Dr. Longstreet circled D. If it strikes you that full-scale G.I. work-ups come high for that group, that makes two of us.

By now, I hope you've got some food for thought. Perhaps your patient load isn't what it should be. Maybe you think you ought to get more referrals. You may even be stewing about the number of former patients who, though they've moved, still don't live all that far away from your office.

Yet you *know* you're a good doctor. So you say, "What next, Professor?" I'll tell you what's next: a long, hard look at some specific parts of your practice, starting with its home base—your office. That's where we'll go in the next chapter.

36

Sizing up location, layout, and appearance of your office

O ne of the most important sections of the quiz sheet I use when I'm surveying a doctor's practice deals with his office. I mean his actual working space—its location, size, and layout. Most of the information I collect for this part of my survey comes, of course, from the inspection I make on my own when I visit him. I can see for myself, for example, whether his examining rooms are too small or whether there's a traffic snarl.

Other items, such as the amount of the rent and the cost of utilities, I get from the doctor's records. I judge the suitability of a given office for a given doctor by putting together my own observations and my client's answers to questions about his patient load and working habits.

To help you through this second phase in the do-it-yourself survey you're making of your own practice, I will reproduce six questions from the eight-page survey form I use in my work. Circle your own answers, and interpret them in the light of the commentary beneath each set of answers. You can also form a judgment on the office of Dr. Mapleton, a G.P. whose practice I recently studied by checking his answers to the following questions:

1. Where is your office located?

(A) Heart of downtown. (B) Fringe of downtown. (C) In the hospital zone. (D) In a suburban shopping area. (E) It's a neighborhood practice. (F) In a rural area.

275

If you've answered F, that's that. You're a country doctor, and there's only one possible location for you—on or near the main street of your hamlet. But if you're a city doctor and circled A or B, there's a chance that you're practicing in the wrong place.

You've noticed, I'm sure, how many doctors have deserted downtown areas in recent years. Have you visited any of them in their new quarters? They're likely to rave about their modern layouts and the relief from parking troubles. The basic advantage of a downtown office used to be its accessibility by streetcar and bus. Today, almost everyone drives a car—to suburban shopping centers and to suburban doctors. It's just too tedious to buck the the traffic and parking problems downtown. (By "downtown," I mean where the stores are. There's nothing wrong with practice on Park Avenue or Central Park West in Manhattan—but one on Fifth Avenue and 42nd Street might give me pause.)

I'll concede that there will always be room for some doctors in any downtown area: A practice can be built out of office workers' ailments. But the workers' families prefer to stay near home. So if you're a downtown doctor and your practice load is stagnating, ask yourself: "Am I giving my practice a fair chance to grow by staying here? Or should I move?"

If you're a downtown doctor who regularly visits a hospital a mile or more away, the case for a move is strengthened. You could turn the time you spend waiting at traffic lights into working time, and you could save yourself a lot of tension. Conservatively, I'd say I know nearly a thousand physicians who have quit downtown in the past 10 years. The move helped them all.

If you circled C or D, you're probably sitting pretty (assuming you're not a G.P. trying to scratch out a practice in the shadow of Massachusetts General or a neurosurgeon waiting for housewives to choose between the A. & P. and a frontal lobotomy). There's nothing wrong with E, either, if you haven't set your sights on something bigger.

Dr. Mapleton, whom I mentioned above, practiced just outside his city's downtown area. But the downtown area hunched like a

276

linebacker between him and the hospital he visited twice daily. And many of his patients had to bull through the downtown traffic to get to his office. "I seem to have a lot of canceled appointments," he told me. I made a note of that.

2. Do you have enough working space?

(A) My consultation room is cramped. (B) I need more examining rooms. (C) My reception room gets pretty crowded at times. (D) My aides grumble about the cramped business space. (E) Storage is a problem. (F) I've got space to spare.

If you circled F, it doesn't follow that you can pass on to the next question. I've known lots of doctors with space they couldn't use—and a bad arrangement of the space they did use. "Enough working space" means adequate space well laid out. It should, for example, be all on one level. And it should be organized in four distinct areas: reception, business, technical, and treatment.

If your consultation room isn't at least 10 feet square, you should have marked A. If your consultation room doubles as an examining room, you should have marked B. And you should have marked B if you don't have at least two examining rooms. (In a multidoctor practice, this means two examining rooms per doctor. For a busy man, two examining rooms may not be enough; I know an OBG man who has six.) And if the rooms you do have are smaller than 10 feet by 8 feet, they're too small.

Did you circle C? Maybe you weren't sure whether to circle it or not. Look at your appointment book. How many patients come to your office in the peak hour of a typical day? Let's say six. Add as many again for relatives and friends. That makes 12. Allowing 20 square feet per person, you need 240 square feet in your reception room. A 17 by 14 room would do fine.

Did you fail to circle D? Is it because your aide doesn't grumble—or because you don't hear her? Your aide spends a lot of her working day in your business office. She needs a work station, room for files, room for supplies, and room to walk about. Every day I see girls struggling to do good work in cubbyholes smaller than apartment kitchens. It irritates them. And their irritation gets passed on to your patients. Mark D if your business office is smaller than your consultation room. If you have two girls, mark D if it's smaller than 160 square feet. For each additional girl you have up front, add 60 square feet.

Finally, here's how to decide if you rate an E. Walk through your office. If you see any cartons or boxes atop cupboards, file cabinets, and bookcases you merit an E. If you don't, you don't.

Dr. Mapleton answered B and C. At the end of a day in his office I circled D and E, too. His consultation room, incidentally, was larger than his reception room.

3. Are you making the best use of your space?

(A) My business office looks out on the reception room. (B) Next nearest the reception room is the technical area (lab, X-ray, shots). (C) After this come the nurse's station, toilets, and storage closets. (D) The treatment area starts with my consultation room. (E) My examining rooms adjoin each other. (F) The minimum width of corridors in my office is 4 feet.

I hope you've circled all six answers. If you missed A, yours is the kind of reception room patients like least. Entering it for the first time, they don't know whether to knock on the door opposite, cough discreetly, or yell, "Anyone home?" And your aide has to pop her head out constantly to see if anyone new has arrived. Direct supervision of the reception room by your aide is a must. How about planting her right in the reception room? Better than nothing—but not much better.

B is a good mark. Since paramedical procedures are generally performed by an aide, keeping the technical area up front avoids congestion in the doctor's domain. The same reasoning calls for a C. Patients shouldn't get into your bailiwick until they have to.

D and E make life easier for you. It's bad to tuck your consultation room away in the farthest reaches of the office. If your examining rooms don't adjoin, you'll use up too much shoe leather. If you have 4-foot corridors, fine. If they're 5 feet wide, finer.

Even if you circled all six answers, you may still be able to ring in some improvements. Are there odd corners in your office? Build cupboards into them. Do you have irregularly shaped rooms in which it's hard to fit conventional furnishings? Use unconventional furnishings. Figure them out yourself, and get a local man to make them. And remember that a lab can go into an alcove. It doesn't have to be in a room.

Dr. Mapleton missed out on several questions. He had a "blind" reception room, with his secretary next door. His consultation room came next, then an examining room, then his lab. He had another examining station set up in a corridor, along with his X-ray equipment. The only john adjoined the reception room. "They bring urine specimens from home," his nurse told me. "You can hardly ask people to go in there in front of everybody— and come out sheepishly with a towel draped over an outstretched hand."

4. How attractive is your office?

(A) It's in good repair. (B) It's adequately heated, cooled, and lighted. (C) The paint is fresh, and the floors are clean. (D) The reception room furnishings are of recent vintage. (E) The décor is pleasing. (F) The magazines are current and plentiful.

Here again, I hope you've circled all six. And I hope you'll do something about any item you couldn't circle.

Given two doctors of equal ability, one with an attractive office and the other with an unattractive one, the first doctor will pull in the crowds. It's unfortunately true that an attractive office will draw patients even to a doctor who's less capable than his colleague down the street—if the colleague offers nothing better than a flyblown pad.

I've met lots of physicians who thought their offices were in mint condition when in fact they weren't. Granted that your office isn't an icehouse in the winter and a Turkish bath in the summer, but what about the lighting? Does your reception room have dim, dreary bulbs encased in opaque cardboard shades? If so, you can't circle B. Nor can you circle A or C till you've checked for chipped walls and ceilings, leaky toilets, doors that stick, sweat-stained paintwork, and scuffed floors. If D or E is your sticking point, throw out that rumpus-room furniture you brought from home too many years ago. Replace those malodorous smoking stands with bright ceramic ashtrays. Paint the doors in your office different colors. Give your aide some cash for flowers. Hang attractive prints on the walls. Go all the way—treat the reception room to wall-to-wall carpeting.

As for F—magazines—either pay attention to them or make sure no patient ever has to wait. If yours is a busy office, you need a lot of magazines. Don't bring your copies from home after the family has read them; take the office copies home when the patients are through with them. As each new issue of a magazine arrives, replace the previous issue. If a magazine gets torn or dirty, take it out of the reception room. Don't try to save by filling your magazine rack with giveaway periodicals. And warn your aide that Medical Economics magazine has no place in a doctor's reception room.

Dr. Mapleton's office passed this particular test with honors. Its chief flaw was a shortage of chairs—not seats, but chairs. When I visited him, I had a choice of two seats, each in the middle of a three-seater settee. I decided to stand. Leaning against the same wall with me were two other men.

5. What parking facilities does your office have?

(A) Off-street parking, and it's adequate. (B) Off-street parking plus street parking; adequate. (C) Metered street parking. (D) Free street parking. (E) I rent parking spaces for patients and personnel. (F) I rent parking spaces for personnel only.

The best mark of course is A. But make sure you're not kidding yourself. One of my clients claimed an A without ever realizing that half his patients, finding his small parking lot full, often circled the block for 20 minutes looking for an empty street space. And one doctor who thought he deserved a B overlooked the fact that his own and his aides' cars occupied half his parking lot.

This question has to be answered from the patient's point of view, not yours. If you work by appointment, chances are you need a minimum of six parking spaces always available for patients. If you're a busy man who often runs late, you may need twice as many. If you don't work by appointment and are in a metered area, your aide had better have a drawer filled with nickels and a deaf ear.

Dr. Mapleton rented 10 spaces on a commercial lot a block from his office. Six of them were available for patients; he and his aides occupied the others. "I pay $60 a month for them," he told me. "That's cheap for this part of town." I agreed it was cheap. Then I borrowed a nickel and sprinted the two blocks to my own car. I hadn't managed to get one of his spaces.

6. How much do you pay for your office?

(A) It's free, courtesy of the drugstore below. (B) It's cheap, being in an old building. (C) The rent is fair, considering the space I have. (D) For what I have, it's a bit stiff. (E) It's high, but what can I do? (F) Boy, am I being taken!

Your answer to this one is bound to be subjective, unless you circled A (and I hope you didn't). How much rent can you afford to pay for your office? A high rent in a well-kept building is a better bargain than a low one in a place that's in bad shape. If rent plus utilities comes to less than 5 per cent of your gross receipts from practice, and it's good space, you've got a bargain. But if more than 10 per cent of your gross is spent on rent, even in the most luxurious building, you're in over your head.

Here's another way to judge whether you or your landlord has the better deal. Figure out the number of square feet you occupy and multiply that by five. The figure you get should be within hailing distance of your annual rent. If the figure is much more than your rent, you've got a bargain; if it's much less, your landlord may have found a pigeon.

If you want to refine that rough guide, throw in your location and your specialty as factors in rent. A colleague of mine, Allison Skaggs of Battle Creek, Mich., once worked up some statistics on the rent paid by 3,000 doctors in 15 states. He found that the bigger the city, the higher the rent. On average, doctors in towns under 20,000 population paid around 4.5 per cent of their gross income in rent; doctors in medium-size cities (20,000 to 250,000 population) paid a little more than 5 per cent; and doctors in big cities paid closer to 6 per cent. By specialty, OBG men, radiologists, pathologists, internists, and dermatologists paid most—6 per cent or more. And ENT men, ophthalmologists, general surgeons, thoracic surgeons, and psychiatrists paid least—4.5 per cent or less.

Dr. Mapleton, I found, gave 8 per cent of his annual gross to his landlord. Figure out for yourself whether he had a bargain.

If you scored poorly on this self-test, you're taking a big risk. You may be losing desirable patients to colleagues of inferior professional skill who, when it comes to pleasing patients, can make *you* look second-best.

37

Sizing up your equipment and furnishings

In surveying upwards of 400 medical practices in 20 states, I've learned one quick way to gauge a doctor's attitude toward office efficiency. It's simply to walk around the office with the doctor —that's the first order of business in any practice survey—and note the variety, age, and condition of his professional and business equipment. If it's plentiful, new, and well kept, I know I've met a man intent on doing the best possible work with the best available tools. If it's sparse, antique, and rickety, I suspect that my client doesn't realize that a doctor often has to spend money to make money.

I don't claim that laying out huge sums on fancy doodads will guarantee a jump in your tax bracket. But hanging on to out-worn, outmoded equipment can be the worst kind of economy. As head of an international airline, you wouldn't use piston-engined planes on the New York-Paris run, would you? Not in this year of grace.

For this third stage of your do-it-yourself practice survey, therefore, I've selected from my master sheet half a dozen queries on equipment, each with a choice of six answers and a brief commentary. I've included also the answers given me recently by a G.P. I'll call Dr. Johnson. He'd lost more patients than expected when a shiny new clinic opened nearby. He wanted to know why.

Circle the answers that fit your own situation. Read the commentaries. Decide whether *your* tools help or handicap you in giving top-quality care. And see how you compare with Dr. Johnson.

1. What's in your reception room?

(A) I have enough seats to guarantee that no patient or escort has to stand. (B) The furniture is varied enough to let people choose a seat they like. (C) The main lighting is overhead, with floor and table lamps for accent. (D) There's a place for coats, hats, umbrellas, and overshoes. (E) Separate toilets for both sexes are near at hand, and their location is plainly indicated. (F) The patients find suitable little extras in the reception room.

If you circled all six answers, you pitched a perfect game. Perhaps you weren't too sure about one or two. You shouldn't, for example, have circled A if your reception room won't seat all the people liable to be in it at one time. How many seats is that? To find out, take the number of patients you're likely to see in one hour on a busy day, then multiply that number by two. That's how many seats you need to accommodate patients and their escorts. To allow one seat per person when there's a pile-up due to an emergency, and a choice of two or more seats on a normal day, multiply by three, not two.

If you circled B, I'd expect to find that your seating consists mainly of chairs, some contoured and some straight, some with arms and some without, some upholstered and some not. There'd be one or two peewee seats for kids. Loveseats and other couches for two? Avoid them. Patients don't like to sit thigh-to-thigh with strangers. Also avoid deep lounge chairs. They're lovely to sit in but awkward to get in and out of.

Older patients especially will appreciate your scoring well with C. It's hard on failing eyes to read by the glimmer of a heavily-shaded lamp two yards distant. Diffused overhead lighting is best.

I hope you didn't miss out on D, since people shouldn't sit around with wet topcoats on their backs or knees. As for E, it's a basic human need.

Hesitant about claiming an F? Complimentary coffee isn't

called for, although I know an office that serves it—on silver trays. But a rug on the floor, pictures on the walls, flowers here and there, and a plenitude of *new* magazines are proven patient-pleasers. So is piped-in music. A phone's a boon, too, even if it's a pay phone. Will you be having kids around? Think about toys, picture books, and the ever-fascinating tropical fish tank.

If you circled fewer than four answers, you have some jobs to do, as did Dr. Johnson. His reception room had plenty of seats— but they were hardly comfortable. There were three long benches and a dozen straight-backed kitchen chairs. And there was a big round table on which stood a lamp with an opaque shade and a litter of old magazines. That was all.

2. How's your business office equipped?

(A) My aide has a work station designed for her job. (B) She files charts on open shelves. (C) She keeps patients' account cards in open trays. (D) Her typewriter and adding machine are electric. (E) She has a copier, a postal scale, a cash box, and a safe. (F) All of the office supplies are stored in closets.

Did you circle all six? I hope so. Chances are, though, you missed out on A. Most doctors' aides work at conventional desks. When a girl has to manage a phone, a transcribing machine, a type-writer, an adding machine, a daybook, several trays of account cards, and general secretarial bric-a-brac, she needs more surface space than most desks provide. Have a carpenter build her some.

If you didn't mark B, C, and D, you're not with it. Push-pull drawers for charts and cards are out. They require too much office space, time, and energy. And electric typewriters and adding machines displaced the manual models back in the fifties, because they're faster, easier, and neater. Get your girl some power tools.

Circle E if you have a copying machine, even if you lack the other E items. The office copier is the 20th century's gift to physicians' aides. It can churn out patients' monthly statements at better than 100 per hour, reproduce charts or parts thereof in nothing flat—and without transcribing errors. It even enables her to rush replies to your correspondents by mailing them copies of their own letters with your yeas or nays written in the margin.

You didn't mark F? Then your front office may be like **Dr.** Johnson's—a rat's nest of half-empty stationery boxes, cartons, bottles, and jars. And the bottom drawers of his old filing cabinets were stuffed with discarded folders and out-of-date phone books. In fact, he failed to score in the whole section. How did you do?

3. What's in your consultation room?

(A) I have a large desk that suits my taste and harmonizes with the other furnishings. (B) I have comfortable chairs for myself and two visitors. (C) My books are on shelves; my medical journals, in a rack. (D) There are curtains at the window, a carpet on the floor, and pictures on the walls. (E) I have all the communication devices I can use. (F) The drawers of my desk are filled with old drug samples.

I'll bet F hit a nerve. Call your Girl Friday and start unloading— now! If their "use by" dates have passed, they're worthless. If they're samples of drugs you never use, they're clutter. If they're still good, they should be sorted and stored.

If you've made a poor showing on the rest of this question, you have plenty of company. I've seen some odd-looking desks in consultation rooms: battered rolltops, steel hulks bought at bankruptcy sales. I've seen some handsome things, too: an antique table worth a small fortune and a set of Louis Quatorze chairs. As for your chairs, they should have arms—and padded seats. You flunk if they're garden chairs.

Did you miss circling C? Many doctors do. I know one whose medical books are strewn over his consultation-room floor. They've been that way since the day he moved in five years ago. And I've peered at so many doctors around head-high piles of musty medical journals that I have a permanent case of torticollis.

It's O.K. to circle the D for pictures even if yours are only framed diplomas. If they're flyspecked though, score a very small d.

To rate an E, you don't necessarily have to have a dictating machine, office intercom, or a buzzer to summon your aide—if you don't really need any of them. Intercoms, for example, are more useful in large offices than in small ones. But if you lack *any* communication device that would save you time, you're handicapping yourself. Did you know you could get a recorder that will repeat your aide's messages to you after she's closed the office? I know a G.P. who regularly calls his office from the hospital before heading for home. After listening to the recording he decides whether he'll go straight home or detour to see a patient.

Dr. Johnson? He fooled me. There was only one word for *his* consultation room: plush.

4. Do you have everything you need for examining patients?

> *(A) My examining tables are adapted to my specialty. (B) Each examining room is equipped with all needed accessories— treatment stand, lamp, stool, waste receptacle, and so on. (C) I keep a full set of instruments in each room. (D) Each room has its own supplies—from drugs to paper clips. (E) Each room is fitted with a writing shelf and stationery rack. (F) There's a designated place in each room for patients' garments.*

You probably circled A without hesitation. But if you're, say, an orthopedist or a pediatrician, there's a chance you erred. I often see standard tables in these doctors' offices, and they're wrong. Their patients need flat, unbroken surfaces to lie on, not tables that spell M when a handle is turned.

If you circled B, C, and D, you're the man for me. It costs plenty to fit up each room with a full set of instruments and supplies. But it's a great investment. The time you save by not having to wait for your nurse to bring the frammis scraper from the next room may not be much in itself. But if she's eternally carting it from room to room, you're both out a few hours a year—and *your* hours are worth at least $20 apiece, I trust.

287

You drew the correct inference from E, I hope: Desks and chairs aren't needed in examining rooms. Make progress notes standing up. You'll save time two ways: Patients won't confabulate so much, and you'll learn to boil down your comments.

You probably didn't circle F. Remedy that. Mount a small shelf at eye level in each examining room. Beneath the shelf, place two hooks. The shelf is for underwear, the hooks for outer garments. Now you won't have to lift patients' clothing off your examining stool before you sit down.

Dr. Johnson didn't circle F. But he scored on A through E.

5. How complete are your technical resources?

(A) I have a separate waiting area for patients needing tests, etc. (B) My nurse has her own work station where she sorts records, takes weights, pulses, temperatures, and so on. (C) My lab is equipped for all the tests I regularly order. (D) I have a room set aside for special procedures such as ECG. (E) I have a "shot room." (F) I have my own X-ray equipment.

This time, I don't hope for six bullseyes. The few physicians I know who can circle all the answers are G.P.s. I push hard for A and B, though, in almost every office. That special waiting area near the lab eases congestion everywhere. And any nurse with a niche all her own will tell you it's the next best thing to a raise.

If yours is a medical rather than a surgical practice, C is a must. To conserve your own time and your patients' shoe leather, you can't afford to be without a lab for your most-often-run tests. If your practice is geared toward older patients, you need D. And E gets patients out of your examining rooms faster.

F, I know, can be a problem. Resolve it this way: If you can't get X-rays of chests and extremities from outside *fast,* consider doing them in your own office. But if prompt service is available, think twice about investing in your own equipment.

Dr. Johnson circled D and E. You may have tagged his major problem by now. His office was equipped to save *him* time and energy. Where he fell down was in his lack of consideration for his patients and his aides.

6. How old is your equipment?

(A) It was fully depreciated long ago. (B) I admit it's old, but there's still some good mileage in it. (C) Some of it's old, some new—but it's all in good shape. (D) I've been meaning to retire some items, but I haven't gotten around to doing so. (E) There are some new gizmos I'd like if I could afford them. (F) I'm new here, and so is my equipment.

The good mark here is C. To me, it means that you don't keep equipment that doesn't function 100 per cent.

Sure, dozens of items of a physician's equipment have a long life. But why slug away with obsolete, malfunctioning tools? If it doesn't work, get it repaired or replace it.

If you circled D, there's hope for you. Get hold of some catalogs. Compare this year's examining tables with your own 15-year-old ones. True, yours aren't bad. But you may be surprised at how much better the new ones are.

Were you tempted to circle E? Go ahead, but I wouldn't advise you to load up with everything shiny the salesmen show you. But don't be too conservative, either. Motorized tables, for example, may strike you as space-age hardware. But you're in the space age, aren't you? Dr. Johnson, an E man, bought one. He likes it.

If you're an A man, and retirement isn't staring you in the face, I suggest you move fast. Item by item, compare what you've got with what the manufacturers are offering this year. Then get busy on the order blanks. Scared by the cost? Uncle Sam will help you with tax write-offs. Or you can lease the new equipment.

Scored an F, did you? Good luck to you. And here's a tip: Every year from now on, have your accountant make a list of items he's depreciated taxwise down to, say, 20 per cent of cost. Compare each listed item with the manufacturer's new offering. You'll make more trade-ins than you might think.

289

38

Sizing up
your aides and what
you pay them

The Wright brothers certainly cut the earth down to size. Not long ago, I breakfasted with a G.P in a rooftop restaurant overlooking the Atlantic Ocean. That same night, I dined with a pediatrician in a patio fanned by a Pacific breeze. Each was worried about his net income.

"The trouble lies with your gross," I told my breakfast companion. "You need more help." I told my dinner partner: "Your expenses are too high. You can do with less help."

Each doctor had been wondering whether his payroll was right for his practice. If you've never done the same, you're unusual. Only one of the hundreds of doctors whose practices I've surveyed has failed to ask, "Do you think I have enough help or too much?" He had no employes at all.

When a doctor asks me whether he has too few or too many aides, I usually fire off a few questions. You might like to answer my six key questions on personnel. To give you a basis for comparison, I've thrown in the answers given me by the California pediatrician. I'll call him Dr. Wills.

1. How much help do you employ?

(A) A Girl Friday is all. (B) One girl out front and another in back. (C) One business aide, one nurse, and one technician. (D) Two out front, two in back. (E) Three business aides, two nurses. (F) Three out front, three in back.

291

In posing these questions, I'm assuming that you don't belong to a large group practice and that your practice doesn't require such specialized workers as physiotherapists and opticians.

Solo surgeons circle A more frequently than other doctors. That's because they're often in their offices only for half-days. Most solo G.P.s, internists, pediatricians, and OBG men answer to B and C. Occasionally, an extra-busy solo man gives me a D. Generally, though, only multidoctor offices have more than three aides.

It's risky for a consultant to be dogmatic about the amount of help any given practice needs. But in a solo office averaging no more than 100 patient visits a week, a lone Girl Friday has a hard life. Two girls, however, should be able to cope in an office averaging 200 visits a week. So, by and large, two aides per average busy doctor is my working yardstick. If a medical office's payroll is loaded down with more than two aides per doctor, I expect to find a special reason for it.

Dr. Wills, the California pediatrician, answered D—and his workload averaged out at only 200 patients a week in the office.

2. How busy are your aides?

(A) They're never pushed. (B) They sure scuttle around while I'm in the office. (C) They must be busy; they're always behind in their work. (D) The front office is hectic, but things are easy in the back. (E) The back's a rat race, but the front isn't overworked. (F) They work hard all day and stay late every night.

In medical offices, as in others, work tends to expand to occupy all the time of all available employes. If you circled A or B and have two full-time aides, consider whether you could get by with one full-timer augmented by part-time help. If A, you probably could. If B, maybe so or maybe not—just consider the possibility.

If you marked C, look again. Take a look at the piled-up paper work in your office some morning; it might have been there for days. And walk through your treatment area and check that everything's ready for the day's expected load.

D and E are obvious problem cases. It's possible you're short-handed front or back. Or you may not be distributing the work fairly. Maybe one girl could catch the phone more than she does or lend a hand with the filing.

F is a black mark. If your aides regularly work more than 40 hours a week (about one in five of all aides does), chances are you're understaffed. Hire extra help, full time or part time—or at least pay your girls for their overtime work.

Dr. Wills answered C. But the backlog was due to inefficiency.

3. What days and hours do your aides regularly work?

(A) Five and a half days, 40 hours. (B) Five and a half days, 38 hours. (C) Five days, 40 hours. (D) Five days, 35 hours. (E) Four days, two half-days, 35 hours. (F) Four days, one half-day, 32 hours.

Some offices seem to have enough girls, but somehow they don't get the work done. Often the explanation is that their working hours are too short. Contrariwise, in some offices with long hours, there's a permanent backlog of work. In these offices, an extra pair of hands may be needed to break the logjam.

If you circled E, you're in the majority according to my observations. Your aides work four 7-hour days—not counting the luncheon break—and two half days.

This 35-hour week works well enough for a solo doctor; he simply closes the office on his midweek afternoon off. But in multi-doctor practices, it can mean that the office is short one aide almost every afternoon.

The other 35-hour workweek, D, is made up of five 7-hour days and no Saturday work. It's becoming increasingly popular.

In A offices, the girls commonly work five 7½-hour days (no midweek time off) and alternate Saturday mornings. Most C offices work five straight 8-hour days and don't open òn Saturdays.

If yours is a specialty practice, there's a lot to be said for the straight five-day office week. I've persuaded many doctors to adopt it. Their aides appreciate it, the doctors themselves like it, and it doesn't seem to discombobulate the patients a bit. I haven't sold any G.P.s on the idea, though.

In F offices, aides get a full day off midweek, working four 7-hour days plus Saturday mornings. Dr. Wills's four girls had this working week. Among them, they put in 128 hours a week. It's an A office now, with one girl less, but only 8 hours a week less.

4. What qualifications do you require of your aides?

(A) To help with patients, I want graduate nurses and registered technologists. (B) I want experienced helpers in back, but they needn't be R.N.s or R.T.s. (C) I can train any savvy girl to help me with patients and do simple tests. (D) For the front office, I want girls who've worked in other medical offices or in hospitals. (E) For the front, commercial-office experience or business-college training will do nicely. (F) A high school certificate is all a front-office girl needs.

I trust you've circled two answers, one in the top three and one in the bottom three. Whatever combination you pick, I'll keep mum —if you and your patients are satisfied. I've been around medical offices long enough to know that pins and diplomas aren't everything.

Some of the best aides I know are B and E girls. The head nurse in a four-man internists' group I know doesn't even have an L.P.N., but a total of 18 years in four different offices has made her a Florence Nightingale. As for good E girls, they abound.

I'll confess that C and F girls bother me a bit. A physician *can* train a totally inexperienced girl to help him with patients, give shots and so forth. Trouble is, too many doctors half-train their C girls. And too many blithely assume that their F girls are doing their work well when they're not.

If you left it to me to pick your office force, I'd scout around for A and D girls. And if I knew where to get certified aides, I wouldn't settle for anything less. What do I mean by that? Well,

294

The American Association of Medical Assistants holds annual examinations and awards the diploma of Certified Medical Assistant (C.M.A.). I'd sure hire a C.M.A. if I had the chance.

Pediatrician Wills had the right idea as far as quality went. He answered A for the two aides who helped him with patients, D for the other two. Too bad they had him snowed; he was top-heavy as to quantity.

5. What jobs do you delegate outright to your aides?

(A) They organize my working day under broad directives from me. (B) Consulting me only when they're stumped, they act as the communicating link between me and my patients. (C) Guided by my accountant, they handle the finances of my practice. (D) They obtain in advance all the information I'm likely to need on every patient, including personal and family medical histories. (E) They do all tests and procedures that a non-M.D. may legally and ethically do. (F) I don't delegate. I tell them what to do and watch them do it.

I hope you circled A through E; if F, you're keeping a watchdog and doing the barking yourself. Hiring aides merely to fetch and carry ignores their real use, which is to free you of nonmedical tasks, thus maximizing your professional potential.

Good aides don't need to be told daily how you want your time parceled out. To claim an A, just block out a typical day for your aides, and they'll get the idea. If they don't, change 'em.

You didn't circle B? Then you're losing lots of time in the office. If a patient asks you a question in the examining room, by all means answer it. But if the same patient phones her question and one of your aides knows the right answer, stay out of the discussion. And if you're called on to rule, don't be in a hurry to grab the phone. Let the aide relay your reply.

Circling C doesn't require you to abandon all control of your practice finances. It does, though, mean that you've set up, with help from your accountant, a money-handling system for the girls to follow that you can check with a minimum of time and effort. If you haven't got such a system, you need one.

D reminds me that I've never understood why more doctors don't delegate history-taking to their aides. Those who do will tell you that it pays off heavily. Maybe you're afraid that your girl will miss out on something. What if she does? You're going to run through it with the patient and add things anyway. The scut work in history-taking is getting the routine stuff on paper.

As for E, simple tests and procedures, the only reason for not letting an aide do them is that she does 'em wrong. That doesn't mean you should do them. It means you need a new aide.

Dr. Wills claimed A through E, but he was kidding himself. He should have circled F. His bookkeeper told me, "I've been after him for months to decide something about these old accounts." And his senior nurse said, "We hand him the syringes and he sticks the kids himself."

6. What proportion of your gross income goes to payroll?

(A) Less than 10 per cent. (B) 10 to 15 per cent. (C) 15 to 20 per cent. (D) 20 to 25 per cent. (E) Over 25 per cent. (F) I don't know.

That F answer isn't there to raise a smile; half the doctors I meet can't answer this question. Of those who do know the answer, surgeons with one-girl offices are most apt to circle A. Most internists, pediatricians, and OBG men reply B and C. Internists who subspecialize in gastroenterology often answer to D or E. Good X-ray technicians aren't cheap.

Typically, the payroll accounts for about 15 per cent of a doctor's gross practice income. So I wouldn't expect your payroll to exceed 20 per cent of the gross. A doctor grossing $4,000 a month and spending $1,000 of it on help is geared for a larger practice. On the face of it, he should have either more patients or less help.

Dr. Wills had to take a D. Now he's in category C—where he belongs.

39

Sizing up the way you employ your time

I'll always remember Dr. Hopcroft. The first time I met him he seemed to be one of the busiest G.P.s I'd ever seen. But after I'd spent a day in his office, I realized his busyness was bad business. He ran hard and got nowhere.

At the end of the day, I threw lots of questions at Dr. Hopcroft about his working day. After answering them, he said: "You don't have to spell out your conclusion. I've already figured out that I'm not using my time intelligently."

There may have been days when you've wondered whether you're spinning *your* wheels. So I've picked out six key questions concerning the use of time. Circle your own answer to each question, then read the commentary along with Dr. Hopcroft's answers. You might discover the causes of some troubles of your own, and you should be able to develop a few good ideas as to what to do about those problems.

1. When does your working day start?

(A) At 7:30 or earlier, at the hospital. (B) At 8, when I make my first house call. (C) At 8, when the floor nurse at the hospital puts my charts out. (D) At 8:30, at the hospital. (E) At 9, when I get to my office; I go to the hospital later. (F) I'm a sackhound; I don't leave home till 9.

Most surgeons I know (and OBG men on their surgery days) are

297

A men. They like to be in the O.R. early, operate, and make rounds later. The sleepyheads make rounds while they're waiting their O.R. turn. The nonsurgeons are usually B, C, or D men. G.P.s and pediatricians are the likeliest to start their day with a house call; internists rarely do.

E goes mostly to general practitioners who don't do much hospital work and to men in such specialties as allergy, dermatology, and so on. Their reasoning is sound: Start at the office and, if you do have a patient in the hospital, drop in there either at lunchtime or on the way home.

There are F men in all specialties. They're the ones who most often complain to me of inadequate incomes. Ten o'clock scholars don't fit into private practice too successfully. What's more, it's my impression that the early starters among my clients are the best-tempered. When I mentioned this to one of them, he said: "That shouldn't surprise you. There's nothing like the morning sun for dispelling grouchiness."

Dr. Hopcroft barely scraped by with a D. "I'm usually at the hospital by a quarter to 9," he told me defensively.

2. When do you start seeing office patients?

(A) Not till after lunch. (B) Around 11 A.M. (C) I usually make it to the office by 10:30. (D) I see my first office patient at 10. (E) I'm at the office by 9:30 most days. (F) Nine sharp. I'm the guy who makes his rounds later.

If you're a surgeon, you probably circled A or B, depending mainly on your average time in the O.R. One or two major procedures, a couple of minors, rounds on a dozen patients, and a spell of chart dictation make up a fair morning's work. A or B for a busy OBG man is also predictable—especially if, like some of my clients, he delivers 6 to 10 women each week and operates on Tuesdays and Thursdays.

Most of the high-volume internists I know would circle B. Even a fast man needs three hours to get through a couple of new admissions, visits to 8 or 10 other rooms, a consultation or two, and, of course, the not-to-be-dodged chart work.

Are you a nonsurgeon who usually has fewer than 10 hospitalized patients? I hope you didn't circle anything higher than E. Too many do. They don't simply go to the hospital, see their patients, and leave. They hang around. They drink coffee. They swap scuttlebutt. Finally, they head for the office and a room filled with irritated patients. If they'd get to their offices by 9:30, they'd be thousands of dollars ahead at the end of the year. And they'd get home earlier at night.

I've already said that the man who doesn't hospitalize many patients can safely dispense with a routine trip to the hospital before going to the office. But for men who must visit the hospital daily, F is a bad mark. Generally, it doesn't pay to split the office day.

Dr. Hopcroft answered D. But on the day I was at his office, he arrived at 10:20, after seeing only six hospital patients.

3. How good is your appointment system?

> *(A) Perfect. Nobody waits, and I get out on time. (B) Pretty good. Few people have to wait, and those not for long. (C) O.K., except that we can't seem to solve the squeeze-in problem. (D) It seems O.K., except that the no-shows bother me. (E) It creaks. I run late all the time. (F) I don't work by appointment. They come and I see 'em—eventually.*

The A physicians I know are almost all high-income men. They've figured out their hourly earning potential and set up a working schedule designed to realize it.

B, however, is a perfectly acceptable mark. Doctors get it by avoiding the traps that produce a C, D, or E. Let's take a closer look at them.

If you circled C, the chances are that you haven't learned that squeeze-ins must be budgeted for. An internist who knows he can finish a one-hour work-up in 50 minutes can, if need be, squeeze in a short emergency-type visit without risking a pile-up. Similarly, a G.P. who at a push can get through four office visits in 50 minutes—an hour's work by the book—can squeeze in one more. His troubles start when he lets his aide *book* patients at five to the hour.

If you circled D, you're probably so overbooked that patients figure you won't even miss them if they default. You'd better be more realistic about your working speed. The percentage of no-shows who never show again is high.

E, if you circled it, is self-incriminating. I'd bet that you overbook, often start late, have a poor time sense, and permit interruptions. I'd also bet that talkative patients have you at their mercy. Worst of all, you probably haven't learned that a routine revisit that reveals a new problem is no longer routine. It's an *initial* visit—and that takes longer. So, if possible, have the patient come back another day.

As a patient, I hope the day will come when F has no adherents. As a management man, I try to speed that day. If yours is a non-appointment practice, I've a question for you: Would you like to do more work in less time? You can, if you'll switch to appointments. Maybe you're a G.P. and you hold as an article of faith that appointments are for specialists only. Not so. I know hundreds of G.P.s who work by appointment. In fact, the only kind of doctor I know who can't schedule most of his day is the hospital resident on emergency-room duty.

How did Dr. Hopcroft do? He managed a forthright E.

4. *In what order do you do things on a normal office day?*

(A) I start the day by seeing my aide, and we talk fast. (B) I see patients next—the new followed by the old. (C) Then I look at the call-backs and charts before lunch. (D) Afternoon patients are seen in that same order. (E) The last part of the office day is for nonpatients, call-backs, and charts. (F) I have no special order; I just look after the squeakiest wheel.

All really good managers I know circle A. They lead off with the mail and the day's appointment sheet. They say: "You answer those, Mary; I'll answer these. So far, I see, we have three patients to squeeze into this morning's schedule. You got any problems that need discussing now? No? O.K., then let's start stamping out disease."

It's a good idea to get into the habit of inviting your aide to bring her problems into the open. Take appointment-scheduling problems, for instance. She knows just what they are—and she may have some good suggestions about how to solve them. But you may never hear of those good ideas unless you make it clear that you *want* to hear about them.

Smart B and D men hardly ever shuffle new patients in with those already under care. And the smartest ones of all, knowing that misery loves company, group their current-care patients by sex, age, and ailment. Not inflexibly, of course. But they try, for example, to see their cardiacs on one day, ulcer patients on another, diabetics on a third. The idea is to get some momentum going—fueled by the kind of concentration you can get only by tuning in on a single subject. Chances are, you'll see more patients in less time—and maybe do an even better job with each of them. Are you a G.P. who sees well babies? Try setting aside a special afternoon for 'em.

Most of the C and E men do their best to shun the phone during appointment hours. They write up or dictate their charts twice a day. They don't keep patients waiting while they listen to detail men, equipment salesmen, or charity solicitors. Heroic? Sure, but their way pays.

I'll lay even money you circled F. Most of my new clients do. Dr. Hopcroft did. And the hurrieder he went, the behinder he got.

5. *Do you normally perform these office procedures in the times stated?*

(A) Full diagnostic work-up: 45 minutes. (B) Limited work-up: 30 minutes. (C) Initial office visit with regional examination: 15 minutes. (D) Office revisit: 10 minutes. (E) Prenatal check: 6 minutes. (F) Well-baby check: 10 minutes.

301

I'm assuming you did your circling on the basis of the time *you* spend with a patient; he may be in your office considerably longer. By a limited work-up (B) I mean a periodic physical, a consultative examination for an opinion on a specific situation, and so on. And in D I'm talking about checking response to treatment, postoperative and postnatal progress, and so on.

Missed 'em all? So did Dr. Hopcroft. So do many other physicians. Yet all over the country I know men who work at these speeds to the satisfaction of their patients and the envy of their colleagues. They just don't waste time.

"Work-up patients fill out a health questionnaire of my design and get their routine lab tests done before I see them," says an A internist. "With these aids, I need only 20 minutes to complete a history. Then comes 25 minutes in the examining room. I don't take patients back into my consultation room; I talk all the time I'm examining them."

The same internist, circling B, adds: "I can update an existing history—mine or a referring physician's—in 10 minutes. The physical exam also takes less time if I've been seeing the patient regularly."

Explaining his C and D marks, a G.P. with a larger-than-usual practice told me: "When a regular patient turns up with a new U.R.I., I don't test his patellar reflexes. And when a hypertensive comes in for his monthly visit, I don't routinely check his fundi. I do all that needs to be done and keep 'em moving."

An OBG man who claimed an E pointed out: "I have two nurses and four examining rooms. I can see three prenatals in 15 minutes. One nurse stays with me; the other sets the girls up. If anything seems to be abnormal, the patient gets a special appointment for the following day."

Similar techniques help a pediatrician-client of mine who claimed an F. He comments: "Many men in my specialty say it takes longer to check a well baby than to diagnose a sick one. That's a half-truth; it all depends on what the sick child is suffering from. With two nurses and three examining rooms, I see six well babies every hour. If there's any problem, the youngster goes off the well-baby schedule until the problem is solved."

6. *What time do you usually close your office?*

(A) Last appointment at 4:30 P.M.; out by 5. (B) Last appointment at 5; out by 5:30. (C) Last appointment at 5:30; out by 6:30. (D) Last appointment at 6; out by 7:15, if I'm lucky. (E) I close twice—at 6 for two hours and at 10 for the day. (F) I have no closing time. As long as people want to see me, I'll stay open.

If you circled A, I'll bet that you do a good day's work and still have enough strength to visit the hospital on the way home—and to turn out in an emergency later if need be.

B is good. You're probably home in time to see the kids at supper. And a "Doctor, please come" call or an SOS from the hospital, though unwelcome, won't seem like the end of the world.

Most of the C and D men I know are already whipped when the waiting room finally empties. Then they face the choice of going home by way of the hospital or a patient's home or of making rounds after dinner. To a tired man, neither choice is attractive.

Our friend Hopcroft? He was a D man. To him, an emergency was almost any request for his services—and in an emergency, of course, he couldn't say No. So even though his last appointment was for 6 o'clock, it was usually 7:30 and often 8 before he locked the office door behind him. He then went home by way of the hospital. Some nights he was too tired to bother with dinner. And his kids? They scarcely knew him.

As for E: Evening office hours do nothing to lengthen the span of human existence. But they can shorten the duration of doctors' lives—and of doctors' wives' patience. If a woman gets fed up being married to a man she seldom sees, who can blame her?

And though F men all tell themselves they stay on at the office for people who need them—and, of course, all patients say that's the case—I've a hunch the doctors need the people more.

40

Sizing up
the way you keep track
of money

Whenever I'm asked to survey a medical practice, I try to discover what triggered the invitation. Almost always, some recent—and often unpleasant—happening has prompted the doctor to seek outside help. Sometimes he suspects that he himself is doing some things the wrong way. Sometimes he has discovered that someone in his office is doing things wrong. A group of anesthesiologists, for example, yelled for help when they learned that their ex-bookkeeper's legacy to them was a cash shortage of $11,000. And an orthopedist called me when an agent for the Internal Revenue Service found that his bookkeeper had in a single year made more than 200 errors of addition and subtraction in her daybook.

So it's for good reason that a section of the eight-page checklist I use in my practice surveys is devoted to money-handling routines. For this chapter, I've picked out the half-dozen most important questions. Circle the answers that fit your own situation. Read the commentary. And study the answers I got recently from a Virginia G.P. I'll call Dr. Rawsen. I'll wager you'll spot what he was doing wrong as easily as I did. And you just may find you're making some of the same mistakes.

1. How are your charges to patients first recorded?

(A) On the patient's chart, by me. (B) On the patient's ledger card, by me. (C) On a daily list of patients, by me. (D) On

*a daybook (or daysheet, service sheet, log sheet, or other equiva-
lent), by my aide at my direction. (E) On a daybook, by my
aide according to a schedule I've given her. (F) On a service
slip, by me [service slips are also called charge slips, charge
tickets, routing slips, etc.].*

Fifteen years ago lots of doctors would have circled A. But today
the dual-purpose chart, combining the patient's medical and financial records, is out of favor—for three reasons. First, clinical
records are privileged and shouldn't be seen by accountants,
I.R.S. agents, or others whose job it is to check fiscal records. Second, clinical records necessarily travel around the office, while
financial records should stay put. And lastly, you can't run dual-
purpose records through the office copying machine to produce
patients' bills.

B is most often marked by the doctor who likes to know the
current state of each patient's account. His aide slips each patient's ledger card inside his chart. With the card before him, it's
as easy for the doctor to jot down the new charge as it is to mark
a list. Occasionally, though, he returns Mrs. Brown's card to Mrs.
Green's chart or otherwise misplaces it, and thus Mrs. Brown
isn't billed. If you circled B, you'd better find another way to bone
up your patients' pay status. Leave those ledger cards up front.

Did you circle C? Many doctors do. I've observed, though, that
many of them don't mark up their lists each day as they should.
Some men accumulate them for as much as a week. Their pro-
crastination is almost always expensive. They forget and fail to
bill for some of the services they've rendered. So it's become my
habit to advise avoiding C altogether.

D works pretty well if doctor and aide get together on it before
closing time every day. Too often they don't. Also, D men face the
extra hazard of a wrong entry by a harassed aide. Maybe it's not
a big risk, but it's there.

If you circled E, you're a rara avis. A top aide, able to read
charts and interpret a fee schedule, can set fees as easily as you
can. But few doctors believe it.

For my money, F beats them all. Set the fee yourself. Write it down in the patient's presence. Give him the paper it's written on and send him along to your aide to settle with her how he'll pay. Medical stationers offer quite a selection of service slips. If none of the stock items suit you, you can always design your own. Don't forget to have your service slips numbered consecutively. If you don't do so, some will go a-missing, as will the money.

Dr. Rawsen, the Virginia G.P., claimed a C. But he marked his lists only once a week. "Sometimes I can't remember everything I did for a patient," he conceded. "When that happens, I play safe and charge only for the visit." *Safe!*

2. How are your patients' payments first recorded?

> *(A) They're entered on the patient's chart, and that's all. (B) We record them in the daybook first. (C) We put all incoming payments, both cash and checks, through our receipt book first. (D) For cash, the first record is the receipt book; for checks, it's the daybook. (E) We write out service slips for all incoming payments, cash or checks. (F) At one writing, we enter all payments on a service slip, the daybook, and the ledger card.*

If you circled A, I hope you make the entries yourself. If you let your aide post payments this way, you're putting temptation in her path. Sure, most medical assistants are straightforward and true, but there's no reason why your financial records shouldn't be the same. The entries should be vouched for by prior entries in a chronological journal such as a daybook.

The chances are that you circled B. It's the traditional way. It's fast, uncomplicated, and the entries are chronological. By itself, though, B is as vulnerable as A. In fact, most embezzlements in medical offices seem to involve false daybook entries. So if you circled only B, you clearly need to do more.

You need C, for instance. Method C will give you worthwhile vouchers—provided the receipts used in your office are consecutively numbered and provided, further, that the original of each receipt goes to the payer. If the payer doesn't get the original, the duplicate is no more valid than a direct daybook entry.

D offices, realizing that a canceled check is an original receipt, don't bother putting patients' checks through the receipt book. Nothing wrong with that. So either C or D is O.K.

If you circled E and use numbered service slips, you're on the right track. Without numbers, service slips are mere memos. If you use a bookkeeping machine, E (with numbered slips) is the method of choice. It's neat—and fast.

For the small office, though, F is the mark I like to see. A single hand operation can create an acceptable voucher for each payment and, by carbon impression, post it to the daybook and ledger card. This write-it-once method eliminates accidental posting errors. And of course it saves time.

Dr. Rawsen claimed a C. Then he showed me a receipt for $10 signed by his aide and made out to a patient.

"My daybook doesn't show this payment," he said. "And there's no duplicate of this receipt in the receipt book. Yet the patient's ledger card shows that she paid."

An unhappy combination of errors—or deliberate omissions? Well, a search of his front office turned up *two* receipt books. One lay on his aide's desk. The other was in the back of a desk drawer. The receipt had come from the hidden book.

"Looks as though you'd better deal out receipt books one at a time to your next aide, Doctor," I suggested.

3. What's your routine for banking office receipts?

(A) They go into a checking account reserved for business use. (B) We bank every penny of professional income. (C) Every business day before closing, we make up the next day's deposit slip. (D) If we ever miss out on C, we still make up a slip for each separate day. (E) Our deposit slips are made up from funds on hand, then checked against our records, not vice versa. (F) We deposit every day unless the banks are closed.

Six circles win the Kewpie. It really *does* pay to be a stickler about your banking routine.

Most doctors today would circle A. They've found that by separating their professional and personal banking they can control business and domestic expenditures more easily. Also, they have a pretty fair idea of where they stand financially. And of course everyone likes to know how he's doing.

You did circle B, didn't you? I'm relieved. Doctors who miss this one worry me. They deposit checks, hang on to cash. I've met one who even endorsed checks and gave them to his wife to use on shopping expeditions. He called me after an I.R.S. agent had given him a hard time. He's a B man now, but even so he'll be audited regularly for years to come.

You probably missed C. In most offices, the deposit slip for each day's take is made up the next day. I've disliked that routine ever since a burglar made off with a boxful of a friend's cash, checks, and unposted service slips. If it ever happens again, the doctor will at least know how much is missing. Now his aide makes up the deposit each night and puts the carbon copy of the deposit slip under her desktop blotter.

D satisfies my yen for fiscal tidiness. I like to see the daybook and deposit slip matched day by day. Another thing: Juggling deposits is a standard routine with embezzlers, and I don't enjoy punching a doctor's adding machine to verify that a fat deposit represents 10 days' receipts.

You might think that E is just a quirk of mine. But some years ago I came up against an aide who, having missed entering a patient in the daybook, found herself with $50 more than the book called for, and she pocketed it. So I'm convinced that the deposit slip should be written up before its total is matched against the daybook's. A small matter, but every little cash control counts.

Why circle F? Does it really matter whether your aide goes to the bank once a day or once a month? It sure does. I'm not thinking only of the risk of leaving sizable amounts of cash in the office for days at a time. What concerns me more is that checks aren't money until they've cleared a bank. If you'll be an F man, you'll get fewer notices of insufficient funds.

Dr. Rawsen answered A and B. "I don't know enough about what goes on to go any further," he told me. He knows more now.

4. How do you pay your office bills?

> *(A) By check, except for trifling outlays such as postage due. (B) Checks are written by an aide, signed by me. (C) Before signing any check, I examine the bill it's written for. (D) I don't sign any check if it's been detached from the checkbook. (E) I never sign a blank check. (F) I've set up a petty cash fund for expenses that can't be paid by check.*

Six circles, please. Your outgoings need to be watched as attentively as your incomings.

If yours is an office where all receipts are banked, you could hardly miss out on A. If you bank it all, you have to write checks to get the money out. Banks can cite you a score of reasons for paying bills by check. One is enough for me: A canceled check is the best proof of payment. These days, you need proof.

When you're running short of cash, you don't merely help yourself, do you? I hope not. If so, you're heading for the worst kind of tax trouble. Some doctors I know leave an i.o.u. That's O.K., as long as repayment is made promptly and without fail. Even better: Write a check to yourself, and leave it rather than an i.o.u. in the cashbox. Then there's nothing to remember. You'll have the cash you need, your check will be banked with the others, and the I.R.S. man will be impressed with your tidiness.

Go ahead and circle B if your wife signs the checks. Ye twain are one flesh. Just don't give your aide the open sesame to your office checking account. It's quite enough for her to write the checks without signing them.

If you missed out on C, you're running the risk of paying for goods you don't get. My favorite example: the doctor who unwittingly signed checks written for higher amounts than the invoices called for. When the credit memos came in, his aide quietly returned them and asked for refund checks. When they came in, she just as quietly exchanged them for cash.

D is a protection against another kind of skulduggery. I once came up against an aide whose gambit was to write a higher amount on a check stub than appeared on the check itself. Then she pocketed the difference. So get in the habit of checking the stubs.

To flunk E is inexcusable. Yet it happens all the time. The most unlikely people make use of the blank check dodge. You wouldn't expect an accountant to take a doctor for $6,000 that way, would you? I know one who did. He got a year in prison. The doctor got a bill for unpaid withholding taxes, *plus* penalties and interest.

I hope you circled F. Start your petty cash fund with a check for $25 or $50. Have your aide jot down how it's spent. Replenish the fund by check when it runs low. That's all. It's the safest way to make sure of a tax deduction for the office Cokes.

Dr. Rawsen? He missed C and D, scored on all the others.

5. What books of account have you set up for your practice?

(A) A daybook and a checkbook. What more do I need? (B) My aide keeps single-entry books. (C) We're on double entry; my aide keeps the journals, my accountant the ledgers. (D) My aide keeps double-entry books all the way to a balance sheet. (E) My accountant (or outside bookkeeping service or management consultant) keeps my books; they're double entry. (F) The accountant keeps my books; I don't know his system.

Every now and then I meet a physician who prides himself on having cut his bookkeeping chores to the bone. He tells me: "In April I hand my daybook, bank statements, deposit slips, and canceled checks to my accountant, and he prepares my tax return. I've been audited several times and come out unscathed." I answer: "For tax purposes, nothing more is needed. But such primitive records don't give you any control over your finances."

311

B, then, is much better. With single-entry books, you put down your income and expenses daily and carry each day's figures to a monthly summary. The monthly totals add up to a summary for the whole year. Outlays are categorized under selected headings—payroll, rent, supplies, etc. All income entries are verifiable against deposit slips and all expense entries against canceled checks. Except for your depreciation allowance, your yearly summary is a ready-made Schedule C for your tax return.

Answers C, D, and E are better still. Single entry tells what you're earning and spending, period. Double entry shows how your earnings and spending build up—or reduce—your net worth.

If you circled F, as Dr. Rawsen did, you probably believe that a shoemaker should stick to his last. You've turned your accounting over to a specialist, and you're willing to let him do his job without hindrance. I'll go along with that, provided you're sure he's keeping a full set of books—i.e., a double-entry set.

6. What do you personally do to make sure your money is being handled correctly?

> *(A) I often examine my daybook for errors in addition and subtraction. (B) I examine my aide's deposit slip every day. (C) I look through my canceled checks each month. (D) I glance inside the petty cash box now and then. (E) Once a month I check a few daybook entries against patients' ledger cards. (F) I ask my accountant to do a full audit once a year.*

Six circles wanted, please. There's a specific reason for each, and there's this overriding reason for the full set: If you don't make *any* checks yourself, you risk being the victim of collusion between your aide and your accountant. It's rare, but not unknown.

The doctor who circles A finds out in a hurry if his aide is a dope at math. And by looking over the daybook every day or two, he's more apt to notice if she fails to record a visit or two—and to ask her why. The omission could be unintentional. Or deliberate.

The B doctor gets a good idea of a normal day's take in cash.

A sharp falloff in currency deposits is often a danger signal. Most pilferers prefer cash to checks.

C will alert you to checks you don't remember signing, to names you can't recall as those of creditors, and to dollar amounts that don't square with your recollection of the month's bills.

D is a worthwhile exercise, even though petty cash defalcations don't often involve much money. A box regularly stuffed with i.o.u.s can be the tip-off that someone in the office is flat broke. And a hard-up aide isn't the best fiduciary.

E is a chore heartily disliked by most doctors. Yet it's easy. Do it after closing time. Pick four pages in the daybook, one in each week. From each page pick four or five entries showing charges unaccompanied by payments. Dig out the relevant ledger cards and match them with the book. If a card shows a payment, pull it out and ask about it next day. Maybe she just goofed. Maybe not.

Don't confuse F with your accountant's routine job of figuring out your taxes—as Dr. Rawsen did. That doesn't require an audit. An audit means *verification* of your book entries and of your patients' accounts. It takes time, and it costs money. But it's worth the cost. It's the *only* way to catch a skilled embezzler.

F, by the way, was Dr. Rawsen's reply. But it turned out there was no actual audit. There is now.

41

Sizing up your collections

One day about a year ago I accepted three phone calls. The first was from a Virginia G.P. who said: "Five of us pooled our practices a year ago. As of today, our patients owe us $100,000 for care we've given them during that time." The second call was from Texas. A surgeon told me: "My partner and I have been together two years. So far, our patients have piled up $78,000 in unpaid accounts." Caller No. 3, a New Jersey internist, reported: "In three years of solo practice I seem to have accumulated delinquent accounts totaling $26,000."

All three physicians asked the same question: "What's wrong?" And to all three, when I subsequently met them, I put some questions of my own. I've reproduced in this chapter the half-dozen I consider most important. Read them and the answers I've provided, and circle the answers that come closest to fitting your own situation. Then study the brief commentaries that accompany each question. And finally, just for fun, compare your results with those of the Texas surgeons.

1. What percentage of your total charges did you collect during the past 12 months?

> *(A) I don't know. (B) 80 per cent or less. (C) 81-85 per cent. (D) 86-90 per cent. (E) 91-95 per cent. (F) Above 95 per cent.*

I'll bet even money that you circled A. Half of all the doctors I meet do. Yet it's the one money question every physician ought to be able to answer instantly. If you don't know *what* you're doing, you can't possibly know *how* you're doing. And if you don't know how you're doing, how can you possibly know when you're doing badly?

Please, if you're an A man, get with it. Total your charges to patients for the past 12 months. Divide this amount into your actual receipts for the same period. Multiply by a hundred. The result is your collection percentage. Calculate it that way every month. Watch it like a hawk. Any time it drops, make it your business to find out why.

Perhaps you circled B. If so, your collection system is suffering from pernicious anemia. To lose 20 cents or more on the dollar, you must be doing *something* wrong. I'm assuming, of course, that you don't put down fees you have no intention of collecting.

C is better than B, but not much. C represents a collection loss that's about equal to your payroll expense. You'd scream at the thought of doubling your payroll, wouldn't you?

D is the country doctor's bracket. Many rural physicians fall into this slot. Yet even they, if they really put their minds to it, can do better. I know it's so because I've helped many of them to shift up a notch or so.

After A, the answer most often circled is E. If you're a surgeon, it's an acceptable mark; don't settle for less, though. Health insurance plans pay out so much to surgeons that a collection loss exceeding 10 per cent is a sign of inefficiency in gathering in the rest of the money.

If, though, you're a G.P. practicing in a city or suburb, or an internist or a pediatrician practicing anywhere, E is nothing to brag about. Most of your charges are small, and small charges are easier to collect than large ones. You should be unhappy if you're collecting less than 95 per cent.

If your specialty is OBG, you should have circled F. Obstetrical patients ought to pay as they grow. They see you a dozen or more times during pregnancy. Train 'em to bring $20 at each prenatal visit, and then when they enter the hospital for delivery they'll be completely paid up.

Those two Texas surgeons I mentioned? They chose A, naturally. So I put their bookkeeper to work totaling the previous year's charges and receipts. She came up with a C.

2. *When does a new patient first discover (without asking) what your services cost?*

> *(A) At the end of the month in which he receives his care. (B) More than a month after he receives his care. (C) Within two weeks of receiving his care. (D) Within a week of receiving his care. (E) As soon as he has received his care. (F) Before he receives his care.*

Any patient who meets a doctor for the first time has money on his mind. So if you circled A, as most doctors do, *it's the wrong answer.* The patient doesn't want to wait up to 30 days to find out what it costs to get well.

B is even worse. I know surgeons, for example, who delay billing patients until they've been home from the hospital a full month. Sometimes it takes as long as 90 days for their patients to get the bad news. A delay like that makes the news three times as bad.

The number of doctors who circle either C or D is inching up. Some offices, anxious to cut down the month-end billing rush, have switched to semimonthly mailings. Some centralized billing services have obtained their clients' permission to send out statements weekly. According to all the reports I've had, no one objects.

If you circled E, take a bow. Your office patients are told what they owe before they leave. Your hospital patients know what they owe you the day they head for home.

Did you circle F? Then I know your collections are good. To your patients, your bill, when it comes, is merely a confirmation of a bargain they've made. You or your aide told them what their care would cost and they said, "Go ahead." Most people keep their bargains.

Oh yes, those fellows in Texas—they came up with a B.

317

3. What percentage of your charges do you collect without even sending a bill?

> *(A) 10 per cent or less. (B) 11-20 per cent. (C) 21-30 per cent. (D) 31-40 per cent. (E) 41-50 per cent. (F) Over 50 per cent.*

Surgeons usually circle A. That's expectable. It'd be dandy if every discharged hospital patient left you a check and a thank-you note on leaving. If, however, they don't know what they owe you, they can't do it. And they *don't* know, do they?

If you're not a surgeon, you flunked if you circled A. You should educate your patients to pay as they go.

For a G.P. or an internist, B is just barely acceptable. If your aide knows her job, she should be able to get you a C at least.

For a pediatrician, D is the passing mark. A smart aide can get cash for half of all your office work. And office work is the backbone of your practice.

If you're an OBG man, you should have circled either E or F. In this specialty, a heavy monthly billing is a tip-off that the collection procedure is defective. As I've already indicated, prepayment of OB fees can be arranged more easily than any other kind.

The Texas surgeons got a big A. Their secretary said: "How can I collect cash when two weeks pass before they tell me the fee?"

4. What's your definition of a slow-paying patient?

> *(A) One who doesn't send a check within 10 days of getting my bill. (B) One who takes longer than 30 days to pay. (C) One who takes more than 60 days to settle up. (D) One who lets his bill go 90 days past due. (E) One who doesn't pay within six months. (F) I don't worry my head about it, and I still make enough to get by.*

Recently I met a Pennsylvania G.P. who falls into the A category. He observed: "Anyone who sends me a check by return mail is a fast payer. By comparison, all others are *slow*." I'm sure some doctors agree secretly with him, but not many will circle A.

B won't be circled often, either. Actually, relatively few doctors get overly excited if a patient delays his payment for a few weeks. "My wife gets 30 days' credit on her charge accounts," they say. "I think I should extend the same consideration to my patients."

My bet is that you put a circle around either C or D. Either answer means you suspect that a patient who doesn't pay your bill within two or three months may never pay at all. And you're darned right.

E, if you chose it, tags you either as easygoing or timorous. And an F indicates that your tax bracket is a gasser. The only doctors I know who shrug off delinquent accounts don't make merely "enough to get by." They make so much that making more doesn't really matter.

The good mark? It's a B. A patient who doesn't pay within 30 days of being asked has to be asked again. You can't call anyone who has to be nudged a prompt payer, can you?

My Lone Star friends, after some hesitation, indicated D. They explained the hesitation thus: "We don't *do* anything about slow payers for at least 90 days. But by that time we're worried sick."

5. *When do you start putting pressure on slow payers?*

   (A) When they're two months past due. (B) After three months. (C) After four months. (D) After five months. (E) After six months. (F) I never press 'em; I quit billing them after awhile.

I'd be surprised if you circled A. But you should have. An account that's two months past due has been billed twice. Anyone who has to be asked a third time is a potential delinquent.

Most likely you circled B. You're willing to ask three times for your money before inquiring why you haven't yet got it. Anyone in the collection business can tell you that a debtor who can ignore three requests for payment won't worry about three more unless they're stiffened up a bit.

If B's a poor score, as I think it is, C, D, and E are still worse.

319

And if you circled F, either you flinch from conflict or you don't really need the money. I'm betting on the former alternative.

My two Texas surgeons were C men. They said: "We felt we should allow people plenty of time to pay. But our leniency doesn't seem to be appreciated." They were wrong. Appreciated was just what their leniency was.

6. What do you do to encourage people to pay?

(A) All my office patients are given the opportunity to pay on the spot. (B) "Send me a bill" patients receive two statements. (C) After the two statements, I ask for payment four times by letter. (D) The first letter asks if the bill was correct, the second appeals to the patient's honesty, the third appeals to his pride. (E) The final letter tells him I intend to call for outside help. (F) If there's no response, I call for the outside help.

If you circled all six of the answers, you may proceed to the head of the class. You have the best collection system I know of, and your collections prove it.

I'm always meeting doctors who'd like to claim A but apparently don't know how to go about it. "When you're seeing 30 patients a day, you can't stop to tell your aide what to charge each one," they say. It isn't necessary to stop. Jot down the charge on a slip of paper and have the patient take it to her. The patient has only two options: Either he pays your aide right then and there, or he asks her to send him a bill.

In B offices, patients who don't respond to the first bill get a second, identical with the first. There's no sticker saying "Please." There's no scribbled "Past due" notation. But the slow-payer has now been asked twice.

If you'd claim a C, D, and E, first write and ask the slow-pay patient if the bill was wrong. It wasn't, of course. But it's a nice way to administer a gentle prod. Then wait another month and write again. In this letter, give him a hint that it's dirty pool to renege on a bargain. Wait another month, then write a third letter.

This time, let him see how surprised you are that he, of all people, hasn't even acknowledged his debt, much less paid it. If, after these three gentle reminders, his silence continues, you should invest one more postage stamp: Tell him that the next voice he hears will be that of a debt collector.

You can claim an F by actually putting the collector to work. How to choose one? A collection agency endorsed by your local medical society is best. But not every society will make an endorsement. If yours won't, you'll have to start asking your colleagues about the local collectors. You'll want to find one that's firm—but fair. If there's one in your community whose letterhead carries the logo of the Medical-Dental-Hospital Bureaus of America, be sure to consider it. The M.D.H.B.A. doesn't give out its imprimatur casually.

The Texans? Skunked. Not one solitary right answer. "They do let me write little notes on the oldest bills," their secretary told me, "but they don't do much good." She showed me one. The patient had owed $300. She'd written: "A partial payment will be accepted." And the patient replied: "Thanks for your consideration. I enclose $100 in full settlement."

42

Sizing up your fees

Dr. Vaughan, as I'll call him, is a 41-year-old surgeon in a small city who asked me to have a look at his practice. "I think I'm a fair enough doctor," he told me on the phone. "At least, my patients seem to like me all right, and I've got plenty of them. Trouble is—well, I collect 94 per cent, but I stay poor. The other surgeons in town aren't a bit busier than I am, but they all seem a lot better fixed. My wife thinks it must be my fees, and I guess it is—but I don't know. If I raised them, I could lose half my practice to these other boys. How about coming over and telling me what to do?"

Almost every doctor I work with on a practice survey asks me if I think his fees are about right. He'd like me to equip him with a surefire fee schedule. Unfortunately, I can't. Every physician has to arrive at his own optimum fees.

Yet a management man can help. The survey questionnaire I use for collecting practice data contains some leading questions about fees. From the answers a doctor gives—plus some follow-up discussion—he's usually able to draw his own conclusions as to whether his fees are right.

For this Part 8 of our do-it-yourself practice survey, I've adapted five fee questions from my master list. They appear on the following pages, each with a choice of six answers and a short commentary. Circle the answers that apply to your own practice, read the commentary, and then decide if your fees are good and proper. I've

323

also included the answers given me by Dr. Vaughan when, as requested, I went to visit him. See how your answers compare with his. I hope yours are somewhat better than his were!

1. What's your basic philosophy about fees?

> *(A) Charge everyone the same for the same service. (B) Vary the fees a bit according to the patient's means. (C) Charge the local going rates. (D) Charge what I think the service is worth. (E) Charge what my patients will cheerfully pay me. (F) Charge what the traffic will bear.*

These days, the popular answers are A, B, and C. About 9 out of 10 doctors now routinely stick to standard charges. Nearly all who vary fees reduce them for hard-up patients but rarely or never hike them for the better-off ones. And most doctors who charge standard fees tell me they simply follow the going rates—the fee levels that most of their local colleagues stay at or below.

A good many doctors, however, say they really don't know what the going rates are. These men usually choose D. Their ideas of what their work is worth can oscillate alarmingly. For example, I know one pediatrician whose fee for a well-baby check goes from $6 to $7 whenever he finds things are slack, and it bounces back to $6 as soon as they perk up.

Almost nobody chooses E. Yet in a way it's an excellent answer, believe it or not. How does one estimate such fees? It's quite simple. You do it like this:

¶ You want to know the fees that your patients will cheerfully pay you. Not just any doctor. *You.* So first you must honestly appraise what you have to offer.

¶ Ask yourself this: By and large, are your professional abilities fair, good, or excellent? Having candidly answered yourself, be equally truthful about the time you take with your patients: Are you generous or stingy? Next take into account the quality of your facilities—e.g., modern office, topflight equipment, efficient aides, and so on. Take into account, too, your willingness to put the

324

patient first and your degree of success in winning the faith and trust of sick people. Finally, identify the income group to which most of your patients belong.

¶ In the light of all that, set your fees at the level you feel the quality of your service deserves. If an all-around increase is indicated, don't back off in alarm. If you've figured all the factors correctly, your patients can be relied on to pay up cheerfully. Believe me, patients know what's fair.

If you'll think about it, you may find you're already doing this. If not, it's worth thinking about a little longer.

As for F—well, all I can say is that this fee philosophy is completely out of style among doctors I work with—or would care to work with.

My client Dr. Vaughan selected A and D. In his town, I happened to know, the going rate for an appendectomy was $175. Dr. Vaughan's fee for the operation: $125. His wife was right.

2. *When did you last review and revise your fees?*

(A) Within the past 12 months. (B) One to three years ago. (C) Three to five years ago. (D) Five to ten years ago. (E) Longer ago than that. (F) Never have.

The answers I get most often are B and C—from about three out of every five doctors. And I'd estimate that one in five gives me A. The remaining doctor answers D, E, or F—most usually it's E. A good number of those who have revised fees during the last three years have done it by shifting to a relative value scale. More and more doctors are doing so. Some of them have been surprised by the number of fees they've *decreased* as a result.

In any case, nearly all the physicians who have upped their charges have done so because, they say, their practice costs have risen so much. And of course that's true. In the last 10 years or so, the cost of living has gone up about 20 per cent; the overhead expenses of medical practice have risen some 75 per cent.

Do rising costs always justify fee increases? Not necessarily.

You can cover your increased expenses in other ways—to a point.

One way is by making extra charges for extra services. In the late 1950s, the office-visit fee usually covered everything. Today it's standard to get $1 or $2 extra for urinalysis, $3 or $4 for shots, and so on. Another way to cover increased costs is by adding patients. The general practitioner of a decade ago, for instance, saw 25 patients a day; now he sees 30. Many a doctor has discovered that he can handle an even bigger volume by spending *more* on his practice, not less. If a new $100-a-week aide can enable you to put $200 a week more on the daybook, you can hold the line on fees for quite a while.

What happens when you're treating all the patients you can? What happens when you've got all the help you can use? Then you can no longer cover increased costs without hiking fees.

In the past 10 years, physicians' fees have risen roughly 30 per cent. In the light of that rise, let's look at *your* fees—especially if you circled D or E or (unless you're new to practice) F. Jot down your fees for the six procedures you do most frequently. Next to those figures, list the fees you charged for the same procedure 10 years ago. See if you've even kept pace with that *average* increase recorded by the index figures.

You haven't? And you've no other way in prospect to cover your increased costs except to raise your fees? *Then do it.* If you let things ride, you'll fall behind in more than your mortgage payments. Underpaid doctors cut corners—and their practices suffer.

Dr. Vaughan, though he'd been in practice a dozen years, indicated F. That kept his wife's diagnostic average at a neat 1.000.

3. If you haven't revised your fees recently, what's been stopping you?

(A) The competition. (B) Fear of patient reactions. (C) I make a good living as it is. (D) My practice growth makes it unnecessary. (E) I don't quite know how to go about it. (F) It's too much trouble.

On this one, Dr. Vaughan, as I expected, gave me A and B. In doing so, he showed poor judgment. If you also go for A and B, I'd say that you too are under some misconceptions. Here's the gist of what I said to Dr. Vaughan and probably would say to you:

Ignore the competition. Whose evaluation of your worth are you going to take, Doctor? Your own—or that of the price cutter two blocks away? Trust that sober analysis you made of yourself.

Trust your patients, too. They don't shop for medical care as they shop stores for 1-cent sales. Fee revisions do not, as many doctors fear, bring irate patients into the office wrathfully waving their monthly statements. Patients can be pretty understanding when fees go up. They've seen everyone else raise prices. So they generally don't react adversely if the doctor finally follows suit. Patients come to you by referral, by hearsay, by accident. If they think you're good, a reasonable fee change won't drive them away.

If you circled C or D, you'll get no argument from me. My mission in life isn't to push up the price of medical care in the U.S. But I do suggest that you think about (1) the number of hours you work each week and (2) the number of patients you see each day. Too many to allow you a reasonable amount of time to yourself? If so, and if your fees are under the local going rates, mightn't it be wise to shorten your hours and see fewer patients—for the same acceptable income? Hike your fees to the going rates, at the least.

If you marked E, let me point to what the doctors in a Medical Economics fee study said they do when they raise fees. About half the fee raisers said they favor across-the-board increases. (If you use a relative value scale, the new conversion factor you select automatically does the job.) The others said they raise fees "selectively," meaning they raise some fees and leave others unchanged.

I'm for the across-the-board method. I'm also for applying the new fees to *all* patients. Limiting the revisions to new patients only leads to trouble, as any dual-fee system must.

How do doctors announce fee revisions? They don't, in most cases. Two-thirds of those surveyed said they simply start charging the new amounts. (That's my recommendation, incidentally.) Most of the others tell the patients personally. Only a few mail a formal announcement or post a notice in the office.

Not many of my clients ever give F for an answer. But human nature being what it is, I suspect that this is often the real reason. I know this: It's a hellishly expensive form of inertia.

4. Do you voluntarily discuss sizable fees with your patients?

(A) Routinely before the service. (B) Immediately after the service. (C) Before and after the service. (D) I state my fees, but I discuss them as little as possible. (E) I state them, but I won't discuss them. (F) I state my fees in advance only when patients request it.

Two-thirds of your colleagues would choose A. One-fourth would take B. About a tenth would mark C. Only hard-shells go for D and E these days. And, oddly enough, few doctors would mark F. Yet I'm always meeting physicians who admit that F is the one that really fits their everyday policy.

If you did circle A, you made the best choice. A patient wants to know what it will cost to have you take care of him. Unless it's a minor service, he'll fret about your charge until he knows for sure what it's going to be.

Now I can hear the G.P.s and the internists muttering, "If he thinks I'm going to discuss 10 or 15 bucks with everyone who comes to the office, he's crazy."

I'm not crazy. I don't say you have to present a short course in medical economics for every routine office visit. Small charges can well be disclosed to the patient *after* he has had the laying on of hands. Many a doctor just writes them down on an itemized charge slip. He asks the departing patient to give the slip to the receptionist before he leaves.

While she's arranging the patient's next appointment with him, she can also answer his questions, if any, about the figures he's seen on the charge slip.

The larger the charge, the more important it is to broach the subject *before* going ahead with the service. If it embarrasses you to talk money with patients, see that your front-office girl does it. *But the talking should be done.* Posting a fee schedule in the reception room is no substitute.

The plain truth is, people are likely to come through with payment in full if they've agreed to your charges beforehand. They're less likely to do so if they're startled by the size of your bill.

But, you say, what if a patient is upset by the amount when you mention it? Don't get your hackles up. Don't be defensive. Ask if a special paying arrangement would be helpful. Installments? Delayed payment? A reduced fee because of his circumstances? Give him a chance to tell you about his situation. Let him see that you want to be fair.

And Dr. Vaughan? On this one the diffident surgeon did well. He chose A.

5. How does health insurance figure in your fee situation?

> *(A) Two-thirds of my fee income is paid through health insurance. (B) At least a third is. (C) Very little is. (D) I charge insured patients more than my regular fees. (E) I charge them my regular fees. (F) I accept insurance benefits as full payment, even if they're lower than my regular fees.*

Well, now, shouldn't there be an answer or two concerned with Medicare in this section of the practice-survey questionnaire? Not yet—but that'll certainly change before long. I'm one of those who fear that Medicare will eventually set fees that participating doctors will have to accept as full payment. And if the Medicare fees are lower than a doctor's regular fees, many of his under-65 patients may be disinclined to pay those regular fees. I admit that all this may never happen, but if it does, there'll be an additional possible answer to the question in my survey: "I bar Medicare patients."

For the present, most doctors would circle either A or B. It's a rare man—usually a pediatrician or a medical subspecialist—who would mark C.

Not many would choose D. But if, thinking of the major-medical forms you sign, *you* circled D—then, Doctor, I'd like a word with you. This time I'm speaking with two voices: the voice of a management man and the voice of an insured patient. As the former, I warn you against killing the goose—and you know what goose I'm talking about.

As the latter, I'd like to ask you why I, a provident, thrifty breadwinner, should pay you more than you ask from the improvident individual who carries no insurance and who probably won't pay you at all until you set the collection agency on his track. Charge me your *regular* fee. It will be paid—cheerfully. But don't fine my insurance company 25 per cent extra. If you do, who'll pay in the end? I will, through higher premiums.

Now, if you marked F, I'd still like a word with you, again speaking with two voices. As a management man, I advise you against accepting cut-prices—unless, of course, the patient has a service-benefit policy. As a patient, I say: "If my insurance doesn't provide enough to pay your regular charge, and I'm not entitled to service benefits, ask me for the difference, Doctor. I don't want favors; I just want to be treated the same as others."

You say I'm not a typical patient? Tell you what: Bring this insurance question up at your next civic gathering or cocktail party for nondoctors. You'll soon find out how typical I really am.

Dr. Vaughan, who gave a B reply, also gave an F one. By now it was clear that his financial unhappiness had one simple basis: He couldn't bring himself to charge what his services were worth. He's promised to rectify matters. Frankly, he's doubtful if it will work. But he's in for a pleasant surprise. He doesn't spend all that time in the O.R. because he's cheap. He's *good*.

43

Sizing up your practice goals

Dr. Wallis—that's not his real name, of course—apologized for calling me at home on a Sunday. "I'm working 70 hours a week," he said. "I flinch at the sight of a new patient, my practice is a financial disaster, and I'm thoroughly dissatisfied with the life I'm living—or *not* living. Yet, according to your articles in Medical Economics, I do most things right. So I want you to fly down here and tell me, if you can, what's wrong."

Dr. Wallis, as I discovered when I met him, had reported his situation accurately. His fiscal troubles and his depression weren't due to lack of help, low fees, lagging collections, or any of the other nuts-and-bolts causes I've reviewed in the eight preceding chapters of Part II. They were, as I told him bluntly, directly due to an inability to manage himself. And that's the point of this concluding chapter: It isn't enough to size up your practice. You also have to size up yourself.

The eight-page checklist I use in my practice surveys has a whole section devoted to the doctor. The answers I get to my questions help me visualize him as a physician, an employer, an organizer, a human being. I've chosen six of the key questions I ask the Dr. Wallises I meet. I've added, in each case, the half-dozen answers they most frequently give me.

Ask yourself the questions. Circle the answers that best fit your situation. Compare your answers with Dr. Wallis's. Then you may feel better—or worse.

1. What triggered your decision to size up your practice?

(A) My practice isn't growing as I'd hoped it would, and I'd like to know why. (B) I work harder than most doctors I know, yet I don't get ahead financially. Why? (C) I want to know how other doctors manage to see so much of their families. (D) I'm overworked. Do I need a partner? (E) I'd like to straighten out the mess in my office. (F) I've no special problems; I just want to know how I'm doing.

As you might expect, doctors who choose A are often young men in a hurry. Occasionally they're older doctors who've put down new roots and wonder whether it wouldn't have been better, after all, to have stayed put. I've known men of 60 to stake out fresh claims. For the eager beavers, the best prescription, I've found, is patience. When a doctor chooses a locality already well covered in his specialty, he can't expect the walls to tumble down instantly. If, therefore, you circled A, ask yourself: Have I really allowed my community enough time to discover my merits?

B is a common response. It used to surprise me that busy doctors had money troubles. Now that I've met so many of them, I've developed a knack for classifying them. Most numerous are the Innocents. Absorbed in their work, they let economics go hang. Then come the Extravagants. They earn well, but they overspend. Finally, there are the Hesitants. They rate their own worth too low and that of others too high. The Innocents have too much faith, the Extravagants too much hope, the Hesitants too much charity. Which do you have too much of?

It's quite usual for doctors to claim both C and D. The desire for more free time motivates many physicians to look for partners. Trouble is, a practice that's too much for one man may not be enough for two. If work is really plentiful, there's another danger: By taking yourself a partner you can create two rat races instead of one—and maybe even make an enemy out of your colleague.

Doctors who circle E are popular with management men. So often, the mess in the office is easy to diagnose. Often, the cause is a nitwit aide. Oftener still, it's a lack of method in some key operation: a hit-or-miss appointment system, for example. There's one E man, though, I gladly sidestep. He's the one who, having personally created the mess in the office, demands that I make it work —as is. Well, it just doesn't happen that way. In medical practice, as in driving nails, you get as good as you give.

I used to welcome F men. These days I'm wary of them. Too many men who say they have no special problem actually have more troubles than a football field has stripes. But an honest-to-goodness F man is always a joy to meet. I always learn something from him that I can teach to others.

Dr. Wallis, as of course you've guessed, claimed B. I classified him in the Innocent category.

2. *How do you really like private practice?*

> *(A) Wouldn't swap it for any job going. (B) I like the individualism of it. (C) It's no picnic, but I keep at it and the pay is good. (D) I gripe a lot, but I realize you can't have everything. (E) I think I'd have liked academic medicine better. (F) I wouldn't choose private practice again on a bet.*

When a doctor doesn't claim an A, I get ready for the hardest task of all: How to help a square peg fit into a round hole.

The doctor who circles B can pose a problem. He's often so individualistic that he'll insist on doing things his own way in the face of proof that it's the wrong way. Case in point: the man who refuses to set up an appointment system although his best patients are switching to doctors more considerate of their time.

Most of the C men I've met have been good organizers, seeking to find ways to become even better. Believe me, I run out of ideas fast when my client's already running a taut ship.

D men are favorites with me. They're men who have come to terms with reality. They're usually receptive to new ways of doing things and cooperative in putting changes into effect.

E men are almost always rewarding clients to work for. Once

convinced a suggestion is right, they don't settle for half measures.

It's just possible that you circled F. If you did and you're below the age of 60, quit now. Good salaries for doctors were never so plentiful as they are today.

Dr. Wallis? You should know him by now. He took A and D.

3. *What are your working habits?*

(A) I get 'em in and get 'em out. (B) I take all the time I need, but I don't dawdle. (C) I probably stay too long with each patient. (D) I stay right on schedule. (E) I run behind, but I wish I didn't. (F) I don't watch the clock.

To me, it's vital to know whether a doctor works fast or slow. It's frankly foolish to suggest that a man should practice medicine in a way that's foreign to his nature. I also need to know whether he has a sense of time. Two answers, if you please: Check A, B, or C. Also be sure to check D, E, or F.

If you're not skimping on anything, A *plus* D spells top efficiency. A *plus* E spells overwork. A *plus* F is worse; that combination spells curtains at an early age, if I'm any judge.

B *plus* D is great. It means your appointment system is working well. B *plus* E probably means you're kidding yourself: You *do* dawdle, and you like it. B *plus* F stamps you as a nice guy, but it gets you home late every night.

C is a loser in any company. Paired with D it means you haven't enough patients to keep you busy. With E it explains why so many of your best patients drift off to other physicians. With F it's the reason so many of their worst patients drift to you.

Dr. Wallis coupled B with E. Then he appealed to his secretary to confirm his self-rating. She changed his B to C. If you gave yourself a B, a check with your aide may be revealing.

4. *How would you describe your temperament?*

(A) Aggressive is the word, I suppose. (B) Kind of spastic; I'm up and down. (C) I'm Cheerful Charlie. (D) Cautious; I like to

think things out. (E) Quiet; I stay on an even keel. (F) Is sensitive too fancy a word? I'm easily crushed.

Not too many doctors would circle A, but those who do so can usually be classified in one of two categories. They're either tremendously successful or tremendously unsuccessful. The successful ones, I've found, are aggressive in a positive sense. They're the ones who initiate large professional buildings and found medical groups. The unsuccessful ones are negatively aggressive; having refused to join in the building project, they'll tell you—angrily—how they were squeezed out of it.

Did you mark B? Oh-oh. If you did, I'll have a pretty good idea of what to expect if you ever consult me. You'll issue a blanket O.K. on everything I suggest, from a new filing system to a change of collection agencies. And I'll find three months later that you've backtracked on every single decision.

If you're a C man, you're an even tougher nut. You'll grin and agree to everything. And when I come to see you in three months' time, it's likely that you'll have moved not one inch in any direction. Then you'll grin again and agree that you ought to have moved a lot. Two like you in the same week, and *my* patience begins to slip.

Maybe, being the canny type, you circled D. I'll suggest this and that improvement in your office routine. You'll tell me you'll think about it. When I meet you a year later and ask how you made out, you'll say:"Well, I haven't actually changed anything yet. But I'm still thinking about it." You're a pea out of the same pod as B and C, and I'm no happier about your prognosis than I am about theirs.

If you circled E, you're my man. That quiet, even temperament of yours is usually a determined one. Once you accept a suggestion, you go through with it. You're hard to sell; but when you buy, you make sure you get the most out of your purchase. You're a good bet to accept my Rx for curing what ails your practice.

I don't meet many F men. They rejigger their entire offices on my say-so, often at considerable expense. Then an aide gripes about some piffling detail, and down comes half the new edifice. At the frown of a transient patient, half of what's left disappears. The rest vanishes when the doctor's wife repeats some trivia garnered from a bridge partner. Then the doctor tells his colleagues that it was a mistake to have listened to me in the first place.

Dr. Wallis chose B. That shows you how wrong a doctor can be in classifying himself. In my book, he's a perfect E. Maybe you marked the wrong answer for yourself, too. Review your answer, please.

5. What do you do when your aide pulls a boner?

> *(A) I blow my top. (B) If it makes me look bad, I tee off, but not otherwise. (C) It depends on how important the mistake is. (D) It depends on whether the same mistake has been made before. (E) I remind myself that no one is infallible. (F) I only wish I had a temper.*

If you circled A, you're entitled to credit for honesty. But that's all. As personal managers, top-blowers are at the bottom of the heap. Practice counting up to 10—slowly.

B is no better. A smart girl will soon learn which bloopers to cover up. If your *amour propre* is overdeveloped, she'll quickly find that the best way to bolster it is to hide anything that might deflate it.

Most doctors rate a C. They can overlook minor errors, but when Girl Friday really bombs, they cut loose. Sometimes that's justifiable. Other times, it would be lots better to put a tight rein on your emotion and simply use the blunder as a teaching experience. Blue-ribbon aides don't just happen; they're the product of patient training.

D is a good mark. Even a blue-ribbon aide can err. But she shouldn't repeat her errors.

An honest E proclaims a saintliness possessed by few of the physicians I know. In fact, most of those who circle it do so rather than admit that F is the answer that really fits them. It takes a brave man to admit that his aide has him hog-tied.

Dr. Wallis consulted his aides before choosing his answer. They voted him an A. With acclamation. And he bowed his head.

6. How far will you go to remedy management faults?

(A) Show me what's needed, and it'll be done. (B) I can be sold—on any particular change. (C) I'll think over every suggestion carefully. (D) You're not going to run me into any new expense, are you? (E) As long as you don't ask me to fire Miss Klopman. (F) H'mm.

I hope you circled A. Management men, like doctors, do best when they're given a clear mandate.

There's nothing wrong with B, though. You've a right to be convinced of the merits of every suggestion offered. But if you marked C I'll be a bit troubled. You'll probably accept every suggestion that fits in with your own thinking and throw out all those that don't—like the patient who swallows the green pills and throws away the red ones because they have a bitter taste.

I hope you skipped D. Economy doesn't consist of not spending. It consists of wise spending. If you did circle D, though, you're hardly alone. It's a mistake that's commonly made.

E is a commoner choice than you might think. Often it's a tip-off that Miss Klopman is a problem the doctor hasn't been able to solve. Most times I can't solve her, either.

Dr. Wallis, at the end of a long day, chose F. A week later, he called and changed it to A.

Now that you've sized up your own practice, what's *your* choice? I hope it's to face up to what ails your practice and to swallow all of the cure. In the long run, you'll be lots better off.

Index

341

342

343

Insurance—*continued*
  business overhead, 35
  correspondence on, 109, 110
  disbursements, 245, 251, 253
  starting capital for, 257
  See also Health insurance
Intercom systems, 51, 63, 66, 287
Interest:
  calculation on credit buying, 264-265
  calculation on loans, 261-262
  disbursements, 245, 251
Internal Revenue Service, 217, 241, 305, 309
  patient charts and, 306
Internists:
  aides, 292, 296
  collection percentages, 316, 318
  fee schedules, 179, 182, 208, 211
  location and, 12
  office space, 19
  overhead, 249, 252, 254
  patient loads, 21, 269, 272
  telephone advice, 153
  time allotment, 298, 302
Internships, 115-116
Interviewing techniques, 69, 77, 78, 79-85
Investment:
  building ownership group, 36-39, 256
  capital, 255-265
  lease protection of, 29
  overhead as, 250-254, 326

Janitors, 42, 250, 251, 252
Joint Commission on Accreditation of Hospitals, 117
Journal of the American Hospital Association, 117
Journal of the American Medical Association, 11

Kirk, Paul, 18

Laboratories, 26, 99, 122
  equipment, 54, 288-289
  overhead, 251
  report records, 172, 173, 174
  space for, 25, 278, 279, 288
Labor unions, 197
Laundry, 250, 251, 252

Law:
  on age discrimination, 76
  expense-sharing agreement, 44-45
  fee justification in, 181
  health insurance, 197, 198
  leases and, 27, 31
  licensing, 12, 114
  on loans, 258, 260, 262
  on race discrimination, 117
  record keeping and, 163, 172, 174
  zoning, 9, 12, 14, 25, 29
Leases, 27-31
  of equipment, 58, 289
  office ownership versus, 33-34
Lectures, 121, 131-132
  to the profession, 133-134
Ledger-posting machine, 51, 59, 61, 229-232, 233
  charge slips and, 308
Liabilities, 243, 246
  defined, 242
Licensing:
  of accountants, 96
  state medical requirements, 12, 114
Lighting, 52, 53
  reception room, 21, 50, 51, 279, 280, 284
Loan companies, 258, 264
Loans:
  capital sources, 255, 256-260, 263
  credit buying, 100, 263-265
  interest calculation, 261-262
  interest disbursements, 245, 251
Location, 3, 5-15, 68, 332
  competition and, 6, 7, 12, 13, 14, 119-120, 269, 270
  hospital privileges and, 6, 113-114, 115, 117
  office construction, 34, 35
  office selection and, 17-19, 275-277
  referrals and, 272-273
  rents and, 281-282
L.P.N.s, 76
  discounts to, 203, 205

Magazines, *see* Reading
Major-medical insurance, 199
Malpractice, 47, 155, 163
Management, importance of, 1-3, 267, 332-333. *See also specific aspects*
Management consultants, 104-105, 226

345

346

347

348

349

350